Boundary Value Problems of
MATHEMATICAL PHYSICS

Volume I

Boundary Value Problems of

MATHEMATICAL

PHYSICS   *Volume I*

I V A R S T A K G O L D

Professor of Mathematics and Engineering Sciences
Northwestern University

THE MACMILLAN COMPANY

COLLIER–MACMILLAN LIMITED, LONDON

Fourth Printing, 1969

Library of Congress catalog card number: 66-10304

THE MACMILLAN COMPANY
COLLIER-MACMILLAN CANADA, LTD.,
TORONTO, ONTARIO

Printed in the United States of America

Preface

The present book is an outgrowth of a series of courses which I taught, first at Harvard and later at Northwestern, to classes consisting primarily of graduate students in engineering and in the physical sciences. Addressing myself to a similar audience, I have attempted here to present a modern, comprehensive treatment of boundary value problems. By definition, a boundary value problem consists of an ordinary or partial differential equation with associated boundary or initial conditions. When E. P. Wigner, a Nobel Laureate in Physics, spoke of "the unreasonable effectiveness of mathematics in the physical sciences," he must have had boundary value problems in mind, for nearly every branch of the physical sciences has been enlightened by the mathematical theory of boundary value problems.

Attention will be directed to both analytic and approximate methods for the solution of linear boundary value problems. The principal analytic methods employ either an eigenfunction expansion or a Green's function. Their full understanding will require the development of a number of mathematical topics such as the theory of distributions, generalized solutions of differential equations, extremal principles, and the spectral theory of differential and integral operators. The subject matter can be divided, in a natural and convenient way, into the parts which correspond to the two volumes of this work.

The first volume is devoted primarily to the mathematical topics just cited and to their application to ordinary differential equations and integral equations. The second volume deals with boundary value problems for partial differential equations.

I have tried to make the material accessible to a wide circle of readers by adopting a frankly pedagogical approach and by postulating modest mathematical prerequisites—standard courses in advanced calculus and in elementary complex variables. In keeping with this objective, I have often stated theorems in somewhat less than their most general form; occasionally I have also omitted

v

or merely sketched a proof which appeared to be beyond the scope of the book. Usually I have started with simple concrete examples before proceeding to the general theory and, sometimes, the same topic is discussed at increasing levels of sophistication as progress is made; I have therefore sacrificed compactness for the sake of greater ease in understanding.

Considerable effort has been spent in devising exercises that are more than routine drill and yet do not require the time and ingenuity of a doctoral dissertation. In fact, these exercises are important extensions of the text; often I have either sketched the method of solution or else offered clues as to how to proceed. The serious reader is encouraged to look over all exercises with care and to solve a substantial fraction of them.

There remains the pleasant task of acknowledging the valuable help which I received through the years from a great many students and colleagues; their constant encouragement provided an essential stimulus for this book.

I. S.

Table of Contents

1. THE GREEN'S FUNCTION

1.1 The String Subject to Transverse Loading   1
1.2 The Dirac Delta Function   18
1.3 The Theory of Distributions   28
1.4 Preliminary Results on Linear Equations of the Second Order   58
1.5 Boundary Value Problems   64
1.6 Alternative Theorems and the Modified Green's Function   79
    Suggested Readings for Chapter 1   91

2. INTRODUCTION TO LINEAR SPACES

2.1 Functions and Transformations   92
2.2 Linear Spaces   96
2.3 Metric Spaces, Normed Linear Spaces, and Inner Product Spaces   99
2.4 Properties of a Separable Hilbert Space   116
2.5 Functionals   135
2.6 Transformations   139
2.7 Linear Transformations on $E_n^{(c)}$ 146
2.8 The Inverse of a Linear Transformation in Hilbert Space   165
2.9 The Spectrum of an Operator   180
2.10 Completely Continuous Operators   184
2.11 Extremal Properties of Bounded Operators   187
    Suggested Readings for Chapter 2   190

3. LINEAR INTEGRAL EQUATIONS

3.1 Introduction   191
3.2 The Neumann Series (Method of Successive Approximations)   206
3.3 The Spectrum of a Self-adjoint Hilbert-Schmidt Operator   212
3.4 The Solution of the Inhomogeneous Equation with a Symmetric Hilbert-Schmidt Kernel   220
3.5 Extremal Principles   223
3.6 Approximations Based on Extremal Principles   226
3.7 Questions Relating to Continuity and Uniform Convergence—The Bilinear Series for the Kernel and the Iterated Kernels   236
3.8 Approximate Methods for the Solution of Integral Equations   241
3.9 Nonsymmetric Hilbert-Schmidt Operators   250
Suggested Readings for Chapter 3   258

4. SPECTRAL THEORY OF SECOND–ORDER DIFFERENTIAL OPERATORS

4.1 Introduction   259
4.2 The Regular Boundary Value Problem   268
4.3 Introductory Examples of Singular Problems   283
4.4 The General Singular Problem   295
Suggested Readings for Chapter 4   322

APPENDIX A

A.1 Static and Dynamic Problems for Strings and Membranes   323
A.2 Static and Dynamic Problems for Beams and Plates   326
A.3 The Equation of Heat Conduction   327

APPENDIX B

B.1 Bessel Functions   329
B.2 Wronskian Relationships   330
B.3 The Modified Bessel Function   331
B.4 The Behavior of Cylinder Functions at Zero and at Infinity   332

INDEX   333

Boundary Value Problems of
MATHEMATICAL PHYSICS

Volume I

Chapter 1

THE GREEN'S FUNCTION

1.1 THE STRING SUBJECT TO TRANSVERSE LOADING

To acquire some insight and confidence in the concepts of this chapter, we introduce these concepts in relation to the simple problem of determining the static deflection of a taut string subject to transverse loading. The analysis of this example will guide us in the formulation of a general mathematical theory which will then be applied to problems of greater physical interest.

A string under tension T is stretched on the x axis between the fixed end points $x = 0$ and $x = l$. A given arbitrary transverse load $f(x)$, measured in units of force/length, is applied to the string; a load of this type will be called a *pressure* to distinguish it from a load consisting of concentrated forces. We wish to calculate the deflection $u(x)$ resulting from the applied pressure $f(x)$. According to Appendix A, the differential equation

$$-T\frac{d^2u}{dx^2} = f(x)$$

must be satisfied in the open interval $0 < x < l$. Since the ends of the string are fixed on the x axis, $u(x)$ must also obey the two boundary conditions†

$$u(0) = 0, \qquad u(l) = 0.$$

If $f(x)$ is given as a continuous function in $0 \le x \le l$, we will show subsequently that there exists one and only one function $u(x)$ which satisfies the differential equation and the boundary conditions. As a simple example

---

† The requirements that the string does not break implies that $u(x)$ is continuous in $0 \le x \le l$, so the boundary conditions can equally well be characterized as

$$u(0+) = 0, \qquad u(l-) = 0,$$

where

$$u(0+) = \lim_{x \to 0+} u(x) \qquad \text{and} \qquad u(l-) = \lim_{x \to l-} u(x).$$

1

consider the case where the pressure is constant along the string, say $f(x) = q$. The general solution of the differential equation $-Tu'' = q$ is

$$u(x) = -\frac{qx^2}{2T} + A + Bx;$$

the boundary conditions yield $A = 0$, $B = ql/2T$, so that the deflection is

$$u(x) = -\frac{qx^2}{2T} + \frac{qlx}{2T}.$$

There are important reasons, both mathematical and physical, for considering problems in which the applied pressure $f(x)$ is not continuous, but merely piecewise continuous; for instance, one can easily envisage a situation in which the applied pressure is the one of Figure 1.1; that is,

$$f(x) = \begin{cases} 0, & 0 \le x < x_0 - \dfrac{\varepsilon}{2}; \\[2mm] p, & |x - x_0| \le \dfrac{\varepsilon}{2}; \\[2mm] 0, & x_0 + \dfrac{\varepsilon}{2} < x \le l. \end{cases} \qquad (1.1)$$

Of course there are those who will insist that the actual pressure must rise sharply but continuously from 0 to p in the neighborhood of $x_0 - \varepsilon/2$ and must exhibit a similar decrease near $x_0 + \varepsilon/2$ (as in Figure 1.2). We do not choose to refute this argument on physical grounds; it suffices to point out that the pressures of Figures 1.1 and 1.2 are essentially equivalent, for they give rise to nearly the same deflections (a preliminary result in this direction is found in Exercise 1.7), and, needless to say, the calculations based on the discontinuous model are much simpler.

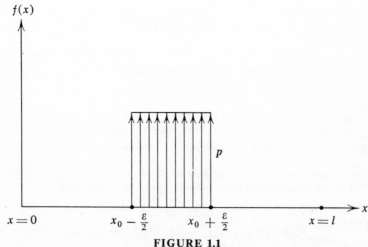

FIGURE 1.1

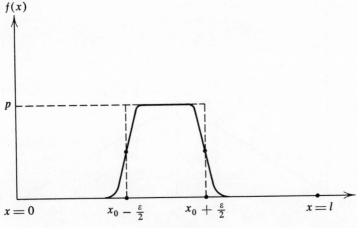

FIGURE 1.2

The deflection $u(x)$ corresponding to the pressure (1.1) can be obtained by integrating the differential equation; we find after applying the boundary conditions,

$$u(x) = \begin{cases} Ax, & 0 \le x < x_0 - \dfrac{\varepsilon}{2}; \\[2mm] C + Dx - \dfrac{px^2}{2T}, & |x - x_0| \le \dfrac{\varepsilon}{2}; \\[2mm] B(l - x), & x_0 + \dfrac{\varepsilon}{2} < x \le l. \end{cases}$$

Now $u'(x)$ is an integral of the piecewise continuous function $-f(x)/T$, hence $u'(x)$ is continuous and of course $u(x)$ is continuous; by using these properties at $x = x_0 - \varepsilon/2$ and $x = x_0 + \varepsilon/2$, we can calculate A, B, C, D, to obtain

$$u(x) = \frac{p\varepsilon}{T} \begin{cases} \dfrac{(l - x_0)x}{l}, & 0 \le x < x_0 - \dfrac{\varepsilon}{2}; \\[3mm] -\dfrac{x^2}{2\varepsilon} + x\left(\dfrac{x_0}{\varepsilon} - \dfrac{x_0}{l} + \dfrac{1}{2}\right) - \dfrac{1}{2\varepsilon}\left(x_0 - \dfrac{\varepsilon}{2}\right)^2, & |x - x_0| \le \dfrac{\varepsilon}{2}; \\[3mm] \dfrac{(l - x)x_0}{l}, & x_0 + \dfrac{\varepsilon}{2} < x \le l. \end{cases} \qquad (1.1a)$$

The deflection is shown in Figure 1.3. We note that u'' is discontinuous at $x = x_0 - \varepsilon/2$ and $x = x_0 + \varepsilon/2$, the two points at which $f(x)$ is discontinuous. At every other point, $-Tu'' = f$; and, of course $u(0) = u(l) = 0$.

In the light of the above example, we now formulate the mathematical problem for the deflection of a string, with fixed end points, subject to a piecewise continuous transverse pressure.

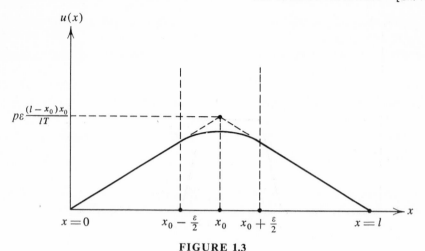

FIGURE 1.3

Let $f(x)$ be piecewise continuous, $0 \le x \le l$. We seek a function $u(x)$ which is continuous, has a continuous derivative, and a piecewise continuous second derivative, such that at all points of continuity of $f(x)$

$$-T\frac{d^2u}{dx^2} = f(x);$$

(1.2)

moreover, $u(x)$ must satisfy the boundary conditions $u(0) = u(l) = 0$.

Such a combination of a differential equation and boundary conditions will be called a *boundary value problem* or *system.*

Uniqueness of the Solution

Consider two solutions $u_1(x)$, $u_2(x)$ of system (1.2). Their difference $w(x)$ is continuous and has a continuous derivative and a piecewise continuous second derivative. Moreover, $w(0) = w(l) = 0$, and, at all points of continuity of $f(x)$, $w(x)$ satisfies $-Tw'' = 0$. In each subinterval in which f is continuous we have $w'' = 0$ and therefore $w' = $ constant. We can therefore say that w' is piecewise constant in $0 \le x \le l$. Since w' is continuous, the constant values in the various subintervals must be the same and $w' = A$, $0 \le x \le l$. Every continuous function $w(x)$ whose derivative is A must be of the form $Ax + B$, where B is another constant. Applying the boundary conditions, we find $w(x) \equiv 0$, $0 \le x \le l$. Therefore, system (1.2) has at most one solution. We will see later that such a solution actually exists.

Superposition Principle

Let $u_1(x)$, $u_2(x)$ be the deflections corresponding to the pressures $f_1(x)$, $f_2(x)$, respectively, in system (1.2). Then, if c_1 and c_2 are arbitrary constants,

$c_1 u_1(x) + c_2 u_2(x)$ is the deflection corresponding to the applied pressure $c_1 f_1(x) + c_2 f_2(x)$.

The proof of the principle of superposition is simple and is left to the reader. It is a direct consequence of the linearity of the differential operator $-T(d^2/dx^2)$ and of the fact that the boundary conditions are linear and homogeneous. A discussion of linear operators is found in Chapter 2.

The Green's Function for the String with Fixed End Points

We wish to solve system (1.2) in as economical a manner as possible for a variety of applied pressures. To accomplish this task, it is useful to introduce an accessory problem where a concentrated unit force acts on the string at the arbitrary point $x = x_0$. This force is indicated by a spike in Figure 1.4, the corresponding deflection being shown in Figure 1.5.

Although normally careful to distinguish between force and pressure (force/length), we now try to express the unit concentrated force in Figure 1.4 as an equivalent pressure $p(x)$. Since the total force acting in any interval (a, b) is the integral of the pressure, we must have

$$\int_a^b p(x)dx = 1, \quad \text{if the interval } (a, b) \text{ contains } x_0;$$

$$\int_a^b p(x)dx = 0, \quad \text{if the interval } (a, b) \text{ does not contain } x_0.$$

The second condition implies that $p(x) = 0$ for $x \neq x_0$; on the other hand, $p(x)$ must be infinite near $x = x_0$ so as to satisfy the first of the above conditions. It is clear that $p(x)$ is not an ordinary piecewise continuous function. We introduce the new symbol $\delta(x)$ to represent the *pressure* (as a function of x) corresponding to a unit force at $x = 0$. Thus $\delta(x - x_0)$ will represent the pressure

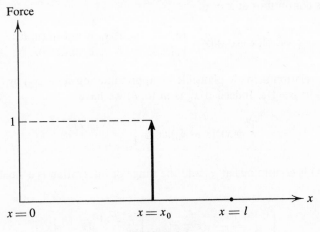

FIGURE 1.4

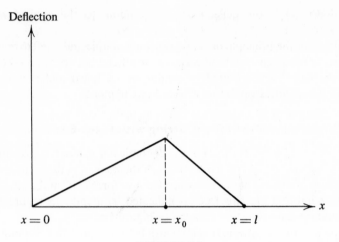

Deflection

$x=0$ $x=x_0$ $x=l$ x

FIGURE 1.5

corresponding to a unit force at $x = x_0$. The "function" $\delta(x - x_0)$ is known as the *Dirac delta function*. One can visualize $\delta(x - x_0)$ as a limit of piecewise continuous functions; for instance, if we let $\varepsilon \to 0$ and $p \to \infty$ with $\varepsilon p = 1$ in (1.1), we obtain $\delta(x - x_0)$. We tentatively list below some of the properties of the delta function (subject to careful reexamination in subsequent sections.)

$$\delta(x - x_0) = \begin{cases} 0, & x \neq x_0; \\ \infty, & x = x_0. \end{cases} \tag{1.3a}$$

$$\int_a^b \delta(x - x_0)dx = \begin{cases} 0, & \text{if } x_0 \text{ is not in } (a, b); \\ 1, & \text{if } x_0 \text{ is in } (a, b). \end{cases} \tag{1.3b}$$

If $\varphi(x)$ is continuous at $x = x_0$,

$$\int_a^b \varphi(x)\delta(x - x_0)dx = \begin{cases} 0, & \text{if } x_0 \text{ is not in } (a, b); \\ \varphi(x_0), & \text{if } x_0 \text{ is in } (a, b). \end{cases} \tag{1.3c}$$

This last relation is made plausible by approximating $\delta(x - x_0)$ by (1.1), with ε small and $p = 1/\varepsilon$. Indeed if x_0 is in (a, b) we have

$$\int_a^b \varphi(x)\delta(x - x_0)dx \cong \int_{x_0 - \varepsilon/2}^{x_0 + \varepsilon/2} \frac{\varphi(x)}{\varepsilon} \, dx;$$

since $\varphi(x)$ is continuous at x_0 and the range of integration is a small interval about x_0,

$$\int_{x_0 - \varepsilon/2}^{x_0 + \varepsilon/2} \frac{\varphi(x)}{\varepsilon} \, dx \cong \varphi(x_0) \int_{x_0 - \varepsilon/2}^{x_0 + \varepsilon/2} \frac{1}{\varepsilon} \, dx = \varphi(x_0).$$

The Dirac delta function and related symbolic functions are presented in a more serious mathematical framework in Sections 1.2 and 1.3.

Our accessory problem is the boundary value problem

$$-T\frac{d^2g}{dx^2} = \delta(x - x_0), \qquad \text{with } g|_{x=0} = 0 \text{ and } g|_{x=l} = 0. \qquad (1.4)$$

The solution of this system is denoted by $g(x \mid x_0)$ and is known as the *Green's function* for $-T(d^2/dx^2)$ with vanishing boundary conditions at $x = 0$, $x = l$. Physically, $g(x \mid x_0)$ is the deflection at x due to a unit force applied at x_0. This physical interpretation justifies the name *influence function*, which is often given to $g(x \mid x_0)$.

REMARK. It is extremely important to understand the distinction between system (1.4) and the completely homogeneous system

$$-T\frac{d^2u}{dx^2} = 0, \qquad \text{with } u(0) = u(l) = 0. \qquad (1.5)$$

System (1.5) has no load or pressure of any kind applied to it; therefore, the unique solution for the deflection is $u(x) \equiv 0$, as was shown earlier.

System (1.4) differs from (1.5) in only one respect, the unit force applied at $x = x_0$. The corresponding deflection is certainly not identically 0 in $0 \le x \le l$. Therefore, changing the right side of the differential equation at the single point $x = x_0$ radically alters the nature of the solution.

It must be realized that the change made at the point $x = x_0$ is enormous, the pressure being changed from 0 for system (1.5) to infinity for system (1.4). It will be shown that this implies that the solution of (1.4) has a discontinuous first derivative at $x = x_0$.

We now solve for the Green's function [system (1.4)]. Since the pressure is 0 whenever $x \ne x_0$, the differential equation reduces to

$$\frac{d^2g}{dx^2} = 0, \qquad 0 \le x < x_0, \quad x_0 < x \le l.$$

Therefore,

$$g(x \mid x_0) = Ax + B, \qquad 0 \le x < x_0;$$

and

$$g(x \mid x_0) = Cx + D, \qquad x_0 < x \le l.$$

Since the deflection vanishes at $x = 0$ and at $x = l$ we find that $B = 0$ and $D = -Cl$, so that

$$g(x \mid x_0) = \begin{cases} Ax, & 0 \le x < x_0; \\ C(x - l), & x_0 < x \le l. \end{cases}$$

To determine A and C we require first that the solution be continuous at $x = x_0$; that is,

$$g(x_0 + |x_0) = g(x_0 - |x_0).$$

This yields $Ax_0 = C(x_0 - l)$, or $C = Ax_0/(x_0 - l)$, and

$$g(x|x_0) = \begin{cases} Ax, & 0 \le x < x_0; \\ Ax_0 \dfrac{(l - x)}{(l - x_0)}, & x_0 < x \le l. \end{cases}$$

The shape of the string for various values of A is shown in Figure 1.6, the different curves corresponding to concentrated forces of different magnitudes applied at x_0. The curve with $A = 0$ corresponds to a zero force at $x = x_0$. The requirement that there be a unit upward (that is, positive) force at $x = x_0$ enables us to determine A. The forces acting on an infinitesimal portion of the string, directly under the load, are shown in Figure 1.7.

The equilibrium conditions are

1. $S_+ \cos \theta_+ = S_- \cos \theta_- = T$, where T is the horizontal component of tension.

2. $S_- \sin \theta_- + S_+ \sin \theta_+ = 1$.

Combining these equations, we find $T(\tan \theta_+ + \tan \theta_-) = 1$, or

$$\left. \frac{dg}{dx} \right|_{x = x_0+} - \left. \frac{dg}{dx} \right|_{x = x_0-} = -\frac{1}{T}.$$

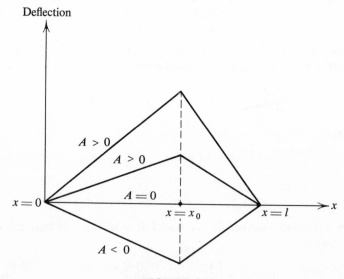

FIGURE 1.6

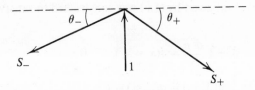

FIGURE 1.7

As expected, the slope of the string is discontinuous at $x = x_0$, the amount of the discontinuity being determined by the magnitude of the concentrated force. In our case

$$\frac{Ax_0}{x_0 - l} - A = -\frac{1}{T} \quad \text{and} \quad A = \frac{l - x_0}{lT}.$$

The Green's function is therefore

$$g(x \mid x_0) = \begin{cases} \dfrac{(l - x_0)}{lT} x, & 0 \le x < x_0; \\[2mm] \dfrac{(l - x)}{lT} x_0, & x_0 < x \le l. \end{cases} \qquad (1.6)$$

Let us introduce the notation

$$x_< = \begin{cases} x, & x \le x_0; \\ x_0, & x \ge x_0. \end{cases}$$

$$x_> = \begin{cases} x_0, & x \le x_0; \\ x, & x \ge x_0. \end{cases}$$

We can then write (1.6) in the more compact form

$$g(x \mid x_0) = \frac{1}{lT} [x_<(l - x_>)], \qquad 0 \le x, x_0 \le l. \qquad (1.6a)$$

Since dg/dx is *discontinuous* at $x = x_0$, g is not a solution of the class described in connection with system (1.2); but we can consider g as a limit of solutions of this class! Setting $p\varepsilon = 1$ in (1.1) and letting $\varepsilon \to 0$, we see that the applied pressure degenerates into a unit concentrated force at $x = x_0$; by inspection of (1.1a) we observe that the corresponding deflection approaches $g(x \mid x_0)$.

From (1.6) one verifies that $g(x \mid x_0)$ is symmetric in the variables x and x_0:

$$g(x \mid x_0) = g(x_0 \mid x). \qquad (1.7)$$

The deflection at x due to a unit force at x_0 is equal to the deflection at x_0 due to a unit force at x. In Section 1.5 it will be shown that this symmetry property holds for a wide class of problems.

The function $g(x \mid x_0)$ given by (1.6) was constructed to satisfy the *equivalent* systems

$$\begin{cases} -T\dfrac{d^2g}{dx^2} = \delta(x - x_0), & 0 \le x \le l; \\[2mm] g(0 \mid x_0) = g(l \mid x_0) = 0. \end{cases} \tag{1.8a}$$

$$\begin{cases} \qquad\qquad -T\dfrac{d^2g}{dx^2} = 0, & 0 \le x < x_0, \ \ x_0 < x \le l; \\[2mm] g(x_0 + \mid x_0) - g(x_0 - \mid x_0) = 0, \\[2mm] \left.\dfrac{dg}{dx}\right|_{x=x_0+} - \left.\dfrac{dg}{dx}\right|_{x=x_0-} = -\dfrac{1}{T}, \\[2mm] \qquad\qquad g(0 \mid x_0) = g(l \mid x_0) = 0. \end{cases} \tag{1.8b}$$

The compactness of the delta function notation is apparent. But let us not be deceived! Although (1.8a) has a strong intuitive appeal, it means no more and no less than (1.8b); in the theory of distributions, which will be developed in the next two sections, it will be possible to assign a direct meaning to (1.8a) and then *derive* (1.8b) from (1.8a).

We have shown that if (1.8b) has a solution it is given by (1.6), but we have not yet proved that (1.6) is actually a solution of (1.8b) [or of its equivalent form (1.8a)]. We conclude by inspection of the formula for g that the boundary conditions, the continuity requirement at x_0, and the jump requirements on the derivative at x_0 are all satisfied. By straightforward differentiation, we check that $-T(d^2g/dx^2) = 0$ in $0 \le x < x_0$ and $x_0 < x \le l$.

The function $g(x \mid x_0)$ exhibited in (1.6) is the *one and only solution* of system (1.8b) [or of its equivalent form (1.8a)].

Uses of the Green's Function for the String

We return to the problem of finding the deflection of a string subject to an arbitrary piecewise continuous pressure $f(x)$. This deflection $u(x)$ satisfies system (1.2), repeated below:

$$-T\frac{d^2u}{dx^2} = f(x), \qquad 0 \le x \le l;$$
$$u(0) = u(l) = 0. \tag{1.9}$$

Divide the interval $(0, l)$ in n equal parts. The center of the kth subinterval is called ξ_k, and the length of each subinterval is $\Delta\xi = l/n$. The deflection of the string subject to the piecewise continuous pressure $f(x)$ is closely approximated by the deflection of a string subject to small concentrated forces, $f(\xi_1)\Delta\xi, \ldots,$ $f(\xi_n)\Delta\xi$ located at $\xi_1, \ldots, \xi_n$, respectively (see Figure 1.8). According to the

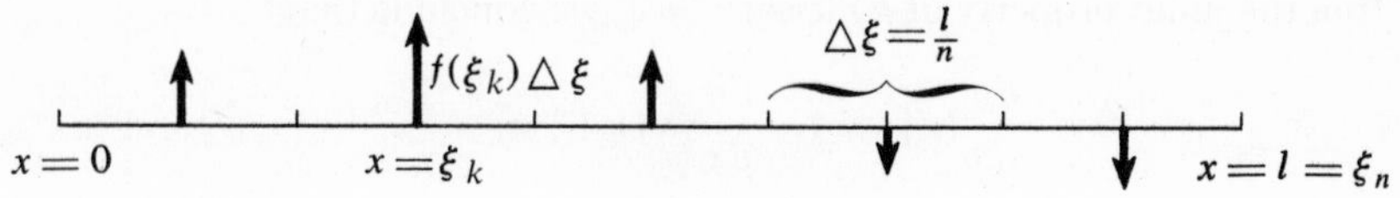

FIGURE 1.8

principle of superposition extended to concentrated loads, the deflection at x due solely to the small load at $x = \xi_k$ is $g(x \mid \xi_k) f(\xi_k) \Delta \xi$, and the deflection at x due to all the small concentrated loads is $\sum_{k=1}^{n} g(x \mid \xi_k) f(\xi_k) \Delta \xi$. As $n \to \infty$ (and $\Delta \xi \to 0$), we conclude

$$u(x) = \int_0^l g(x \mid \xi) f(\xi) d\xi. \tag{1.10}$$

Formula (1.10) was obtained by an intuitive (or heuristic) argument. Let us now show that (1.10) is the one and only solution of (1.9). Since uniqueness has been previously established, it remains only to verify that (1.10) actually satisfies system (1.9). The boundary conditions of (1.9) are satisfied because $g(x \mid \xi)$ itself vanishes at $x = 0$ and $x = l$. By differentiating (1.10) with care, we will show that $-Tu'' = f(x)$ at any point x where $f(x)$ is continuous. Because the derivative of g is discontinuous at $x = \xi$, it is prudent to split the interval of integration for ξ into the two parts $(0, x-)$ and $(x+, l)$; thus,

$$\frac{du}{dx} = \frac{d}{dx} \left[\int_0^{x-} g(x \mid \xi) f(\xi) d\xi + \int_{x+}^l g(x \mid \xi) f(\xi) d\xi \right].$$

In the separate intervals, we may use the formula for differentiation under the integral sign to obtain

$$\frac{du}{dx} = \int_0^{x-} \frac{dg}{dx} f(\xi) d\xi + \int_{x+}^l \frac{dg}{dx} f(\xi) d\xi + g(x \mid x-) f(x-) - g(x \mid x+) f(x+).$$

Since g is a continuous function and f is continuous at x, the last two terms cancel and

$$\frac{du}{dx} = \int_0^{x-} \frac{dg}{dx} f(\xi) d\xi + \int_{x+}^l \frac{dg}{dx} f(\xi) d\xi = \int_0^l \frac{dg}{dx} f(\xi) d\xi.$$

We see that the precaution of splitting the integral into two parts was unnecessary, but it will be essential in calculating the second derivative. We have

$$\frac{d^2 u}{dx^2} = \int_0^{x-} \frac{d^2 g}{dx^2} f(\xi) d\xi + \int_{x+}^l \frac{d^2 g}{dx^2} f(\xi) d\xi$$

$$+ \frac{dg}{dx} (x \mid x-) f(x-) - \frac{dg}{dx} (x \mid x+) f(x+).$$

From the jump property of dg/dx at $x = \xi$, we conclude that

$$\frac{dg}{dx}(x\,|\,x-) - \frac{dg}{dx}(x\,|\,x+) = -\frac{1}{T}.$$

Hence

$$\frac{d^2u}{dx^2} = \int_0^{x-} \frac{d^2g}{dx^2} f(\xi)d\xi + \int_{x+}^{l} \frac{d^2g}{dx^2} f(\xi)d\xi - \frac{1}{T}f(x).$$

Since $d^2g/dx^2 = 0$ in the intervals $\xi < x$ and $\xi > x$, it follows that

$$-T\frac{d^2u}{dx^2} = f(x),$$

and our proof is complete. The one and only solution of system (1.9) is

$$u(x) = \int_0^l g(x\,|\,\xi)f(\xi)d\xi.$$

As an illustration, consider the case of a uniform pressure $f(x) = q$, $0 \le x \le l$. Then

$$u(x) = q\int_0^l g(x\,|\,\xi)d\xi = q\int_0^x g(x\,|\,\xi)d\xi + q\int_x^l g(x\,|\,\xi)d\xi.$$

In the integral from 0 to x, ξ is smaller than x and we use the *second* line of (1.6), whereas in the integral from x to l, ξ is larger than x and the *first* line of (1.6) must be used (with $x_0 = \xi$ of course). Thus we find

$$u(x) = \frac{q}{lT}\int_0^x \xi(l-x)d\xi + \frac{q}{lT}\int_x^l x(l-\xi)d\xi = \frac{q}{2T}x(l-x),$$

a result previously obtained by elementary means.

We now come to a valuable interpretation of the relation between $g(x\,|\,\xi)$ and the differential expression $-T(d^2/dx^2)$. Consider the operator $L = -T(d^2/dx^2)$, which operates *only* on functions $u(x)$ with the properties: $u''(x)$ is piecewise continuous, $u(0) = u(l) = 0$. Define the integral operator G, which operates on functions $f(x)$, which are piecewise continuous, by the formula

$$Gf = \int_0^l g(x\,|\,\xi)f(\xi)d\xi.$$

Then we have $LGf = f$ and $GLu = u$, where f and u are any two functions in their respective classes. This leads to the terminology: G and L are inverses of each other. This point of view is stressed in Chapter 2.

We have established that the solution of system (1.9) is

$$u(x) = \int_0^l g(x\,|\,\xi)f(\xi)d\xi,$$

where $g(x \mid \xi)$ is given by (1.6). System (1.9) could also have been solved by methods from elementary differential equations. Indeed, the solution of the differential equation in (1.9) can be written by inspection as

$$u(x) = C_1 + C_2 x - \frac{1}{T} \int_0^x (x - t) f(t) dt.$$

We now require $u(0) = u(l) = 0$ to determine C_1 and C_2.

The advantages of the Green's function method are

1. The boundary conditions are incorporated in (1.10). We do not, for each different $f(x)$, have to recompute two constants to obtain the solution of the system.

2. The form (1.10) lends itself to the valuable interpretation that the deflection due to the distributed load is the sum of the deflections due to many small concentrated loads.

3. If the load on the string is a generalized pressure $f(x)$, consisting of a piecewise continuous pressure $f_0(x)$ and concentrated forces $f_1, \ldots, f_n$ located at $x_1, \ldots, x_n$, respectively, then

$$u(x) = \int_0^l g(x \mid \xi) f(\xi) d\xi = \int_0^l g(x \mid \xi) \left[f_0(\xi) + \sum_{k=1}^n f_k \delta(\xi - x_k) \right] d\xi$$

$$= \int_0^l g(x \mid \xi) f_0(\xi) d\xi + \sum_{k=1}^n f_k g(x \mid x_k).$$

Hence (1.10) is valid even if $f(x)$ contains concentrated forces.

4. The Green's function also enables us to solve the completely inhomogeneous system:

$$\boxed{-Tu'' = f(x); \qquad u(0) = a, \quad u(l) = b.} \qquad (1.11)$$

We recall that the Green's function $g(x \mid \xi)$ satisfies

$$-Tg'' = \delta(x - \xi); \qquad g(0 \mid \xi) = 0, \quad g(l \mid \xi) = 0.$$

Multiply the first of these differential equations by g, the second by u, subtract, and integrate from 0 to l to obtain

$$T \int_0^l (gu'' - ug'') dx = - \int_0^l f(x) g(x \mid \xi) dx + \int_0^l \delta(x - \xi) u(x) dx,$$

which reduces to

$$u(\xi) = \int_0^l f(x) g(x \mid \xi) dx + T(gu' - ug') \Big]_0^l.$$

Since g vanishes at the end points, and

$$\frac{dg}{dx} \bigg|_{x=0} = \frac{l - \xi}{Tl}, \qquad \text{and} \qquad \frac{dg}{dx} \bigg|_{x=l} = \frac{-\xi}{Tl},$$

we have

$$u(\xi) = \int_0^l f(x)g(x\,|\,\xi)dx + \frac{l-\xi}{l}\,a + \frac{\xi}{l}\,b.$$

Interchanging the labels x and ξ, and using the symmetry of g,

$$u(x) = \int_0^l g(x\,|\,\xi)f(\xi)d\xi + \frac{l-x}{l}\,a + \frac{x}{l}\,b.$$

It is easy to verify that the above actually satisfies system (1.11); uniqueness is shown in the same manner as for system (1.2).

5. The Green's function is also used in converting an eigenvalue problem consisting of a differential equation and boundary conditions into an eigenvalue integral equation.

As an example consider the free vibrations of a string with fixed end points. In Appendix A it is shown that the deflection $u(x, t)$ must satisfy

$$T\frac{\partial^2 u}{\partial x^2} = \rho\,\frac{\partial^2 u}{\partial t^2}, \qquad u(0, t) = u(l, t) = 0,$$

where ρ is the constant mass density of the string (per unit length). We look for solutions of the form $u(x, t) = X(x)e^{-i\omega t}$. This leads to an ordinary differential equation for the space part $X(x)$ of the solution:

$$-T\frac{d^2 X}{dx^2} = \lambda X, \qquad X(0) = X(l) = 0, \tag{1.12}$$

where $\lambda = \rho\omega^2$. For most values of the parameter λ (which is at our disposal), the only solution of system (1.12) is $X(x) \equiv 0$ in $0 \le x \le l$. Any exceptional values of λ, for which nontrivial solutions of the system exist, are called *eigenvalues*. The corresponding nontrivial solutions X are called the *eigenfunctions*.

System (1.12) is of the form (1.9), with λX playing the role of the inhomogeneous term. Using (1.10) we have

$$X(x) = \lambda \int_0^l g(x\,|\,\xi)X(\xi)d\xi. \tag{1.13}$$

This is an eigenvalue integral equation entirely equivalent to *system* (1.12). Integral equations of this type are studied in Chapter 3.

EXERCISES

1.1 The solution of the system

$$-Tu'' = f; \qquad u(0) = a, \quad u(l) = b$$

can also be obtained by adding the solutions of the two partially inhomogeneous systems

$$-Tu_1'' = f; \qquad u_1(0) = 0, \quad u_1(l) = 0,$$

and

$$-Tu_2'' = 0; \qquad u_2(0) = a, \quad u_2(l) = b.$$

The first system is solved using the Green's function, the second using elementary methods. Compare with the solution obtained under (4) above.

1.2 Another physical problem which leads to the same systems treated in the previous sections is the one-dimensional heat conduction problem (steady state).

Consider a rod $0 \le x \le l$ with a small constant cross section A. The rod is homogeneous, the flow of heat is in the x direction only, and the temperature u is constant over any cross section. By assumption, there is no heat flow through the lateral surface, but heat can flow through the plane boundaries, and there may be heat sources in the interior. We assume that the heat generated by these sources per unit time per unit length is a piecewise continuous function $f(x)$ [$f(x)$ is therefore the density of heat input]. Let k be the thermal conductivity. Then according to Appendix A, an energy balance on an infinitesimal section of the rod yields

$$-kA \frac{d^2u}{dx^2} = f(x).$$

There are a number of boundary conditions at $x = 0, x = l$, which can be associated with this problem.

(a) Temperature given: $u(0) = a, \quad u(l) = b.$

(b) Heat flow given: $\dfrac{du}{dx}(0) = a, \quad \dfrac{du}{dx}(l) = b.$

In (b) a and b cannot be assigned arbitrarily without violating the steady-state condition! To find the relation between a, b and $f(x)$, we integrate the differential equation from 0 to l to obtain

$$kA\left[\frac{du}{dx}\bigg|_l - \frac{du}{dx}\bigg|_0\right] = -\int_0^l f(x)dx.$$

Thus the following relation must hold:

$$kA(a - b) = \int_0^l f(x)dx,$$

which guarantees that the heat flowing out through the plane boundaries is equal to the net heat input in the rod from the interior heat sources. It can be shown that if this relation is satisfied, a solution actually exists but is determined only to an additive constant.

(c) Heat transfer from the ends into a surrounding atmosphere at 0 temperature:

$$\frac{du}{dx}\bigg|_{x=l} = -\theta u(l) \quad \text{and} \quad \frac{du}{dx}\bigg|_{x=0} = \theta u(0),$$

where θ is a given constant describing the heat-transfer properties from the ends of the rod into the surroundings.

(d) A combination of the above conditions, e.g., at one end the temperature is given, at the other the heat flow is specified.

1.3 In the preceding heat-conduction problem, a more general differential equation is obtained if we assume: (a) that the cross section A is a slowly varying function of x (slowly varying so as not to spoil the one-dimensional feature of the problem), and/or that k is a function of x; and (b) that heat transfer is allowed from the lateral surface into the surrounding atmosphere, the amount of heat transferred per unit time through the lateral surface between x and $x + \Delta x$ being $\mu(x)u(x)\Delta x$. Assuming that the temperature over a cross section is constant, the appropriate differential equation for the temperature is

$$-\frac{d}{dx}\left(kA\frac{du}{dx}\right) + \mu u = f(x).$$

Show that if $f(x) = \delta(x - \xi)$, that is, if a concentrated unit source is located at $x = \xi$, then

$$\frac{du}{dx}(\xi+) - \frac{du}{dx}(\xi-) = -\frac{1}{k(\xi)A(\xi)}.$$

(Take a heat balance for a small element of the rod at $x = \xi$.)

1.4 Construct the Green's function for the systems

(a) $\qquad -\frac{d^2g}{dx^2} = \delta(x - \xi); \qquad g(0\,|\,\xi) = 0, \quad \frac{dg}{dx}(l\,|\,\xi) = 0.$

(b) $\qquad -\frac{d^2g}{dx^2} = \delta(x - \xi); \qquad g(0\,|\,\xi) = 0, \quad \frac{dg}{dx}(l\,|\,\xi) - \theta g(l\,|\,\xi) = 0.$

1.5 Consider the motion of a particle along a straight line. The force on the particle is along the line, and the particle starts from rest at the origin.

The displacement $u(t)$ satisfies Newton's law:

$$m \frac{d^2u}{dt^2} = f(t),$$

and the initial conditions

$$u(0) = 0, \qquad \frac{du}{dt}(0) = 0.$$

The Green's function $g(t \mid t_0)$ satisfies

$$m \frac{d^2g}{dt^2} = \delta(t - t_0); \qquad g(0 \mid t_0) = 0, \qquad \frac{dg}{dt}(0 \mid t_0) = 0.$$

Show that

$$g(t \mid t_0) = \begin{cases} 0, & 0 \le t < t_0; \\ \dfrac{t - t_0}{m}, & t > t_0. \end{cases}$$

Hence

$$u(t) = \int_0^\infty g(t \mid t_0) f(t_0) dt_0 = \int_0^t \frac{(t - t_0)}{m} f(t_0) dt_0.$$

We observe that the solution at time t depends only on the force acting before time t.

1.6 (a) For the string problem (1.6) show that $g(x \mid x_0)$ is positive and that the maximum value of g over the square $0 \le x$, $x_0 \le l$, is $l/4T$.
(b) Consider system (1.2) for two "nearly equal" pressures $f_1(x)$ and $f_2(x)$ satisfying

$$|f_1(x) - f_2(x)| < \varepsilon, \qquad 0 \le x \le l.$$

Show that the corresponding deflections satisfy the inequality

$$|u_1(x) - u_2(x)| < \frac{l^2 \varepsilon}{4T}.$$

1.7 Consider again the string problem (1.2). Let us define

$$d(f_1, f_2) = \int_0^l |f_1 - f_2| dx$$

as the numerical measure of the "separation" between the two functions $f_1(x)$ and $f_2(x)$. Since $d(f_1, f_2)$ is just the area between the graphs of f_1 and f_2, the definition appears reasonable. In this sense it is quite clear that the separation between the pressures in Figures 1.1 and 1.2 is small.

Show that if $d(f_1, f_2) < \varepsilon$, then

$$\max_{0 \le x \le l} |u_1 - u_2| < \frac{l}{4T}\,\varepsilon, \quad \text{and} \quad d(u_1, u_2) < \frac{l^2}{4T}\,\varepsilon.$$

1.8 Consider a beam subject to the transverse pressure $f(x)$. It is shown in Appendix A that the differential equation for the deflection $u(x)$ is

$$EI\frac{d^4u}{dx^4} = f(x),$$

where E and I are certain constants.

    (a) Find the Green's function for a beam of length l whose ends are clamped.

    (b) Find the Green's function for a beam of length l whose ends are simply supported.

(HINT: The deflection and its first two derivatives are continuous under the concentrated load, but d^3g/dx^3 is discontinuous under the load.)

1.2 THE DIRAC DELTA FUNCTION

Introduction

In various branches of physics one encounters sources which are nearly instantaneous (if time is the independent variable) or almost localized (if the independent variable is a space coordinate). To avoid the cumbersome study of the detailed functional dependence of these sources, one would like to replace them by idealized sources which are truly instantaneous or localized; such idealized sources are said to be *impulsive or concentrated*. Typical instances of such sources are the concentrated forces and moments in solid mechanics; the point masses in the theory of the gravitational potential; the impulsive forces and pressures in acoustics and in impact mechanics; and the point charges, dipoles, and multipoles in electrostatics.

We wish to develop a mathematical theory of concentrated sources; we expect two things from this theory: (1) a clear and unambiguous way to specify mathematically a concentrated source, and (2) a method for the calculation of the response to a concentrated source, that is, a method for interpreting and solving differential equations whose inhomogeneous term is a concentrated source. In the present section we concern ourselves only with the first of these two aspects of the theory; the program will be fully developed in Section 1.3.

Although it is natural to try to specify a concentrated source as the limit of continuous source distributions, such an approach quickly leads to mathematical difficulties. These difficulties are overcome by adopting an alternative point of view in which a concentrated source is characterized by its "action" on suitable accessory functions.

The Delta Function as the Limit of Sequences of Continuous Functions

To fix ideas, we begin with a description of a point charge as the limiting case of continuous charge distributions on a line. Suppose that charge is distributed continuously on the real axis with the charge density

$$s_k(x) = \frac{1}{\pi} \frac{k}{1 + k^2 x^2},$$

where k is a positive integer. For large k, $s_k(x)$ is very small, except for a peak of height k/π at the origin (see Figure 1.9). The total charge to the *left* of the point x is

$$r_k(x) = \int_{-\infty}^{x} s_k(u)\,du = \frac{1}{2} + \frac{1}{\pi} \arctan kx,$$

where $r_k(x)$ is known as the *cumulative* charge distribution and is shown in Figure 1.10. We note that

$$\lim_{x \to \infty} r_k(x) = \int_{-\infty}^{\infty} s_k(u)\,du = 1, \qquad \text{for every } k.$$

Hence the total charge on the line is always 1, independent of the index k. It is clear that

$$\lim_{k \to \infty} s_k(x) = \begin{cases} 0, & x \neq 0; \\ \\ \infty, & x = 0; \end{cases} \qquad \text{and} \qquad \lim_{k \to \infty} r_k(x) = \begin{cases} 0, & x < 0; \\ \frac{1}{2}, & x = 0; \\ 1, & x > 0. \end{cases}$$

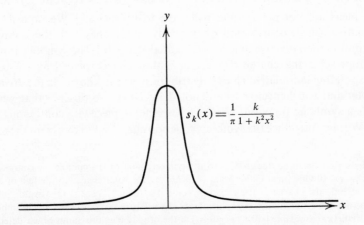

$$s_k(x) = \frac{1}{\pi} \frac{k}{1 + k^2 x^2}$$

FIGURE 1.9

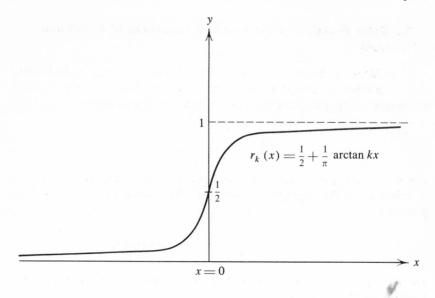

$$r_k\,(x)=\tfrac{1}{2}+\frac{1}{\pi}\ \text{arctan}\ kx$$

FIGURE 1.10

As k increases, the total charge (which is always 1) is pushed relentlessly toward the origin. If we tentatively write $s(x) = \lim_{k \to \infty} s_k(x)$, then $s(x)$ is the charge density due to a positive unit charge located at $x = 0$. The limiting density $s(x)$ is not an ordinary function, since it is infinite at $x = 0$. In spite of this, it is convenient to introduce the symbolic function $\delta(x)$ to represent the limiting density for all x. It appears that $\delta(x)$ vanishes for $x \neq 0$ and is positively infinite at $x = 0$ in such a way that $\int_{-\infty}^{\infty} \delta(x)dx = 1$. (As Exercise 1.11 shows, these ideas are not precise and will have to be revised.) We note that the cumulative charge distribution $r_k(x)$ strictly approaches $r(x)$, the cumulative distribution for a positive unit charge located at $x = 0$.† The symbolic function $\delta(x)$ represents the charge *density* for a unit charge placed at $x = 0$. The corresponding cumulative charge distribution $r(x)$ is known as the *Heaviside function* and will henceforth be denoted by $H(x)$; we observe that whereas $\delta(x)$ is a symbolic function, $H(x)$ is a respectable piecewise continuous function. We also introduce the symbolic function $\delta(x - x_0)$ to represent the charge

---

† There may be some question as to the correct value of the cumulative charge distribution at $x = 0$. One must define what is meant by the total charge to the left of $x = 0$; do we include the charge at the origin or some part of it? There is no sensible physical criterion available, and in fact, the value of $r(x)$ at $x = 0$ is of no consequence. The important fact is that $r(x)$ has a *jump* $[r(0+) - r(0-)]$ at the origin; it is this jump which determines the charge located at $x = 0$.

density for a unit charge placed at $x = x_0$; the corresponding cumulative distribution is clearly $H(x - x_0)$.

EXERCISES

1.9 Consider the sequence of functions $s_k(x) = (k/\sqrt{\pi})e^{-k^2x^2}$. Sketch a few of these functions and the corresponding cumulative distributions. Show that, in the light of all the properties so far mentioned, it is consistent to state

$$\lim_{k\to\infty} s_k(x) = \delta(x).$$

1.10 Same as Exercise 1.9 for the sequences

(a) $s_k(x) = \begin{cases} 0, & |x| > \dfrac{1}{2k}; \\[2mm] k, & |x| < \dfrac{1}{2k}. \end{cases}$

(b) $s_k(x) = \begin{cases} 0, & |x| > \dfrac{1}{2k}; \\[2mm] 4k^2x + 2k, & -\dfrac{1}{2k} \le x \le 0; \\[2mm] -4k^2x + 2k, & 0 \le x \le \dfrac{1}{2k}. \end{cases}$

1.11 The sequence

$$s_k(x) = \begin{cases} -k, & |x| < \dfrac{1}{2k}; \\[2mm] 2k, & \dfrac{1}{2k} \le |x| \le \dfrac{1}{k}; \\[2mm] 0, & \text{otherwise}; \end{cases}$$

should serve to dispel some of the most cherished superstitions about the delta function. A glance at the graph of $s_k(x)$ shows that for k large the charge distribution is equivalent to a unit (positive) charge at $x = 0$, yet $\lim_{k\to\infty} s_k(0) = -\infty$! Thus we must abandon the idea that $\delta(x)$ is $+\infty$ at $x = 0$. The reader should have no difficulty in constructing a sequence for which $s_k(0) = 0$ yet $\lim_{k\to\infty} s_k(x) = \delta(x)$.

1.12 Consider an experiment whose outcome can be described by a single real number x. The cumulative probability distribution $F(x)$ is defined as the probability that the outcome be a number smaller than x. The function

$f(x) = dF/dx$ is the probability density. Note that for any experiment we have $F(-\infty) = 0$, $F(+\infty) = 1$, $\int_{-\infty}^{\infty} f(x)dx = 1$. The situation is exactly the same as when a unit of charge is spread on the x axis (except that the probability density must be nonnegative). The advantage of the delta function notation is that it enables us to treat both discrete and continuous probability distributions in the same framework.

Take the particular example of the toss of a fair coin. The outcome "heads" will be assigned the value $x = 0$, the outcome "tails" the value $x = 1$. Show that

$$F(x) = \begin{cases} 0, & x < 0; \\ \tfrac{1}{2}, & 0 < x < 1; \\ 1, & x > 1. \end{cases}$$

$$f(x) = \tfrac{1}{2}[\delta(x) + \delta(x - 1)].$$

The Sifting Property of the Delta Function

We have seen above (Exercises 1.9, 1.10, and 1.11) that a variety of sequences have the "limit" $\delta(x)$, yet these sequences can behave quite differently at $x = 0$. There is a much more satisfactory way of characterizing the delta function and the sequences which approach the delta function. Let us return to the sequence $s_k(x) = k/\pi(1 + k^2x^2)$ and let us define the *action* of $s_k(x)$ on the function $\varphi(x)$ by the formula

$$A_k[\varphi] = \int_{-\infty}^{\infty} \varphi(x)s_k(x)dx.$$

We regard A_k as a weighted average of $s_k(x)$ with respect to the weighting function $\varphi(x)$. Here $\varphi(x)$ is an arbitrary function, continuous at the origin, and behaving well enough at infinity to ensure the existence of the integral. For simplicity, let φ be bounded; that is, $|\varphi| \leq M$ for all x, $-\infty < x < \infty$.

Theorem. *If $\varphi(x)$ is bounded, integrable, and continuous at $x = 0$,*

$$\lim_{k \to \infty} \int_{-\infty}^{\infty} \varphi(x) \frac{k}{\pi(1 + k^2x^2)} \, dx = \varphi(0). \qquad (1.14)$$

Proof. We first observe that

$$\int_{-\infty}^{\infty} \varphi(x)s_k(x)dx = \int_{-\infty}^{\infty} \varphi(0)s_k(x)dx + \int_{-\infty}^{\infty} \eta(x)s_k(x)dx = \varphi(0) + \int_{-\infty}^{\infty} \eta s_k \, dx,$$

where

$$\eta(x) = \varphi(x) - \varphi(0).$$

To show that $\lim\limits_{k\to\infty} \int_{-\infty}^{\infty} \eta s_k \, dx = 0$, we must prove that for any $\varepsilon > 0$ there exists an index N such that

$$\left| \int_{-\infty}^{\infty} \eta s_k \, dx \right| < \varepsilon, \qquad \text{whenever } k > N.$$

Let A be a positive number (to be chosen below) and divide the interval from $-\infty$ to ∞ into three parts so that

$$\int_{-\infty}^{\infty} \eta s_k \, dx = \int_{-\infty}^{-A} \eta s_k \, dx + \int_{A}^{\infty} \eta s_k \, dx + \int_{-A}^{A} \eta s_k \, dx = I_1 + I_2 + I_3 .$$

We examine first the integral I_3; let the maximum of $|\eta|$ in $-A \leq x \leq A$ be denoted by $p(A)$. Then

$$|I_3| \leq \int_{-A}^{A} |\eta| s_k \, dx \leq p(A) \int_{-A}^{A} \frac{k}{\pi(1 + k^2 x^2)} \, dx = p(A) \left[\frac{2}{\pi} \arctan kA \right] \leq p(A).$$

Since $\eta(0) = 0$ and $\eta(x)$ is continuous at $x = 0$, we have $\lim\limits_{A\to 0} p(A) = 0$. Thus, for any $\varepsilon > 0$, there exists A so small that

$$|I_3| < \frac{\varepsilon}{2},$$

and this holds independent of k.

With A so chosen, it remains to show that $|I_1 + I_2|$ is small for sufficiently large k. Since $|\varphi(x)| \leq M$ and $|\eta| \leq |\varphi(x)| + |\varphi(0)|$, $|\eta|$ is bounded in $-\infty < x < \infty$, say $|\eta| \leq P$. Then

$$|I_1 + I_2| \leq P \left[\int_{-\infty}^{-A} s_k \, dx + \int_{A}^{\infty} s_k \, dx \right] = P \left(1 - \frac{2}{\pi} \arctan kA \right).$$

With A fixed, $\lim\limits_{k\to\infty} (2/\pi) \arctan kA = 1$, so that we can find N such that

$$P \left(1 - \frac{2}{\pi} \arctan kA \right) < \frac{\varepsilon}{2}, \qquad k > N.$$

With this choice of N we have

$$\left| \int_{-\infty}^{\infty} \eta s_k \, dx \right| = |I_1 + I_2 + I_3| \leq |I_1 + I_2| + |I_3| < \varepsilon, \quad k > N.$$

This shows that $\lim\limits_{k\to\infty} \int_{-\infty}^{\infty} \eta s_k \, dx = 0$ and completes the proof of (1.14).

Thus, as k approaches infinity, the action of $k/\pi(1 + k^2 x^2)$ on $\varphi(x)$ approaches the number $\varphi(0)$. Since, as k increases, we regard $k/\pi(1 + k^2 x^2)$

as an increasingly good approximation to $\delta(x)$, it is natural to *define* $\delta(x)$ as the "function" which has the action $\varphi(0)$. It will be shown in the next section that no piecewise continuous function can have the action $\varphi(0)$, so that $\delta(x)$ is a new mathematical object known as *generalized* or *symbolic function*. When $\delta(x)$ acts on suitable accessory functions $\varphi(x)$, it picks out the value of $\varphi(0)$ at $x = 0$; thus symbolically,

$$\int_{-\infty}^{\infty} \varphi(x)\delta(x)dx = \varphi(0). \tag{1.15}$$

Property (1.15) is known as the *sifting property* of the delta function.

DEFINITION.   A sequence $s_k(x)$ is a δ *sequence* if

$$\lim_{k\to\infty} \int_{-\infty}^{\infty} s_k(x)\varphi(x)dx = \varphi(0)$$

for all $\varphi(x)$ which are continuous and bounded $-\infty < x < \infty$.† If $s_k(x)$ is a δ sequence, it is clear that

$$\lim_{k\to\infty} \int_{-\infty}^{\infty} s_k(x - x_0)\varphi(x)dx = \varphi(x_0).$$

Since, for large k, $s_k(x - x_0)$ approximates $\delta(x - x_0)$, we define $\delta(x - x_0)$ as the "function" which has the action $\varphi(x_0)$. Thus $\delta(x - x_0)$ has the sifting property

$$\int_{-\infty}^{\infty} \varphi(x)\delta(x - x_0)dx = \varphi(x_0).$$

We shall write

$$s_k(x - x_0) \to \delta(x - x_0) \qquad \text{or} \qquad \lim_{k\to\infty} s_k(x - x_0) = \delta(x - x_0).$$

EXERCISES

1.13 Show that the sequences in Exercises 1.9, 1.10, and 1.11 have the property

$$\lim_{k\to\infty} \int_{-\infty}^{\infty} \varphi(x)s_k(x)dx = \varphi(0)$$

† Occasionally, as in Exercise 1.18, one encounters sequences which have the property

$$\lim_{k\to\infty} \int_{-\infty}^{\infty} s_k(x)\varphi(x)dx = \varphi(0)$$

for a somewhat smaller class of accessory functions $\varphi(x)$. Such sequences will still be known as δ sequences.

for any $\varphi(x)$ bounded, integrable, and continuous at $x = 0$. Therefore, all these sequences are δ sequences.

1.14 Let a charge $+k$ be located at $x = \varepsilon$ and a charge $-k$ be located at $x = -\varepsilon$. The product $2k\varepsilon$ is known as the *dipole moment* of the charge configuration. Now suppose that the charges are brought together in such a way as to keep the dipole moment equal to 1 (that is, we let $\varepsilon \to 0$ and $k \to \infty$ so that $2k\varepsilon = 1$); the resulting charge configuration is known as a *dipole source* of unit moment. Such a dipole source can be approximated by a continuous charge distribution on the real line, as follows. Let $t_k(x) = -ds_k/dx$, where $s_k(x) = k/\pi(1 + k^2x^2)$, so that $t_k(x) = 2k^3x/\pi(1 + k^2x^2)^2$; we have sketched $t_k(x)$ in Figure 1.11 for a large value of k. We have

$$\int_a^b t_k(x)dx = s_k(a) - s_k(b) = \frac{k}{\pi(1 + k^2a^2)} - \frac{k}{\pi(1 + k^2b^2)};$$

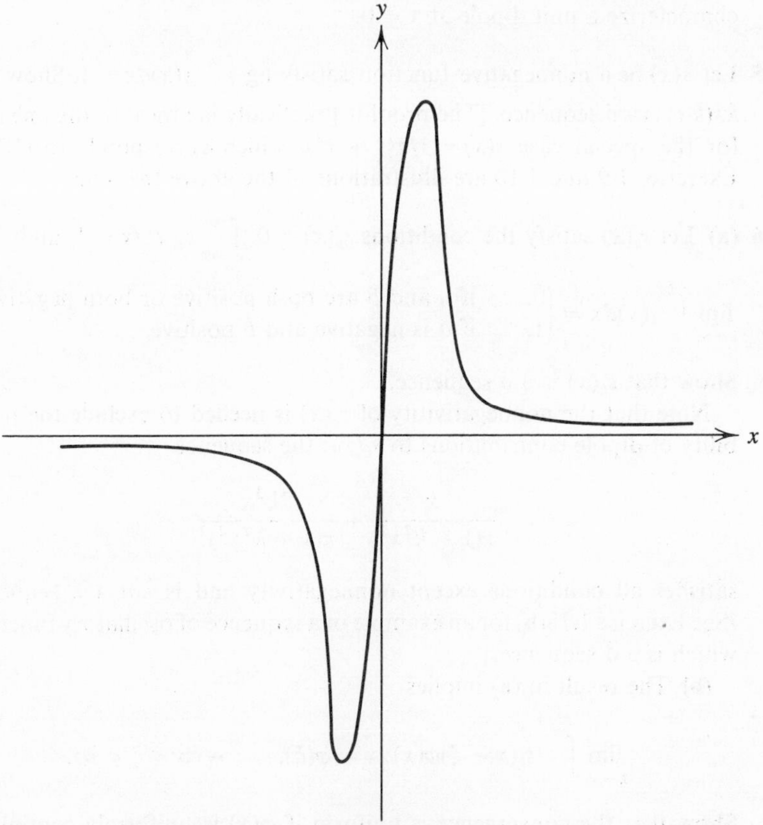

FIGURE 1.11

if neither a nor b is 0, each term approaches 0 as $k \to \infty$, and the total charge in any such interval goes to 0 as $k \to \infty$. On the other hand, $\int_0^\varepsilon t_k(x)dx \to +\infty$ and $\int_{-\varepsilon}^0 t_k(x)dx \to -\infty$; thus, for large k, we have a large positive charge just to the right of the origin and a large negative charge just to the left of the origin. Further, the first moment of the charge distribution about the origin is $\int_{-\infty}^\infty x t_k(x)dx = 1$. Hence, for large k, $t_k(x)$ approximates a dipole of unit moment located at $x = 0$. We note with some surprise that for *each* x, $\lim_{k \to \infty} t_k(x) = 0$, so that the pointwise convergence to 0 does not tell the whole story. To characterize the behavior of $t_k(x)$, consider its action on suitable functions $\varphi(x)$:

$$A_k[\varphi] = \int_{-\infty}^\infty t_k(x)\varphi(x)dx.$$

Show that $\lim_{k \to \infty} A_k[\varphi] = (d\varphi/dx)(0)$. This last property will be used to characterize a unit dipole at $x = 0$.

1.15 Let $s(x)$ be a nonnegative function satisfying $\int_{-\infty}^\infty s(x)dx = 1$. Show that $ks(kx)$ is a δ sequence. [The proof is practically identical to the one used for the special case $s(x) = 1/\pi(1 + x^2)$, which corresponds to (1.14).] Exercises 1.9 and 1.10 are illustrations of the above theorem.

1.16 (a) Let $s_k(x)$ satisfy the conditions $s_k(x) \geq 0$, $\int_{-\infty}^\infty s_k(x)dx = 1$, and

$$\lim_{k \to \infty} \int_a^b s_k(x)dx = \begin{cases} 0, & \text{if } a \text{ and } b \text{ are both positive or both negative;} \\ 1, & \text{if } a \text{ is negative and } b \text{ positive.} \end{cases}$$

Show that $s_k(x)$ is a δ sequence.

Note that the nonnegativitity of $s_k(x)$ is needed to exclude the possibility of dipole contributions to $s_k(x)$; the sequence

$$\frac{k}{\pi(1 + k^2 x^2)} + \frac{2k^3 x}{\pi(1 + k^2 x^2)^2}$$

satisfies all conditions except nonnegativity and is *not* a δ sequence. [See Exercise 1.18(b) for an example of a sequence of oscillatory functions which is a δ sequence.]

(b) The result in (a) implies

$$\lim_{k \to \infty} \int_{-\infty}^\infty s_k(x - \xi)\varphi(x)dx = \varphi(\xi), \qquad -\infty < \xi < \infty.$$

Show that the convergence is uniform if $\varphi(x)$ is uniformly continuous $-\infty < x < \infty$.

1.17 *The Weierstrass approximation theorem.* Consider the sequence

$$f_k(x) = \begin{cases} (1 - x^2)^k, & |x| < 1; \\ 0, & |x| \geq 1. \end{cases}$$

(a) Let $I_k = \int_{-1}^{1} (1 - x^2)^k \, dx$; show that $I_k = 2^{2k+1}(k!)^2/(2k + 1)!$; by using Stirling's formula, $k! \sim k^k e^{-k}\sqrt{2\pi k}$, valid for large k, show that $\lim_{k \to \infty} \sqrt{k} \, I_k = \sqrt{\pi}$.

(b) The sequence $s_k(x) = f_k(x)/I_k$ satisfies the conditions of Exercise 1.16, so

$$\lim_{k \to \infty} \int_{-\infty}^{\infty} s_k(x - \xi)\varphi(x)dx = \varphi(\xi).$$

Let $\varphi(x)$ be a continuous function, $-\infty < x < \infty$, which vanishes identically for $|x| > \frac{1}{2}$. [Note that this implies $\varphi(\frac{1}{2}) = \varphi(-\frac{1}{2}) = 0$, and that $\varphi(x)$ is uniformly continuous $-\infty < x < \infty$.] Show that $\int_{-\infty}^{\infty} s_k(x - \xi)\varphi(x)dx$ reduces to a *polynomial* in ξ when $-\frac{1}{2} \leq \xi \leq \frac{1}{2}$. Therefore $\varphi(\xi)$ has been uniformly approximated by a sequence of polynomials over the interval $-\frac{1}{2} \leq \xi \leq \frac{1}{2}$.

(c) Let $\psi(x)$ be continuous $-\frac{1}{2} \leq x \leq \frac{1}{2}$; show that $\psi(x)$ can be uniformly approximated by polynomials. [HINT: Consider $\varphi(x) = \psi(x) - x[\psi(\frac{1}{2}) - \psi(-\frac{1}{2})] - \frac{1}{2}\psi(\frac{1}{2}) - \frac{1}{2}\psi(-\frac{1}{2}).$] Let $\psi(x)$ be continuous over the finite interval $a \leq x \leq b$; show that $\psi(x)$ can be uniformly approximated by polynomials over this interval.

1.18 (a) A sequence $r_k(x)$ is an H sequence if

$$r_k(x) \to H(x) = \begin{cases} 1, & x > 0, \\ 0, & x < 0, \end{cases}$$

and $\int_{-\infty}^{\infty} r_k(x)\varphi(x)dx \to \int_{0}^{\infty} \varphi(x)dx$. The latter property can be obtained from the pointwise convergence of $r_k(x)$ to $H(x)$ by adding the requirement that $|r_k(x)| \leq r(x)$, where $r(x)$ is integrable over every finite interval. Show that $(1/\pi)\int_{-\infty}^{x} (\sin ku/u)du$ is an H sequence. [HINT: Let $ku = v$, and show that $\left|\int_{a}^{b} (\sin v/v)dv\right| \leq \int_{-\pi}^{\pi} (\sin v/v)dv.$]

(b) Let $s_k(x) = \sin kx/\pi x$. Let $\varphi(x)$ be differentiable with $\varphi'(x)$ continuous and bounded, and $\varphi(\pm\infty) = 0$. Show, by integration by parts, that

$$\lim_{k \to \infty} \int_{-\infty}^{\infty} \frac{\sin kx}{\pi x} \varphi(x)dx = \varphi(0).$$

Thus $s_k(x)$ may be regarded as a δ sequence. Observe that $s_k(x)$ changes signs an infinite number of times in $(-\infty, \infty)$.

1.19. Show that the sequence in Exercise 1.11 is a δ sequence.

1.3 THE THEORY OF DISTRIBUTIONS

Functions Viewed as Linear Functionals

Consider a real-valued, continuous function $y = f(x)$ defined on the real axis $-\infty < x < \infty$.† It is customary to visualize such a function as a table of values which lists the values of the independent variable x in the first column and the corresponding values of the dependent variable y in the second column. Although this table cannot be written in its entirety (the variable x assuming an infinite number of values even in a finite interval), we have no difficulty in regarding this conceptual table as a characterization of the function f. Since a definite value of y is associated with each point x on the real line, f is being viewed as a point function.

We can equally well characterize f by a completely different table of values. Consider $\langle f, \varphi \rangle = \int_{-\infty}^{\infty} f(x)\varphi(x)dx$ for a variety of accessory functions $\varphi(x)$ to be further specified below. The notation $\langle f, \varphi \rangle$ is used to remind us of the interpretation of the integral as an *inner product* (also known as a *dot* or *scalar product*; see Chapter 2). $\langle f, \varphi \rangle$ is termed the *action* of f on φ and is nothing more than the weighted average of $f(x)$ with respect to the weighting function $\varphi(x)$. We have thus constructed a new table of values which lists various accessory functions $\varphi(x)$ in the first column and the corresponding actions $\langle f, \varphi \rangle$ in the second column. Such a correspondence, which assigns to each function $\varphi(x)$ an unambiguous real number $\langle f, \varphi \rangle$, is known as a *functional* [the independent variable being a function $\varphi(x)$ and the dependent variable the number $\langle f, \varphi \rangle$]. If the functional is to characterize the point function $f(x)$ in an unambiguous manner, it is essential to choose the class of accessory functions $\varphi(x)$ so that the two different continuous functions $f_1(x)$ and $f_2(x)$ generate different functionals (that is, there must exist at least one φ for which the actions $\langle f_1, \varphi \rangle$ and $\langle f_2, \varphi \rangle$ are different).

REMARK. The characterization of functions as functionals on a space of accessory functions is not as unnatural as it first appears. In fact, the reader is probably familiar with the following examples, which illustrate the same idea.

1. If mass is continuously distributed on a finite portion of the real line, the mass density $f(x)$ can be characterized by its moments

$$\int_{-\infty}^{\infty} f(x)dx, \qquad \int_{-\infty}^{\infty} xf(x)dx, \qquad \int_{-\infty}^{\infty} x^2f(x)dx, \ldots.$$

† Strictly speaking, the function is the rule that establishes the correspondence between x and y; thus f is the function, whereas $f(x)$ is the numerical value assumed by f at x. Here we shall adopt the classical notation of letting the symbol $f(x)$ stand either for the function or for the value assumed by the function at x; the interpretation to be made should be clear from the context (see Section 2.1 for more about functions).

The functions x^n are the accessory functions. The specification of all the moments determines $f(x)$.

2. If $f(x)$ is a differentiable function in $0 \le x \le \pi$, and $f(0) = f(\pi) = 0$, then $f(x)$ can be characterized by its actions on the accessory functions $(2/\pi)\sin x, (2/\pi)\sin 2x, \ldots$. If we let $b_n = \langle f, (2/\pi)\sin nx\rangle = (2/\pi)\int_0^\pi f(x)\sin nx\,dx$, we can recover $f(x)$ from $\{b_n\}$ by the familiar sine series:

$$f(x) = \sum_{n=1}^{\infty} b_n \sin nx.$$

3. Whenever a physical measurement is made on a function $f(x)$ of time or position (such a pressure, velocity, voltage, etc.), it is never the instantaneous or local value of f which is measured but rather some average of f over a short time or space interval. Thus the observed value of f at x_0 is really of the form $\int \varphi(x_0, x)f(x)dx$, where $\varphi(x_0, x)$ is nearly constant over a short interval about x_0, and vanishes outside this interval.

We have seen that we can characterize f either as a point function or as a functional on a space of accessory functions. This second point of view will enable us to extend the notion of "function" in a very natural manner. The accessory functions which are useful in this connection are the so-called *test functions* defined below.

Test Functions

DEFINITION.   A *test function* $\varphi(x)$ is a function which is infinitely differentiable (that is, differentiable to every order) in $-\infty < x < \infty$, and which vanishes outside some finite interval (which may be different for different test functions). The space of all test functions will be denoted by D.

REMARKS.   1. It is not entirely evident that there exist nontrivial test functions. Suppose that $\varphi(x)$ is positive in $a < x < b$ and vanishes outside this interval; according to the definition of a test function, every derivative of φ must vanish at $x = a$ and $x = b$; it may at first be difficult to see how a function which is so "flat" at $x = a$ and $x = b$ can climb to positive values inside the interval. The following example shows that test functions do exist:

$$\varphi(x) = \begin{cases} \exp\left(\dfrac{1}{x^2 - 1}\right), & |x| < 1; \\ 0, & |x| \ge 1. \end{cases}$$

This even function is sketched in Figure 1.12. It is easily seen that $\varphi(x)$ is infinitely differentiable except possibly at $x = \pm 1$. Because of the evenness of $\varphi(x)$, it is enough to examine the point $x = 1$. Since

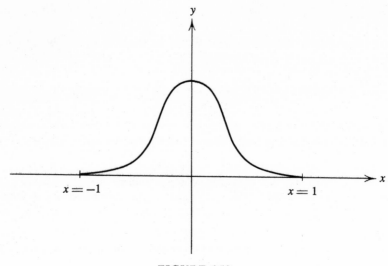

FIGURE 1.12

$\lim\limits_{x \to 1-} \exp[1/(x^2 - 1)] = 0$, $\varphi(x)$ is continuous at $x = 1$. A simple calculation, based on the fact that, for any n,

$$\lim_{x \to 1-} \frac{1}{(x^2 - 1)^n} \exp\left(\frac{1}{x^2 - 1}\right) = 0,$$

shows that all left-hand derivatives of φ vanish at $x = 1$; hence every
derivative of φ vanishes at $x = 1$.

2. If $\varphi(x)$ is the test function in the above example, then $\psi(x) = \varphi\{(1/\varepsilon)(x - x_0)\}$ is also a test function which is positive in $x_0 - \varepsilon < x < x_0 + \varepsilon$ and vanishes outside this interval.

3. If $\varphi_1(x)$ and $\varphi_2(x)$ are test functions, so is $c_1\varphi_1 + c_2\varphi_2$ for any
real numbers c_1 and c_2 ; we can therefore say that the space D of test
functions is a real linear space [see (2.2)].

4. Derivatives of any order of a test function are again test functions.

Convergence in the Space of Test Functions

We introduce an extremely stringent form of convergence in the space of
test functions. The usefulness of this definition will become apparent in what
follows. Let $\varphi_n(x)$ be a sequence of test functions; we write $\varphi_n(x) \to 0$ in D if

1. All the test functions $\varphi_n(x)$ vanish outside a *common* finite interval.
2. $\lim\limits_{n \to \infty} \varphi_n(x) = 0$ *uniformly* in $-\infty < x < \infty$, and, for every integer k,
$\lim\limits_{n \to \infty} [d^k\varphi_n(x)/dx^k] = 0$, *uniformly* in $-\infty < x < \infty$.

Distributions

DEFINITION.   *A linear functional on the space D of test functions* is a rule t which assigns to each test function $\varphi(x)$ a real number $\langle t, \varphi \rangle$ with the property

$$\langle t, c_1\varphi_1 + c_2\varphi_2 \rangle = c_1\langle t, \varphi_1 \rangle + c_2\langle t, \varphi_2 \rangle,$$

for arbitrary real numbers c_1 and c_2 and arbitrary test functions φ_1 and φ_2.

It follows that, for any linear functional, $\langle t, 0 \rangle = 0$ and

$$\left\langle t, \sum_{k=1}^{n} c_k\varphi_k \right\rangle = \sum_{k=1}^{n} c_k\langle t, \varphi_k \rangle.$$

DEFINITION.   A linear functional on D is *continuous* if and only if $\langle t, \varphi_n \rangle \to 0$ whenever $\varphi_n \to 0$ in D (here $\langle t, \varphi_n \rangle \to 0$ refers of course to ordinary convergence of a sequence of numbers). A continuous linear functional on D will also be known as a *distribution*. The space of all distributions will be denoted by D'.

By a slight abuse of terminology we shall also refer to $\langle t, \varphi \rangle$ as the distribution, when in fact $\langle t, \varphi \rangle$ is actually the value assumed by the distribution t at φ (the number $\langle t, \varphi \rangle$ will also be called more picturesquely the *action* of t on φ).

Let t_1 and t_2 be any two distributions and let c_1 and c_2 be arbitrary real numbers; we then define a new distribution $t = c_1t_1 + c_2t_2$ by the formula

$$\langle t, \varphi \rangle = \langle c_1t_1 + c_2t_2, \varphi \rangle = c_1\langle t_1, \varphi \rangle + c_2\langle t_2, \varphi \rangle. \tag{1.16}$$

It is easily checked that t is in fact a linear functional on D and that t is continuous, so that a distribution has been defined. Thus if t_1 and t_2 are in D' so is $c_1t_1 + c_2t_2$; hence D' is itself a linear space.

The simplest kind of distributions (but not the only kind) are those generated by locally integrable functions. A function $f(x)$ is said to be *locally integrable* if $\int_I |f(x)|dx$ exists for every finite interval I.† The class of locally integrable functions includes all piecewise continuous functions and other functions such as $1/x^{1-\varepsilon}$, where $\varepsilon > 0$. An important property of locally integrable functions should be noted: Let $I_1, \ldots, I_n, \ldots$ be a sequence of nested intervals (that is, each interval is included in the preceding one) whose lengths approach 0; then $\lim_{n\to\infty} \int_{I_n} |f(x)|dx = 0$. Consequently the class of locally integrable functions does *not* include the delta "function."

---

† The integral used in this definition is the Lebesgue integral (some of whose properties are discussed in Chapter 2), but the reader who is unfamiliar with this concept may interpret the integral in the Riemann sense for most of what follows.

Theorem. *Each locally integrable function $f(x)$ generates a distribution via the definition*

$$\langle f, \varphi \rangle = \int_{-\infty}^{\infty} f(x)\varphi(x)dx. \tag{1.17}$$

Proof. It is clear that a linear functional on the space of test functions has been defined; to prove continuity, let $\varphi_n(x)$ be a sequence of test functions such that $\varphi_n(x) \to 0$ in D. Then

$$|\langle f, \varphi_n \rangle| = \left| \int_{-\infty}^{\infty} f\varphi_n \, dx \right| \leq \int_{-\infty}^{\infty} |f| \, |\varphi_n| dx \leq M_n \int_I |f| dx,$$

where M_n is the maximum of $|\varphi_n|$ and I is the common interval outside of which all the $\varphi_n(x)$ vanish. The fact that $\varphi_n(x) \to 0$ in D implies the uniform convergence of $\varphi_n(x)$ to 0, so that $M_n \to 0$; hence $\langle f, \varphi_n \rangle \to 0$, and $\langle f, \varphi \rangle$ is a distribution.

The constant point function c is locally integrable and defines a distribution by the formula

$$\langle c, \varphi \rangle = \int_{-\infty}^{\infty} c\varphi(x)dx = c \int_{-\infty}^{\infty} \varphi(x)dx.$$

The same symbol c will be used for the number c, the constant point function c, and for the distribution generated by the constant point function c.

Do different locally integrable functions generate different distributions? The following theorem is a preliminary result in this direction.

Theorem. *The only continuous function $f(x)$ for which $\langle f, \varphi \rangle = 0$ for every test function φ is $f(x) \equiv 0$, $-\infty < x < \infty$.*

Proof. Suppose $f(x_0) > 0$; then there exists an interval $x_0 - \varepsilon < x < x_0 + \varepsilon$ in which $f(x)$ is positive. We have seen that there is a test function $\varphi(x)$ which is positive in $x_0 - \varepsilon < x < x_0 + \varepsilon$ and vanishes outside this interval. For this test function we have $\langle f, \varphi \rangle > 0$, which contradicts the hypothesis. A similar contradiction would have been obtained if we had assumed $f(x_0) < 0$.

COROLLARY. *Two different continuous functions generate different distributions.*

The above theorem and its corollary do not hold (without suitable modification) for locally integrable functions. Indeed the functions $f_1(x) \equiv 0$ and

$$f_2(x) = \begin{cases} 0, & x \text{ not an integer}; \\ 1, & x \text{ integer,} \end{cases}$$

generate the same distribution (the 0 distribution). For the purposes of the present theory (and indeed for nearly all other important applications) such functions are regarded as indistinguishable. The following definition makes the idea precise: Two locally integrable functions $f_1(x)$ and $f_2(x)$ are *equal almost everywhere* if $\int_I |f_1 - f_2| dx = 0$ for every finite interval I.

Theorem. *Two locally integrable functions, equal almost everywhere, generate the same distribution; if they are not equal almost everywhere they generate different distributions.*

The proof of the theorem is omitted (only the second part presents any difficulty).

From now on we shall take the point of view that functions which are equal almost everywhere are the same function. With this understanding, different locally integrable functions generate different distributions.

So far, all we have shown is that locally integrable functions can be characterized as distributions by (1.17). We now make the important observation that there exist distributions which cannot be represented in the form (1.17) for any locally integrable $f(x)$. Consider $\langle t, \varphi \rangle = \varphi(0)$, which is clearly a linear functional; furthermore, if $\varphi_n(x) \to 0$ in D, then the sequence of numbers $\varphi_n(0)$ certainly approaches 0 and hence $\langle t, \varphi \rangle$ is continuous and is a distribution. This distribution is known as the *delta distribution* and will be written $\langle \delta, \varphi \rangle$. We now show that $\langle \delta, \varphi \rangle$ is not generated [via (1.17)] by a locally integrable function $f(x)$. If such a locally integrable function existed, we would have $\int_{-\infty}^{\infty} f(x)\varphi(x)dx = \varphi(0)$ for every test function. Consider the test functions

$$\varphi_a(x) = \begin{cases} \exp\left(\dfrac{a^2}{x^2 - a^2}\right), & |x| < a; \\ 0, & |x| \geq a. \end{cases}$$

We have $\varphi_a(0) = 1/e$, $|\varphi_a(x)| \leq 1/e$; hence

$$\left| \int_{-\infty}^{\infty} f(x)\varphi_a(x)dx \right| = \left| \int_{-a}^{a} f(x) \exp\left(\frac{a^2}{x^2 - a^2}\right) dx \right| \leq \frac{1}{e} \int_{-a}^{a} |f(x)| dx.$$

Since $f(x)$ is locally integrable, we have $\lim_{a \to 0} \int_{-a}^{a} |f(x)| dx = 0$ and $\lim_{a \to 0} \int_{-\infty}^{\infty} f(x)\varphi_a(x)dx = 0$; on the other hand, we must have $\int_{-\infty}^{\infty} f(x)\varphi_a(x)dx = \varphi_a(0) = 1/e$. We have arrived at a contradiction, and consequently there cannot exist a locally integrable function $f(x)$ such that $\int_{-\infty}^{\infty} f(x)\varphi(x)dx = \varphi(0)$ for every test function.

DEFINITION. A distribution is *regular* if it can be generated by a locally integrable function through (1.17). All other distributions are *singular*.

REMARKS.   1. Whether or not a distribution t is regular, we shall always feel free to write $\langle t, \varphi \rangle = \int_{-\infty}^{\infty} t(x)\varphi(x)dx$. If t is regular, the preceding formula is valid with $t(x)$ a locally integrable function; if t is singular, the formula is purely symbolic and $t(x)$ is known as the *symbolic* or *generalized function* corresponding to the distribution t. As we progress we shall pay less and less distinction to the difference between $t(x)$ and $\langle t, \varphi \rangle$. Any property ascribed to $t(x)$ is, by definition, the direct consequence of the same property holding for $\langle t, \varphi \rangle$. For instance, if two distributions are equal (that is, if $\langle t_1, \varphi \rangle = \langle t_2, \varphi \rangle$ for every φ), we say that $t_1(x) = t_2(x)$.

2. A distribution is a generalization of the notion of a real-valued function of a real variable. A similar generalization is easily made for complex-valued functions of a real variable (this, of course, has nothing to do with functions of a complex variable). The test functions $\varphi(x)$ are now infinitely differentiable complex-valued functions of the real variable x; this new space of test functions is denoted by $D^{(c)}$, and the same definition is used for convergence to 0 in $D^{(c)}$ as in D. A distribution t is now a complex-valued functional on $D^{(c)}$ satisfying the conditions

(a) $\langle t, c_1\varphi_1 + c_2\varphi_2 \rangle = c_1\langle t, \varphi_1 \rangle + c_2\langle t, \varphi_2 \rangle$

for any *complex* numbers c_1 and c_2.

(b) $\lim_{n \to \infty} \langle t, \varphi_n \rangle = 0,$

whenever $\varphi_n \to 0$ in $D^{(c)}$.

EXAMPLES

Example 1.   The Heaviside distribution $\langle H, \varphi \rangle$ is generated by the locally integrable function

$$H(x) = \begin{cases} 0, & x < 0; \\ 1, & x \geq 0. \end{cases}$$

Thus $\langle H, \varphi \rangle$ is a regular distribution, and

$$\langle H, \varphi \rangle = \int_{-\infty}^{\infty} H(x)\varphi(x)dx = \int_{0}^{\infty} \varphi(x)dx.$$

The definition used for $H(x)$ at $x = 0$ is arbitrary; any other finite value could have been used for the definition of $H(0)$, and none of our results would be affected.

Example 2.   The rule which assigns to each test function $\varphi(x)$ its value at $x = 0$ is the delta distribution (which has been shown to be singular). We write

$$\langle \delta, \varphi \rangle = \varphi(0) = \int_{-\infty}^{\infty} \delta(x)\varphi(x)dx.$$

The generalized function $\delta(x)$ represents the charge density for a positive unit charge located at $x = 0$.

Example 3.   The rule that assigns to each test function $\varphi(x)$ its value at the fixed point $x = \xi$ is a singular distribution,

$$\langle \delta_\xi, \varphi \rangle = \varphi(\xi) = \int_{-\infty}^{\infty} \delta_\xi(x)\varphi(x)dx.$$

The generalized function $\delta_\xi(x)$ represents the charge density for a positive unit charge located at $x = \xi$. We note that δ_0 and δ are the same distribution; furthermore, it will be shown below that $\delta_\xi(x)$ can be identified with $\delta(x - \xi)$.

Example 4.   Let a positive charge of magnitude $1/\varepsilon$ be located at $x = \varepsilon/2$, and a like negative charge at $x = -\varepsilon/2$. The limiting charge configuration, as $\varepsilon \to 0$, is said to be a dipole of positive unit moment located at $x = 0$. The action of the limiting charge configuration on a test function $\varphi(x)$ is

$$\lim_{\varepsilon \to 0} \left\{ \frac{1}{\varepsilon}\,\varphi\left(\frac{\varepsilon}{2}\right) - \frac{1}{\varepsilon}\,\varphi\left(-\frac{\varepsilon}{2}\right) \right\} = \varphi'(0).$$

The singular distribution $\varphi'(0)$ is known as the *dipole distribution*. We will show later that the corresponding generalized function can be interpreted as $-\delta'(x)$.

Operations with Distributions

1. *Translation.*   If $f(x)$ is locally integrable, it generates the distribution $\langle f(x), \varphi(x) \rangle = \int_{-\infty}^{\infty} f(x)\varphi(x)dx$, whereas $f(x - a)$ generates the distribution

$$\langle f(x - a), \varphi(x) \rangle = \int_{-\infty}^{\infty} f(x - a)\varphi(x)dx$$

$$= \int_{-\infty}^{\infty} f(x)\varphi(x + a)dx = \langle f(x), \varphi(x + a) \rangle.$$

The above relation suggests the definition to be used for $t(x - a)$, where $t(x)$ is an arbitrary generalized function. Thus, we define $t(x - a)$ from

$$\langle t(x - a), \varphi(x) \rangle = \langle t(x), \varphi(x + a) \rangle.$$

This definition makes sense, since $\varphi(x + a)$ is a test function and the action of t on $\varphi(x + a)$ is therefore meaningful. Using this definition we have

$$\langle \delta(x - a), \varphi(x) \rangle = \langle \delta(x), \varphi(x + a) \rangle = \varphi(a).$$

Therefore, $\delta(x - a) = \delta_a(x)$; henceforth we use the notation $\delta(x - a)$ instead of $\delta_a(x)$.

2. *Scale Expansion.* If $f(x)$ is locally integrable, so is $f(ax)$ for any real number a. The distribution corresponding to $f(ax)$ is

$$\langle f(ax), \varphi(x) \rangle = \int_{-\infty}^{\infty} f(ax)\varphi(x)dx = \begin{cases} \dfrac{1}{a} \int_{-\infty}^{\infty} f(u)\varphi\left(\dfrac{u}{a}\right)du, & a > 0; \\ -\dfrac{1}{a} \int_{-\infty}^{\infty} f(u)\varphi\left(\dfrac{u}{a}\right)du, & a < 0. \end{cases}$$

Thus

$$\langle f(ax), \varphi(x) \rangle = \frac{1}{|a|} \left\langle f(x), \varphi\left(\frac{x}{a}\right) \right\rangle, \qquad \text{for } a \neq 0.$$

This suggests that, for any distribution t, we define $t(ax)$ from

$$\langle t(ax), \varphi(x) \rangle = \frac{1}{|a|} \left\langle t(x), \varphi\left(\frac{x}{a}\right) \right\rangle, \qquad a \neq 0.$$

We observe that $\delta(-x)$ is the generalized function corresponding to

$$\langle \delta(-x), \varphi(x) \rangle = \langle \delta(x), \varphi(-x) \rangle = \varphi(0).$$

Therefore $\delta(-x) = \delta(x)$, and $\delta(x)$ is an *even* generalized function.

3. *Multiplication by a Locally Integrable Function.* If $t(x)$ is a generalized function and $f(x)$ is locally integrable, it is natural to define $f(x)t(x)$ from

$$\langle ft, \varphi \rangle = \langle t, f\varphi \rangle. \tag{1.18}$$

Unfortunately $f\varphi$ is not necessarily a test function, so that the action of t on $f\varphi$ may not be defined. If $f(x)$ is *infinitely differentiable*, $f\varphi$ will be a test function, and the definition (1.18) is used for ft.

If c is the constant point function, ct is always defined and $\langle ct, \varphi \rangle = \langle t, c\varphi \rangle = c\langle t, \varphi \rangle$, the last equality being a consequence of the linearity of t. On the other hand, we have previously defined a constant multiple of a distribution by (1.16), namely $\langle ct, \varphi \rangle = c\langle t, \varphi \rangle$; we note with satisfaction and relief that the two definitions coincide. As another example, consider $f(x)\delta(x)$, where $f(x)$ is infinitely differentiable; then, $\langle f\delta, \varphi \rangle = \langle \delta, f\varphi \rangle = f(0)\varphi(0)$. Thus $f(x)\delta(x)$ is the same generalized function as $f(0)\delta(x)$. It is clear that this definition of $f(x)\delta(x)$ can be used even in the case where $f(x)$ is only continuous at $x = 0$. If $f(x)$ is infinitely differentiable and $t(x)$ is the *dipole* distribution [that is $\langle t, \varphi \rangle = \varphi'(0)$], we have from (1.18), $\langle ft, \varphi \rangle = \langle t, f\varphi \rangle = (d/dx)(f\varphi)|_{x=0} = f'(0)\varphi(0) + f(0)\varphi'(0)$, or $f(x)t(x) = f'(0)\delta(x) + f(0)t(x)$. This definition can be used as long as $f(x)$ is continuously differentiable at $x = 0$.

We observe that the product of two distributions *cannot* always be defined; for instance, $\delta^2(x) = \delta(x)\delta(x)$ cannot be defined in a useful way as a distribution.

Values of a Distribution on an Open Interval

The concept of the value of a generalized function at a point x is not particularly useful (and in some cases not even meaningful). On the other hand, we shall have occasion to speak of the values of a generalized function over an open interval; in particular, we may be able to identify a generalized function with a locally integrable function over an open interval.

DEFINITION. Two generalized functions $t_1(x)$ and $t_2(x)$ are said to be equal over the open interval $a < x < b$ if $\langle t_1, \varphi \rangle = \langle t_2, \varphi \rangle$ for all test functions $\varphi(x)$ which vanish outside the interval $a < x < b$.

As an example we see that $\delta(x) = 0$ in $0 < x < \infty$ and $-\infty < x < 0$.

Differentiation of Distributions

If $f(x)$ is a differentiable function whose derivative is locally integrable, $f'(x)$ defines the distribution

$$\langle f', \varphi \rangle = \int_{-\infty}^{\infty} f'(x)\varphi(x)dx.$$

Integrating by parts and recalling that $\varphi(x)$ is 0 outside a finite interval, we find that

$$\langle f', \varphi \rangle = - \int_{-\infty}^{\infty} f(x)\varphi'(x)dx = \langle f, -\varphi' \rangle.$$

Thus the action of f' on φ is equal to the action of f on the test function $-\varphi'$. For any distribution t, the derivative t' is defined by the formula

$$\langle t', \varphi \rangle = \langle t, -\varphi' \rangle = -\langle t, \varphi' \rangle. \tag{1.19}$$

That (1.19) does in fact define a linear functional on D follows from

$$\langle t', c_1\varphi_1 + c_2\varphi_2 \rangle = -\langle t, c_1\varphi_1' + c_2\varphi_2' \rangle = -c_1\langle t, \varphi_1' \rangle - c_2\langle t, \varphi_2' \rangle$$
$$= c_1\langle t', \varphi_1 \rangle + c_2\langle t', \varphi_2 \rangle.$$

To show that t' is a distribution, we must prove further that whenever $\varphi_n \to 0$ in D then $\langle t', \varphi_n \rangle \to 0$. Now if $\varphi_n \to 0$ in D, then $\varphi_n' \to 0$ in D and, since t is a distribution, $\langle t, \varphi_n' \rangle \to 0$. The definition (1.19) then shows that $\langle t', \varphi_n \rangle \to 0$. By repeated application of (1.19), we obtain

$$\langle t^{(n)}, \varphi \rangle = \langle t, (-1)^n \varphi^{(n)} \rangle = (-1)^n \langle t, \varphi^{(n)} \rangle. \tag{1.19a}$$

Since the nth derivative of a test function is also a test function, one can easily see that (1.19a) defines a distribution known as the nth generalized derivative of t. This distribution (or its corresponding generalized function) will be written $t^{(n)}$ or $d^n t/dx^n$.

EXAMPLES

Example 1. Let $H(x)$ be the Heaviside function; then,

$$\langle H, \varphi \rangle = \int_{-\infty}^{\infty} H(x)\varphi(x)dx = \int_{0}^{\infty} \varphi(x)dx.$$

By (1.19) we have

$$\langle H', \varphi \rangle = -\langle H, \varphi' \rangle = -\int_{0}^{\infty} \varphi'(x)dx = \varphi(0).$$

Therefore $\langle H', \varphi \rangle = \langle \delta, \varphi \rangle$ and we write

$$\frac{dH}{dx} = \delta(x). \tag{1.20}$$

An alternative way of defining dH/dx is by the formula

$$\frac{dH}{dx} = \lim_{\varepsilon \to 0} \frac{H(x + \varepsilon) - H(x)}{\varepsilon}.$$

Calculating the distribution on the right side, we obtain

$$\left\langle \frac{dH}{dx}, \varphi \right\rangle = \lim_{\varepsilon \to 0} \left\langle \frac{H(x + \varepsilon) - H(x)}{\varepsilon}, \varphi \right\rangle = \lim_{\varepsilon \to 0} \frac{1}{\varepsilon} \left[\int_{-\varepsilon}^{\infty} \varphi(x)dx - \int_{0}^{\infty} \varphi(x)dx \right]$$

$$= \lim_{\varepsilon \to 0} \frac{1}{\varepsilon} \int_{-\varepsilon}^{0} \varphi(x)dx = \varphi(0).$$

Thus the two natural definitions of dH/dx are in agreement.

In ordinary analysis $H(x)$ has derivative 0 except at the origin, where the derivative fails to exist. One might be tempted to say that $H'(x) = 0$ and not to worry about what happens at $x = 0$; such a definition would be fruitless, since it would violate the desirable property that a function can be recovered by integrating its derivative. On the other hand, the more sophisticated equation (1.20) can be formally integrated to yield

$$H(x) = \int_{-\infty}^{x} \delta(\xi)d\xi = \begin{cases} 0, & x < 0; \\ 1, & x > 0. \end{cases}$$

Example 2. Let $f(x)$ be differentiable except at the points $a_1, \ldots, a_n$, where $f(x)$ jumps by the respective amounts $\Delta f_1, \ldots, \Delta f_n$. It is further assumed that the derivative of f is locally integrable wherever the derivative exists. The generalized derivative of f is obtained from (1.19),

$$\langle f', \varphi \rangle = -\langle f, \varphi' \rangle = -\int_{-\infty}^{\infty} f\varphi' \, dx$$

$$= -\int_{-\infty}^{a_1} f\varphi' \, dx - \int_{a_1}^{a_2} f\varphi' \, dx - \cdots - \int_{a_n}^{\infty} f\varphi' \, dx.$$

Integrating by parts and noting that $f(a_k+) - f(a_k-) = \Delta f_k$, we find

$$\langle f', \varphi \rangle = \int_{-\infty}^{a_1} \frac{df}{dx} \varphi \, dx + \cdots + \int_{a_n}^{\infty} \frac{df}{dx} \varphi \, dx + \sum_{k=1}^{n} \Delta f_k \varphi(a_k).$$

We can therefore write

$$\langle f', \varphi \rangle = \int_{-\infty}^{\infty} [f']\varphi \, dx + \sum_{k=1}^{n} \Delta f_k \varphi(a_k)$$

or

$$\boxed{f' = [f'] + \sum_{k=1}^{n} \Delta f_k \delta(x - a_k).} \qquad (1.21)$$

The symbol $[f']$ stands for the usual derivative of $f(x)$ wherever this derivative exists (at points where the usual derivative does not exist, $[f']$ can be assigned any finite value whatever). The symbol f' stands for the generalized derivative of f. The term $\sum_{k=1}^{n} \Delta f_k \delta(x - a_k)$ in (1.21) ensures that the integral of f' yields f rather than the continuous function which would be obtained by integrating $[f']$ alone. Formula (1.21) can also be derived by considering the function

$$g(x) = f(x) - \sum_{k=1}^{n} \Delta f_k H(x - a_k).$$

The presence of the term $\Delta f_k H(x - a_k)$ removes the jump in $f(x)$ at $x = a_k$, so that $g(x)$ is continuous; furthermore, the derivative of $g(x)$ coincides with $[f']$. It immediately follows that

$$[f'] = f' - \sum_{k=1}^{n} \Delta f_k \delta(x - a_k).$$

A jump in a function results in a delta function appearing in its generalized derivative.

Example 3.   The derivative of the delta function is obtained from (1.19):

$$\langle \delta', \varphi \rangle = -\langle \delta, \varphi' \rangle = -\varphi'(0).$$

Thus $-\delta'(x)$ is the generalized function corresponding to the dipole distribution $\varphi'(0)$. We regard $-\delta'(x)$ as the charge density corresponding to a dipole of positive unit moment located at $x = 0$. It is equally reasonable to define δ' as the limit as $\varepsilon \to 0$ of the difference quotient $[\delta(x + \varepsilon) - \delta(x)]/\varepsilon$, where $\delta(x + \varepsilon)$ is defined as a translation of $\delta(x)$. A simple calculation shows

$$\left\langle \frac{\delta(x + \varepsilon) - \delta(x)}{\varepsilon}, \varphi(x) \right\rangle = \frac{1}{\varepsilon} [\varphi(-\varepsilon) - \varphi(0)].$$

As $\varepsilon \to 0$, we again obtain $-\varphi'(0)$, which agrees with the previous definition (see Exercise 1.22 for the general case).

Example 4. If $f(x)$ is infinitely differentiable, we can calculate $f(x)(d^n t/dx^n)$ as follows:

$$\langle ft^{(n)}, \varphi \rangle = \langle t^{(n)}, f\varphi \rangle = (-1)^n \left\langle t, \frac{d^n(f\varphi)}{dx^n} \right\rangle.$$

Example 5. Let L be the linear differential operator

$$a_0(x)\frac{d^n}{dx^n} + \cdots + a_{n-1}(x)\frac{d}{dx} + a_n(x),$$

where all the coefficients are infinitely differentiable; then, for any distribution t, we have

$$\langle Lt, \varphi \rangle = \left\langle \sum_{k=0}^{n} a_{n-k} t^{(k)}, \varphi \right\rangle = \left\langle t, \sum_{k=0}^{n} (-1)^k \frac{d^k(a_{n-k}\varphi)}{dx^k} \right\rangle.$$

The action of Lt on φ is therefore equivalent to the action of t on the test function $\psi(x)$, where

$$\psi(x) = L^* \varphi = \sum_{k=0}^{n} (-1)^k \frac{d^k(a_{n-k}\varphi)}{dx^k}.$$

The nth-order linear differential operator L^* is known as the *formal adjoint* of L.

Example 6. A distribution is said to be of *order n* if it can be expressed as the nth derivative of a regular distribution, but cannot be expressed as a derivative of lower order of a regular distribution. The higher the order of a distribution, the more singular it is. A distribution of order 0 is a regular distribution (that is, a distribution corresponding to a locally integrable function).

A distribution is of *order n over an open interval* $a < x < b$ if, over that interval, it coincides with the nth derivative of a regular distribution and does not coincide with a derivative of lower order of a regular distribution.

It can be shown that every distribution is of finite order over any finite interval (but it is possible for the order to increase with the size of the interval, so that the distribution may not be of finite order on the whole line).

There is no difficulty in showing that $\delta(x)$ is of order 1, $\delta'(x)$ of order 2, and $\delta^{(n)}(x)$ of order $n + 1$.

EXERCISES

1.20 Construct a test function which has the value 1 in $-1 \le x \le 1$. (HINT: Consider the integral of the test function in Exercise 1.21.)

1.21 Consider the test function

$$\varphi(x) = \begin{cases} k \exp\left(\dfrac{1}{x^2 - 1}\right), & |x| < 1; \\ 0, & |x| \geq 1, \end{cases}$$

where k has been chosen so that $\int_{-1}^{1} \varphi(x)dx = 1$. The function

$$\varphi_\varepsilon(x - \xi) = \frac{1}{\varepsilon} \varphi\left(\frac{x - \xi}{\varepsilon}\right)$$

is then a test function which vanishes for $|x - \xi| \geq \varepsilon$; furthermore, $\int_{-\infty}^{\infty} \varphi_\varepsilon(x - \xi)dx = 1$. Now let $u(x)$ be a continuous function which vanishes outside a finite interval [$u(x)$ is not a test function, since we have not assumed any differentiability properties]. Show that

$$\psi_\varepsilon(x) = \int_{-\infty}^{\infty} \varphi_\varepsilon(x - \xi)u(\xi)d\xi$$

is a test function and that

$$\lim_{\varepsilon \to 0} \psi_\varepsilon(x) = u(x), \qquad \text{uniformly on } -\infty < x < \infty.$$

Thus we have the remarkable fact that, over a finite interval, any continuous function can be uniformly approximated by test functions.

1.22 We have defined t' from $\langle t', \varphi \rangle = -\langle t, \varphi' \rangle$. It is equally tempting to define t' by $\lim_{\varepsilon \to 0} [t(x + \varepsilon) - t(x)]/\varepsilon$, where $t(x + \varepsilon)$ is a translated distribution. From this point of view

$$\langle t', \varphi \rangle = -\langle t, \varphi' \rangle - \lim_{\varepsilon \to 0} \left\langle t(x), \frac{\varphi(x) - \varphi(x - \varepsilon)}{\varepsilon} - \varphi'(x) \right\rangle.$$

For the two definitions to be in agreement, we must have

$$\lim_{\varepsilon \to 0} \left\langle t(x), \frac{\varphi(x) - \varphi(x - \varepsilon)}{\varepsilon} - \varphi'(x) \right\rangle = 0.$$

Since t is a continuous functional on the space of test functions, the desired result follows if it can be shown that

$$\{[\varphi(x) - \varphi(x - \varepsilon)]/\varepsilon - \varphi'(x)\} \to 0 \text{ in } D.$$

Prove this last statement, thereby establishing the concordance of the two definitions of t'.

Convergence of Distributions

Consider a sequence t_n of distributions. If, for each test function $\varphi(x)$, the sequence of numbers $\langle t_n, \varphi \rangle$ has a limit as $n \to \infty$, we will say that t_n converges as $n \to \infty$. The set of limiting values defines a functional, easily seen to be linear, on the space of test functions. It can be shown (but not without difficulty) that this functional is continuous. Consequently, if the sequence of distributions t_n converges as $n \to \infty$, there exists a distribution t such that, for each test function φ,

$$\lim_{n \to \infty} \langle t_n, \varphi \rangle = \langle t, \varphi \rangle.$$

We shall use the notation $\lim_{n \to \infty} t_n = t$, or $t_n \to t$, and say that t_n converges (distributionally) to t.

The same definitions can be used if t_α is a set of distributions which depend on the continuous parameter α; thus we write $\lim_{\alpha \to \alpha_0} t_\alpha = t$ if, for each test function φ, we have $\lim_{\alpha \to \alpha_0} \langle t_\alpha, \varphi \rangle = \langle t, \varphi \rangle$. A series of distributions

$$s_1 + \cdots + s_n + \cdots$$

is said to converge to t provided the sequence of partial sums $t_k = \sum_{n=1}^{k} s_n$ converges to t as $k \to \infty$; we then write $t = \sum_{n=1}^{\infty} s_n$.

When dealing with a sequence of locally integrable functions $f_n(x)$, we may wish to enquire about the relation between ordinary pointwise convergence and distributional convergence. The following theorem will serve our purposes: If $f_n(x)$ converges uniformly to $f(x)$ over each finite interval, then $f_n \to f$ in the sense of distributions. Indeed it follows from uniform convergence that f is locally integrable, and

$$\langle f_n, \varphi \rangle = \int_{-\infty}^{\infty} f_n(x)\varphi(x)dx \to \int_{-\infty}^{\infty} f\varphi \, dx = \langle f, \varphi \rangle.$$

The step $\int_{-\infty}^{\infty} f_n(x)\varphi(x)dx \to \int_{-\infty}^{\infty} f\varphi \, dx$ is a consequence of the uniform convergence of $f_n\varphi$ to $f\varphi$ and of the fact that φ vanishes outside a finite interval. Of course it is possible for $f_n(x)$ to approach $f(x)$ distributionally even if the sequence $f_n(x)$ does not approach $f(x)$ pointwise; for instance, the sequence $f_n(x) = \sin nx$ does not converge pointwise to any function, yet $f_n(x) \to 0$ distributionally, as we shall see below.

The following theorem on term-by-term differentiation plays a central role in the applications of the theory of distributions. *If the sequence of distributions t_n converges to t, then the sequence t_n' must converge to t'.* Let us observe first that t' and t_n' exist because all distributions are differentiable. Furthermore,

$$\langle t_n', \varphi \rangle = -\langle t_n, \varphi' \rangle \to -\langle t, \varphi' \rangle = \langle t', \varphi \rangle,$$

which proves that $t'_n \to t'$. This leads to the remarkable and useful result that *every convergent sequence or series of distributions can be differentiated term by term as often as required*.

In mathematical physics one frequently encounters sequences of functions which fail to converge uniformly in $-\infty < x < \infty$. Such sequences fall into two categories: those which converge pointwise but not uniformly, and those which even fail to converge pointwise. Both categories should be intrepreted distributionally, and the following procedure is usually effective. Let $f_n(x)$ be the troublesome sequence; suppose that an integer k can be found such that $f_n(x)$ is the kth derivative of a sequence $g_n(x)$ which converges uniformly to $g(x)$. It follows that $g_n \to g$ distributionally and, by the differentiation theorem, that $f_n \to g^{(k)}$, where $g^{(k)}$ is the kth generalized derivative of g.

EXAMPLES

Example 1.   It was shown in Section 1.2 that, for every test function φ,

$$\lim_{k \to \infty} \int_{-\infty}^{\infty} \frac{1}{\pi} \frac{k}{1 + k^2 x^2} \varphi(x) dx = \varphi(0).$$

(In fact, this was shown for a much larger class of functions φ.) We have therefore a rigorous interpretation of the formula

$$\lim_{k \to \infty} \frac{1}{\pi} \frac{k}{1 + k^2 x^2} = \delta(x).$$

Example 2.   Consider the locally integrable function $t_\alpha(x) = \sin \alpha x / \pi x$, which depends on the parameter α. We have shown in Exercise 1.18 that, for every test function $\varphi(x)$,

$$\lim_{\alpha \to \infty} \int_{-\infty}^{\infty} \frac{\sin \alpha x}{\pi x} \varphi(x) dx = \varphi(0).$$

Therefore, in the sense of distributional convergence,

$$\lim_{\alpha \to \infty} \frac{\sin \alpha x}{\pi x} = \delta(x).$$

We note further that

$$\frac{\sin \alpha x}{\pi x} = \frac{1}{2\pi} \int_{-\alpha}^{\alpha} e^{i\omega x} \, d\omega;$$

hence

$$\lim_{\alpha \to \infty} \frac{1}{2\pi} \int_{-\alpha}^{\alpha} e^{i\omega x} \, d\omega = \delta(x) \qquad \text{or} \qquad \frac{1}{2\pi} \int_{-\infty}^{\infty} e^{i\omega(x - \xi)} \, d\omega = \delta(x - \xi).$$

The foregoing equations have been popular among physicists (and used effectively by them) for a few decades; the theory of distributions now furnishes a rigorous interpretation of these equations.

Example 3. The sequence $f_n(x) = \sin nx$ fails to converge in the classical sense (unless x is a multiple of π). The sequence $g_n(x) = -\cos nx/n$ approaches 0 uniformly in $-\infty < x < \infty$, therefore $g_n \to 0$ distributionally; by the differentiation theorem $g_n'(x) = \sin nx \to 0$ distributionally.

Example 4. The sequence $f_n(x) = 2n^3x/\pi(1 + n^2x^2)^2$ (discussed previously in Section 1.2; see Figure 1.11) converges pointwise (but not uniformly) to 0 in $-\infty < x < \infty$. The statement that $f_n(x)$ approaches 0 pointwise does not describe the situation satisfactorily, because we know that for large n, $f_n(x)$ has extremely large positive values for $x = 0+$ and extremely large negative values for $x = 0-$. The distributional limit takes this into account. In fact,

$$f_n(x) = -\frac{1}{\pi}\frac{d}{dx}\left(\frac{n}{1 + n^2x^2}\right),$$

so that, from (1),

$$f_n(x) \to -\delta'(x) \qquad \text{or} \qquad \langle f_n, \varphi \rangle \to \varphi'(0).$$

Example 5. Consider the Fourier series

$$\sum_{n=-\infty}^{\infty} c_n e^{inx}$$

If, for large $|n|$, $|c_n| \le M/n^2$, the series converges uniformly and hence distributionally. If all we know is that, for large $|n|$, $|c_n| \le Mn^\alpha$, where α is an integer, the series may diverge pointwise; the related series

$$\sum_{n\ne 0} (in)^{-\alpha-2} c_n e^{inx}$$

converges uniformly to some function $g(x)$. On taking the $(\alpha + 2)$th derivative, we find that

$$\sum_{n=-\infty}^{\infty} c_n e^{inx} = c_0 + g^{(\alpha+2)}(x),$$

where $g^{(\alpha+2)}$ is the $(\alpha + 2)$th generalized derivative of $g(x)$.

Example 6. Consider the function (sketched in Figure 1.13)

$$f(x) = \begin{cases} x + \frac{1}{2}, & -\frac{1}{2} < x < 0; \\ x - \frac{1}{2} & 0 < x < \frac{1}{2}; \end{cases}$$

$f(0) = 0; f(x + k) = f(x)$. The generalized derivative of this locally integrable, periodic function is given by $f'(x) = 1 - \sum_{k=-\infty}^{\infty} \delta(x - k)$. Expanding $f(x)$ in a Fourier series, we obtain

$f(x) = \sum_{n=1}^{\infty} b_n \sin 2n\pi x$

$$f(x) = -\frac{2}{\pi}\sum_{n=1}^{\infty}\frac{1}{2n}\sin 2n\pi x.$$

$b_n = \frac{2}{\pi}\int_0^1 f(\xi) \sin 2n\pi\xi \, d\xi$

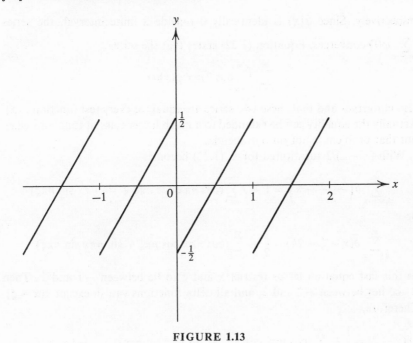

FIGURE 1.13

The above equality holds in the sense of pointwise convergence (from the elementary theory of Fourier series); it is also valid in the distributional sense, because the right side is the term-by-term derivative of a uniformly convergent series (see Example 5). By the differentiation theorem for series which converge distributionally, we have

$$f'(x) = -2 \sum_{n=1}^{\infty} \cos 2n\pi x$$

or

$$\sum_{k=-\infty}^{\infty} \delta(x-k) = 1 + 2 \sum_{n=1}^{\infty} \cos 2n\pi x, \qquad -\infty < x < \infty. \qquad (1.22)$$

A statement like (1.22) would create havoc in classical analysis because the right side is a divergent series, but it hardly causes a ripple of excitement in the theory of distributions. Let us be quite clear about (1.22); we are saying

$$\lim_{k \to \infty} t_k(x) = 1 + 2 \lim_{n \to \infty} s_n(x),$$

where $t_k(x) = \sum_{i=-k}^{k} \delta(x-i)$ and $s_n(x) = \sum_{j=1}^{n} \cos 2j\pi x$; here the distributions $\langle t_k, \varphi \rangle$ and $\langle s_n, \varphi \rangle$ are given by

$$\langle t_k, \varphi \rangle = \sum_{i=-k}^{k} \varphi(i) \qquad \text{and} \qquad \langle s_n, \varphi \rangle = \sum_{j=1}^{n} \int_{-\infty}^{\infty} \cos 2j\pi x \, \varphi(x) dx,$$

respectively. Since $\varphi(x)$ is identically 0 outside a finite interval, the series $\sum\limits_{i=-\infty}^{\infty} \varphi(i)$ converges. Equation (1.22) states that the series

$$\sum_{j=1}^{\infty} \int_{-\infty}^{\infty} \cos 2j\pi x \; \varphi(x) dx$$

also converges and that these two series are equal for every test function $\varphi(x)$. Actually the equality can be extended to a much larger class of functions $\varphi(x)$, but that problem is not on our agenda.

With $(x - \xi)/2$ substituted for x, (1.22) becomes

$$\sum_{k=-\infty}^{\infty} \delta\left(\frac{x-\xi}{2} - k\right) = 1 + 2 \sum_{n=1}^{\infty} (\cos n\pi x \cos n\pi\xi + \sin n\pi x \sin n\pi\xi)$$

or

$$\sum_{k=-\infty}^{\infty} \delta(x - \xi - 2k) = \frac{1}{2} + \sum_{n=1}^{\infty} (\cos n\pi x \cos n\pi\xi + \sin n\pi x \sin n\pi\xi).$$

In this last equation let us restrict x and ξ to lie between -1 and 1. Then $x - \xi$ lies between -2 and 2, and all delta functions vanish except $\delta(x - \xi)$. Therefore,

$$\delta(x - \xi) = \frac{1}{2} + \sum_{n=1}^{\infty} (\cos n\pi x \cos n\pi\xi + \sin n\pi x \sin n\pi\xi); \qquad -1 < x, \xi < 1.$$

$$(1.22a)$$

Formula (1.22a) contains the nucleus of the usual Fourier series expansion for the interval $(-1, 1)$. Indeed, if we multiply both sides by an arbitrary function $Z(x)$ and integrate from -1 to 1, we obtain formally

$$Z(\xi) = \frac{1}{2} \int_{-1}^{1} Z(x) dx + \sum_{n=1}^{\infty} \cos n\pi\xi \int_{-1}^{1} Z(x) \cos n\pi x \; dx$$

$$+ \sum_{n=1}^{\infty} \sin n\pi\xi \int_{-1}^{1} Z(x) \sin n\pi x \; dx.$$

In Chapter 4 we shall develop methods for generating such formulas as (1.22a). The reader familiar with the theory of Fourier series knows that certain mild restrictions must be imposed on $Z(x)$ for the expansion to be valid. The method employed here gives no hint as to the nature of these restrictions.

Example 7. *The Poisson summation formula and transformation of series.* From (1.22) it follows that

$$\sum_{k=-\infty}^{\infty} \delta(x - k) = \sum_{n=-\infty}^{\infty} e^{i2\pi nx},$$

or, setting $\lambda x = y$,

$$\sum_{k=-\infty}^{\infty} \delta\left(\frac{y}{\lambda} - k\right) = \sum_{n=-\infty}^{\infty} e^{i2\pi yn/\lambda}.$$

We multiply by an arbitrary test function $\varphi(y)$ and integrate from $-\infty$ to ∞; noting that $\delta[(y/\lambda) - k] = |\lambda|\delta(y - k\lambda)$, we obtain

$$|\lambda| \sum_{k=-\infty}^{\infty} \varphi(k\lambda) = \sum_{n=-\infty}^{\infty} \int_{-\infty}^{\infty} e^{i2\pi yn/\lambda} \varphi(y) dy. \tag{1.23a}$$

The above formula can be extended to functions φ which are not test functions, but merely satisfy the milder conditions: φ continuous, piecewise differentiable, and $\int_{-\infty}^{\infty} |\varphi| dx < \infty$. We recall that the Fourier transform of $\varphi(y)$ is a function $\Phi(\omega)$ defined by

$$\Phi(\omega) = \int_{-\infty}^{\infty} e^{i\omega y} \varphi(y) dy,$$

so that (1.23a) can be written

$$\sum_{k=-\infty}^{\infty} \varphi(k\lambda) = \frac{1}{|\lambda|} \sum_{n=-\infty}^{\infty} \Phi\left(\frac{2\pi n}{\lambda}\right). \tag{1.23b}$$

This transformation from one series to another often improves the convergence. Let us look at the particular case where $\varphi(y) = e^{-y^2}$; an easy calculation shows that $\Phi(\omega) = \sqrt{\pi}\, e^{-\omega^2/4}$, so that (1.23b) becomes

$$\sum_{k=-\infty}^{\infty} \exp(-k^2\lambda^2) = \frac{\sqrt{\pi}}{|\lambda|} \sum_{n=-\infty}^{\infty} \exp(-\pi^2 n^2/\lambda^2). \tag{1.24}$$

By examining the ratio of successive terms for these two series we see that the series on the left converges rapidly for $|\lambda|$ large, whereas the series on the right converges rapidly for small values of $|\lambda|$.

EXERCISES

1.23 In the next few exercises we consider locally integrable functions whose discontinuities are more severe than the simple jumps included in (1.21). These functions are still differentiable in the distributional sense; investigation of the generalized derivatives will enable us to give meaning to certain divergent integrals.

Consider the locally integrable function

$$f(x) = (\log x)_+ = \begin{cases} \log x, & x > 0; \\ 0, & x < 0. \end{cases}$$

This function defines a distribution

$$\langle f, \varphi \rangle = \int_0^\infty \varphi(x) \log x\, dx = \lim_{\varepsilon \to 0} \int_\varepsilon^\infty \varphi(x) \log x\, dx.$$

What is $\langle f', \varphi \rangle$? We have

$$\langle f', \varphi \rangle = -\langle f, \varphi' \rangle = -\int_0^\infty \varphi'(x) \log x\, dx = -\lim_{\varepsilon \to 0} \int_\varepsilon^\infty \varphi'(x) \log x\, dx.$$

Integrating by parts,

$$\langle f', \varphi \rangle = \lim_{\varepsilon \to 0} \left[\int_{\varepsilon}^{\infty} \frac{\varphi(x)}{x} \, dx + \varphi(\varepsilon) \log \varepsilon \right].$$

Although $\int_{0}^{\infty} [\varphi(x)/x] dx = \lim_{\varepsilon \to 0} \int_{\varepsilon}^{\infty} [\varphi(x)/x] dx$ fails to exist [unless $\varphi(0) = 0$], the limit of the quantity in brackets always exists and is known as the *finite part* of $\int_{0}^{\infty} [\varphi(x)/x] dx$. The function

$$\left(\frac{1}{x} \right)_{+} = \begin{cases} \dfrac{1}{x}, & x > 0; \\ 0, & x < 0, \end{cases}$$

is not locally integrable and therefore does not generate a distribution. In the classical sense $(1/x)_{+}$ is the derivative of $(\log x)_{+}$ *except* at $x = 0$. The distributional derivative of $(\log x)_{+}$ is a singular distribution g defined by

$$\langle g, \varphi \rangle = \lim_{\varepsilon \to 0} \left[\int_{\varepsilon}^{\infty} \frac{\varphi(x)}{x} \, dx + \varphi(\varepsilon) \log \varepsilon \right].$$

We shall write

$$g(x) = \mathrm{pf} \left(\frac{1}{x} \right)_{+},$$

where pf stands for *pseudofunction*. In this notation, we have

$$\frac{d}{dx} (\log x)_{+} = \mathrm{pf} \left(\frac{1}{x} \right)_{+}. \tag{1.25}$$

Show that with appropriate definitions,

$$\frac{d}{dx} (\log |x|)_{-} = \mathrm{pf} \left(\frac{1}{x} \right)_{-}.$$

1.24 Find the generalized derivative of

$$f(x) = \begin{cases} x^{-1/2}, & x > 0; \\ 0, & x < 0. \end{cases}$$

With appropriate definitions show that

$$f'(x) = -\tfrac{1}{2} \, \mathrm{pf} \, (x^{-3/2})_{+}.$$

1.25 Consider the locally integrable function $f(x) = \log |x|$, $-\infty < x < \infty$. For all $x \neq 0$ we have $(d/dx) \log |x| = 1/x$ in the ordinary sense of differentiation; since $1/x$ is not a locally integrable function, the formula cannot hold distributionally. We proceed to compute the distributional derivative of $f(x)$. We have

$$\langle f, \varphi \rangle = \int_0^\infty \varphi(x) \log x \, dx + \int_{-\infty}^0 \varphi(x) \log(-x) dx.$$

Hence

$$\langle f', \varphi \rangle = -\langle f, \varphi' \rangle = \lim_{\varepsilon \to 0} \left[-\int_\varepsilon^\infty \varphi'(x) \log x \, dx - \int_{-\infty}^{-\varepsilon} \varphi'(x) \log(-x) dx \right]$$

$$= \lim_{\varepsilon \to 0} \left[\int_\varepsilon^\infty \frac{\varphi(x)}{x} \, dx + \int_{-\infty}^{-\varepsilon} \frac{\varphi(x)}{x} \, dx + \varphi(\varepsilon) \log \varepsilon - \varphi(-\varepsilon) \log \varepsilon \right].$$

Since φ is differentiable at $x = 0$, $\lim_{\varepsilon \to 0} [\varphi(\varepsilon) - \varphi(-\varepsilon)] \log \varepsilon = 0$; therefore,

$$\langle f', \varphi \rangle = \lim_{\varepsilon \to 0} \left[\int_\varepsilon^\infty + \int_{-\infty}^{-\varepsilon} \frac{\varphi(x)}{x} \, dx \right].$$

Although the limiting values of the individual integrals fail to exist [unless $\varphi(0) = 0$], the sum converges and is known as the *Cauchy principal value* of $\int_{-\infty}^\infty [\varphi(x)/x] dx$. We shall define the pseudofunction $\mathrm{pf}(1/x)$ by

$$\left\langle \mathrm{pf}\left(\frac{1}{x}\right), \varphi \right\rangle = \lim_{\varepsilon \to 0} \left[\int_\varepsilon^\infty + \int_{-\infty}^{-\varepsilon} \frac{\varphi}{x} \, dx \right],$$

so that

$$\frac{d}{dx} \log |x| = \mathrm{pf}\left(\frac{1}{x}\right). \tag{1.26}$$

Referring to Exercise 1.23, show that

$$\frac{d}{dx} \log |x| = \mathrm{pf}\left(\frac{1}{x}\right)_+ + \mathrm{pf}\left(\frac{1}{x}\right)_-,$$

and, therefore,

$$\mathrm{pf}\left(\frac{1}{x}\right) = \mathrm{pf}\left(\frac{1}{x}\right)_+ + \mathrm{pf}\left(\frac{1}{x}\right)_-.$$

1.26 Show that

$$\lim_{R \to \infty} \frac{1 - \cos Rx}{x} = \mathrm{pf}\left(\frac{1}{x}\right).$$

What you must prove is that for each test function $\varphi(x)$,

$$\lim_{R \to \infty} \int_{-\infty}^\infty \frac{1 - \cos Rx}{x} \varphi \, dx = \lim_{\varepsilon \to 0} \left[\int_\varepsilon^\infty + \int_{-\infty}^{-\varepsilon} \frac{\varphi}{x} \, dx \right].$$

1.27 Consider the complex-valued locally integrable function $f_\alpha(x) = 1/(x + i\alpha)$ (where α is real, $\alpha \neq 0$). This function defines a distribution on $D^{(c)}$:

$$\langle f_\alpha, \varphi \rangle = \int_{-\infty}^{\infty} \frac{\varphi(x)}{x + i\alpha}\, dx$$

$$= \int_{-\infty}^{\infty} \frac{x}{x^2 + \alpha^2}\, \varphi(x)dx - i \int_{-\infty}^{\infty} \frac{\alpha}{x^2 + \alpha^2}\, \varphi(x)dx.$$

Show that

$$\lim_{\alpha \to 0\pm} \langle f_\alpha, \varphi \rangle = \mp i\pi\varphi(0) + \lim_{\varepsilon \to 0}\left[\int_{-\infty}^{-\varepsilon} + \int_{\varepsilon}^{\infty} \frac{\varphi}{x}\, dx \right].$$

Therefore, we can write

$$\lim_{\alpha \to 0\pm} \frac{1}{x + i\alpha} = \mp i\pi\delta(x) + \mathrm{pf}\left(\frac{1}{x}\right). \qquad (1.27)$$

1.28 Use the Poisson formula (1.23a) with $\lambda = 1$, $\varphi(x) = e^{-a|x|}$ to show that

$$\sum_{k=-\infty}^{\infty} e^{-a|k|} = \sum_{n=-\infty}^{\infty} \frac{2a}{a^2 + 4\pi^2 n^2}.$$

By noting that the left side is essentially a geometric series, obtain

$$\sum_{n=-\infty}^{\infty} \frac{2a}{a^2 + 4\pi^2 n^2} = \frac{1 + e^{-a}}{1 - e^{-a}}.$$

Can you derive this result by any other method?

1.29 With $0 < \xi < 1$, consider the even function

$$f(x) = \begin{cases} 1, & -\xi < x < \xi; \\ 0, & \xi < x < 1; \\ 0, & -1 < x < -\xi, \end{cases}$$

$f(x + 2) = f(x)$.

Expand $f(x)$ in a Fourier cosine series. By differentiating this series and comparing with the generalized derivative of f obtained directly, show that

$$2 \sum_{n=1}^{\infty} \sin n\pi x \sin n\pi\xi = \sum_{k=-\infty}^{\infty} \delta(x - 2k - \xi) - \sum_{k=-\infty}^{\infty} \delta(x - 2k + \xi).$$

If $0 < x, \xi < 1$, this becomes

$$\delta(x - \xi) = 2 \sum_{n=1}^{\infty} \sin n\pi x \sin n\pi\xi. \qquad (1.28)$$

Show that this is the nucleus for the usual sine-series expansion for an arbitrary function $Z(x)$ in $0 < x < 1$.

1.30 Combine (1.28) and (1.22a) to show that if $0 < x, \xi < 1$,

$$\delta(x - \xi) = 1 + 2 \sum_{n=1}^{\infty} \cos n\pi x \cos n\pi \xi. \tag{1.29}$$

Derive the usual cosine-series expansion for a function $Z(x)$ in $0 < x < 1$.

Differential Equations in Distributions

The equation

$$\frac{dt}{dx} = 0 \tag{1.30}$$

may be considered as a differential equation for an unknown distribution t. We want to find every distribution whose derivative coincides with the 0 distribution, that is, every distribution t with the property $\langle t', \varphi \rangle = 0$, or $\langle t, -\varphi' \rangle = 0$. Thus the necessary and sufficient condition for t to be a solution of (1.30) is that

$$\langle t, \psi \rangle = 0 \tag{1.31}$$

for every test function ψ which is the derivative of a test function.

It is easily seen that the necessary and sufficient condition for a test function $\psi(x)$ to be the derivative of another test function is that $\int_{-\infty}^{\infty} \psi \, dx = 0$. The condition is necessary because $\psi = d\varphi/dx$ implies $\int_{-\infty}^{\infty} \psi \, dx = \int_{-\infty}^{\infty} \varphi' \, dx = \varphi(\infty) - \varphi(-\infty) = 0$. To show that the condition is sufficient, let ψ be a test function with the property $\int_{-\infty}^{\infty} \psi \, dx = 0$; then $\varphi(x) = \int_{-\infty}^{x} \psi(\alpha)d\alpha$ is infinitely differentiable, $\varphi'(x) = \psi(x)$, and φ vanishes outside a finite interval; hence ψ is the derivative of a test function.

We now return to the solution of (1.30). Let $\varphi(x)$ be an arbitrary test function and $\varphi_0(x)$ be a fixed test function with the property $\int_{-\infty}^{\infty} \varphi_0(x)dx = 1$. We can write

$$\varphi(x) = \varphi_0(x) \int_{-\infty}^{\infty} \varphi(x)dx + \left[\varphi(x) - \varphi_0(x) \int_{-\infty}^{\infty} \varphi(x)dx \right]. \tag{1.32}$$

The function in brackets is a test function ψ with the property $\int_{-\infty}^{\infty} \psi \, dx = 0$. If t is a solution of (1.30), it follows from (1.31) that $\langle t, \psi \rangle = 0$; hence

$$\langle t, \varphi \rangle = \left\langle t, \varphi_0 \int_{-\infty}^{\infty} \varphi \, dx \right\rangle = \left(\int_{-\infty}^{\infty} \varphi \, dx \right) \langle t, \varphi_0 \rangle.$$

The quantity $\langle t, \varphi_0 \rangle$ is a constant independent of φ, therefore,

$$\langle t, \varphi \rangle = c \int_{-\infty}^{\infty} \varphi \, dx,$$

so that t is a constant distribution.

We have shown that the only distributional solutions of $dt/dx = 0$ are the constant distributions, in other words, regular distributions generated by constant functions. *The distributional solutions of* (1.30) *therefore coincide with the classical functional solutions of* (1.30) Consider now the inhomogeneous equation

$$\frac{dt}{dx} = f, \tag{1.33}$$

where f is an arbitrary given distribution. This equation is equivalent to $\langle t', \varphi \rangle = \langle f, \varphi \rangle$ or $\langle t, \varphi' \rangle = \langle f, -\varphi \rangle$. Thus the action of t on any test function ψ which is the derivative of a test function is known.

We decompose the arbitrary test function $\varphi(x)$ by (1.32) to obtain

$$\langle t, \varphi \rangle = \left\langle t, \varphi_0 \int_{-\infty}^{\infty} \varphi \, dx \right\rangle + \langle t, \psi \rangle,$$

where $\psi = \varphi - \varphi_0 \int_{-\infty}^{\infty} \varphi \, dx$ is the derivative of the test function $\varphi_1 = \int_{-\infty}^{x} \varphi(\alpha)d\alpha - \int_{-\infty}^{\infty} \varphi(\alpha)d\alpha \int_{-\infty}^{x} \varphi_0(\alpha)d\alpha$. Thus $\langle t, \psi \rangle$ is known ($\langle t, \psi \rangle = \langle f, -\varphi_1 \rangle$); it is easily seen that it is legitimate to define a distribution t_0 by the relation

$$\langle t_0, \varphi \rangle = \langle f, -\varphi_1 \rangle. \tag{1.34}$$

In terms of t_0 we have

$$\langle t, \varphi \rangle = \langle t_0, \varphi \rangle + \langle t, \varphi_0 \rangle \int_{-\infty}^{\infty} \varphi \, dx.$$

Since $\langle t, \varphi_0 \rangle$ is a constant independent of φ, we have

$$\langle t, \varphi \rangle = \langle t_0, \varphi \rangle + c \int_{-\infty}^{\infty} \varphi \, dx = \langle t_0, \varphi \rangle + \langle c, \varphi \rangle,$$

and (1.33) has solutions all of which are of the form $t_0 + c$, where t_0 is defined by (1.34).

We proceed with a discussion of the general linear differential equation of the nth order. Let $a_0(x), \ldots, a_n(x)$ be infinitely differentiable functions, and let L be the differential operator

$$L = a_0(x) \frac{d^n}{dx^n} + \cdots + a_{n-1}(x) \frac{d}{dx} + a_n(x) = \sum_{k=0}^{n} a_{n-k}(x) \frac{d^k}{dx^k}. \tag{1.35}$$

The operation Lt is defined for any distribution t. Indeed we have shown that $\langle Lt, \varphi \rangle = \langle t, L^*\varphi \rangle$, where L^* is the formal adjoint of L:

$$L^*\varphi = \sum_{k=0}^{n} (-1)^k \frac{d_k(a_{n-k}\varphi)}{dx^k}. \tag{1.36}$$

If f is a given distribution, the equation

$$Lt = a_0(x)\frac{d^n t}{dx^n} + \cdots + a_n(x)t = f \qquad (1.37)$$

may be regarded as a differential equation for an unknown distribution t. A distribution t is said to satisfy (1.37) if, for every test function φ, we have

$$\langle Lt, \varphi \rangle = \langle f, \varphi \rangle,$$

or, equivalently,

$$\langle t, L^*\varphi \rangle = \langle f, \varphi \rangle. \qquad (1.38)$$

The solutions of (1.37) may fall in any of the following categories:

1. If t corresponds to a function which is sufficiently differentiable so that the operations in (1.37) can be performed in the classical sense, and the resulting equation is an identity, we say that t is a *classical solution* [of course, t will also satisfy (1.38)].

2. If t corresponds to a function which is not sufficiently differentiable to be substituted in (1.37), but t satisfies (1.38), we say that t is a *weak solution*.

3. If t is a singular distribution (that is, does not correspond to a function), but t satisfies (1.38), we say that t is a *distributional solution*.

The term *generalized solution* is used for all three types of solutions listed above.

There exists a large class of problems for which all generalized solutions of (1.37) are classical solutions. We offer the following theorem without proof:

Theorem.   *If $a_0(x)$ never vanishes and $f(x)$ is a locally integrable function, every generalized solution of (1.37) is a classical solution.*

In particular, for the homogeneous equation ($f = 0$), if $a_0(x) \neq 0$ for all x, all solutions are classical solutions.

The following examples show that nonclassical solutions can arise.

EXAMPLES

Example 1. $x(dt/dx) = 0$ has the solution $t = H(x)$; indeed in the sense of distributions $dH/dx = \delta(x)$ and $x\delta(x) = 0$. This solution is a weak solution, since $H(x)$ is a function but is not differentiable in the classical sense. It can be shown that every generalized solution of the equation is of the form $c_1 H(x) + c_2$, whereas the only classical solutions are constants (see Exercise 1.31).

Example 2. $x^2(dt/dx) = 0$ has the distributional solution $t = \delta(x)$ (see Exercise 1.32).

Example 3. $d^2t/dx^2 = \delta''(x)$ has the solution $t = \delta(x)$, which is a distributional solution. Every generalized solution must be of the form $\delta(x) + c_1 + c_2 x$, since the difference between two solutions satisfies the homogeneous equation $d^2t/dx^2 = 0$, which has only the classical solutions $c_1 + c_2 x$.

Fundamental Solutions and Green's Functions

We assume throughout this section that $a_0(x) \neq 0$ for every x. Let ξ be a fixed but arbitrary real number, and let L be the differential operator (1.35). Any solution of the equation

$$Lt = \delta(x - \xi) \tag{1.39}$$

is said to be a *fundamental solution* for the operator L with *pole* at ξ. We will see below that fundamental solutions are actually functions which are weak solutions of (1.39). We introduce the notation $t(x \mid \xi)$ to remind us of the dependence of the fundamental solution on the point ξ. Since any two fundamental solutions (with the same pole) differ by a solution of the homogeneous equation, the general solution of (1.39) consists of the sum of a particular solution of (1.39) and the general solution of the homogeneous equation.

A particular solution of (1.39) can be obtained by the following heuristic procedure. Let $u(x)$ be a fixed but arbitrary solution of the homogeneous equation, and let $v_\xi(x)$ be a solution of the homogeneous equation still to be determined (as the notation implies, this solution will depend on ξ).

Since $Lt = 0$ whenever $x \neq \xi$,

$$t = \begin{cases} v_\xi(x), & x > \xi; \\ u(x), & x < \xi, \end{cases}$$

where $v_\xi(x)$ is to be computed from $u(x)$ by appropriate matching conditions at $x = \xi$; these conditions will reflect the fact that Lt has a delta-function behavior at $x = \xi$. Integrating (1.39) from $x = \xi - \varepsilon$ to $x = \xi + \varepsilon$, and assuming that $t, \ldots, d^{n-2}t/dx^{n-2}$ are continuous at $x = \xi$, we obtain

$$\lim_{\varepsilon \to 0} \int_{\xi-\varepsilon}^{\xi+\varepsilon} a_0(x) \frac{d^n t}{dx^n} \, dx = 1$$

or

$$a_0(\xi) \left[\frac{d^{n-1}t}{dx^{n-1}} \bigg|_{x=\xi+} - \frac{d^{n-1}t}{dx^{n-1}} \bigg|_{x=\xi-} \right] = 1$$

or

$$v_\xi^{(n-1)}(\xi) = u^{(n-1)}(\xi) + \frac{1}{a_0(\xi)}.$$

We therefore conjecture that a solution of (1.39) is

$$t(x \mid \xi) = \begin{cases} v_\xi(x), & x > \xi; \\ u(x), & x < \xi, \end{cases} \tag{1.40}$$

where $u(x)$ is a fixed arbitrary solution of the homogeneous equation and $v_\xi(x)$ is another solution of the homogeneous equation satisfying the conditions

$$v_\xi(\xi) = u(\xi), \qquad v_\xi'(\xi) = u'(\xi), \ldots, v_\xi^{(n-2)}(\xi) = u^{(n-2)}(\xi),$$

$$v_\xi^{(n-1)}(\xi) = u^{(n-1)}(\xi) + \frac{1}{a_0(\xi)}.$$

According to the uniqueness and existence theorem for ordinary differential equations, $v_\xi(x)$ exists and is unambiguously determined [once $u(x)$ and ξ are fixed]. It is clear from the jump condition on the $(n-1)$th derivative that u and v_ξ are independent solutions of the homogeneous equation.

We now prove that the function $t(x \mid \xi)$ defined by (1.40) is a solution of (1.39) [t is a weak solution since $t^{(n-1)}$ is discontinuous at $x = \xi$]. We must show that, for every test function φ,

$$\langle t, L^*\varphi \rangle = \varphi(\xi).$$

By the definition of t, we have

$$\langle t, L^*\varphi \rangle = \int_{-\infty}^{\infty} t(x \mid \xi) L^*\varphi \, dx = \int_{-\infty}^{\xi-} u L^*\varphi \, dx + \int_{\xi+}^{\infty} v_\xi L^*\varphi \, dx,$$

where

$$L^*\varphi = \sum_{k=0}^{n} (-1)^k \frac{d^k(a_{n-k}\varphi)}{dx^k}.$$

We integrate by parts enough times so that the differentiatons are transferred from φ to u and v_ξ; thus the terms involving $d^k(a_{n-k}\varphi)/dx^k$ will be integrated by parts exactly k times. Since φ vanishes outside a finite interval, there is no contribution from the integrated terms at $x = \pm\infty$. Because $u^{(k)}(\xi) = v^{(k)}(\xi)$ for $k = 0, \ldots, n-2$, the integrated contributions at $\xi-$ and $\xi+$ cancel except for a term involving $u^{(n-1)}$ and one involving $v_\xi^{(n-1)}$ (these terms arising from the nth integration by parts of the terms corresponding to $k = n$). Using the jump condition

$$v_\xi^{(n-1)}(\xi) = u^{(n-1)}(\xi) + \frac{1}{a_0(\xi)},$$

one obtains

$$\langle t, L^*\varphi \rangle = \varphi(\xi) + \int_{-\infty}^{\xi-} \varphi Lu \, dx + \int_{\xi+}^{\infty} \varphi Lv_\xi \, dx.$$

Since both Lu and Lv_ξ vanish, it follows that

$$\langle t, L^* \varphi \rangle = \varphi(\xi).$$

We have shown that $t(x \mid \xi)$ as given by (1.40) is a solution of (1.39). Every fundamental solution is therefore the sum of this particular $t(x \mid \xi)$ and of a solution of the homogeneous equation. Since there exist n independent solutions of the homogeneous equation, n arbitrary constants will appear in the most general fundamental solution.

Let us now introduce the concept of the Green's function; the Green's function is a fundamental solution which satisfies n additional, specified, homogeneous boundary conditions. Whereas the general fundamental solution contains n arbitrary constants, the Green's function is completely determined once the boundary conditions are given. (Certain limitations on the nature of the boundary conditions and the differential operator must be imposed to ensure the existence and uniqueness of the Green's function.) The theory of Green's functions for second-order linear differential operators is developed in the next section.

EXAMPLES

Example 1.   It is easily seen that $t = -|x - \xi|/2$ is a solution of

$$-\frac{d^2 t}{dx^2} = \delta(x - \xi).$$

Formula (1.6) gives another fundamental solution satisfying vanishing boundary conditions at $x = 0$, $x = 1$ (with $T = 1$, $l = 1$). Thus

$$g(x \mid \xi) = \begin{cases} (1 - x)\xi, & \xi < x; \\ (1 - \xi)x, & x < \xi, \end{cases}$$

is also a fundamental solution. We see that $g(x \mid \xi) - t(x \mid \xi) = (x/2) + (\xi/2) - \xi x$, which is a solution of the homogeneous equation.

Example 2.   *The causal fundamental solution* or Green's function for the initial-value problem. This fundamental solution is obtained by setting $u = 0$ in (1.40). Thus

$$t(x \mid \xi) = \begin{cases} v_\xi(x), & x > \xi; \\ 0, & x < \xi, \end{cases}$$

where $v_\xi(\xi) = v'_\xi(\xi) = \cdots = v_\xi^{(n-2)}(\xi) = 0$ and $v_\xi^{(n-1)}(\xi) = 1/a_0(\xi)$. The reason for calling t a Green's function is that, if ξ is restricted to positive values, t satisfies n homogeneous conditions at $x = 0$; indeed $t, t', \ldots, t^{(n-1)}$ all vanish at $x = 0$ (since $t \equiv 0$ for $x < \xi$). If L has constant coefficients, $v_\xi(x) = v_0(x - \xi)$, and

$$t(x \mid \xi) = t(x - \xi) = \begin{cases} v_0(x - \xi), & x > \xi; \\ 0, & x < \xi, \end{cases}$$

where $v_0(0) = v'_0(0) = \cdots = v_0^{(n-2)}(0) = 0$ and $v_0^{(n-1)}(0) = 1/a_0$.

Example 3.   Fundamental solutions are used to solve the inhomogeneous equation

$$Lw = f, \tag{1.41}$$

where f is a given function.

As was done in Section 1.1, we write $f(x)$ as continuous superposition of delta functions $\left[f(x) = \int_{-\infty}^{\infty} \delta(x - \xi) f(\xi) d\xi \right]$. The principle of superposition suggests the solution $w(x) = \int_{-\infty}^{\infty} t(x \mid \xi) f(\xi) d\xi$, where $Lt = \delta(x - \xi)$. As we change t we obtain different solutions to (1.41). Often we are interested in solving (1.41) subject to n additional homogeneous conditions; in that case the Green's function satisfying these n conditions is the most convenient fundamental solution to employ.

EXERCISES

1.31 The observant reader will have noted that the successful solution of (1.30) and (1.33) depended on the decomposition of an arbitrary test function $\varphi(x)$ into two parts, one part proportional to the fixed test function $\varphi_0(x)$ with $\int_{-\infty}^{\infty} \varphi_0(x) dx = 1$ and the other part the derivative of a test function. Other decompositions are required to solve functional equations involving distributions. Consider, for instance, the equation

$$xt = 0. \tag{1.42}$$

We search for all solutions t of (1.42), that is, all distributions t for which $\langle xt, \varphi \rangle = 0$, or by (1.18), $\langle t, x\varphi \rangle = 0$. Thus the action of t is known on all test functions of the form $x\varphi$. The reader should prove that the necessary and sufficient condition for a test function ψ to be of the form $x\varphi$ is that $\psi(0) = 0$. This suggests the following decomposition for an arbitrary test function $\varphi(x)$. Let $\varphi_0(x)$ be a fixed test function such that $\varphi_0(0) = 1$; then

$$\varphi(x) = \varphi(0)\varphi_0(x) + [\varphi(x) - \varphi(0)\varphi_0(x)].$$

The test function in brackets vanishes at $x = 0$. If t is a solution of (1.42), it follows that

$$\langle t, \varphi \rangle = \varphi(0)\langle t, \varphi_0(x) \rangle + \langle t, \varphi(x) - \varphi(0)\varphi_0(x) \rangle.$$

The second term on the right side vanishes; hence

$$\langle t, \varphi \rangle = \varphi(0)\langle t, \varphi_0(x) \rangle.$$

Since $\langle t, \varphi_0(x) \rangle$ is a constant independent of $\varphi(x)$, it follows that

$$\langle t, \varphi \rangle = c\varphi(0) \qquad \text{or} \qquad t = c\delta(x).$$

It is now trivial to show that the general solution of $x(dt/dx) = 0$ is given by $t = c_1 H(x) + c_2$.

1.32 Find the general solution of

$$x^k \frac{dt}{dx} = 0,$$

where k is a positive integer.

1.33 Show that the general solution of

$$x \frac{dt}{dx} + t = 0$$

is

$$t = c_1 \delta(x) + c_2 \, \mathrm{pf}\left(\frac{1}{x}\right).$$

1.34 Show that the solution of

$$Lw = f, \qquad x > 0,$$

with the initial conditions $w(0) = 0, \ldots, w^{(n-1)}(0) = 0$, is given by

$$w(x) = \int_0^x v_\xi(x) f(\xi) d\xi,$$

where $v_\xi(x)$ is defined as in Example 2.

1.4 PRELIMINARY RESULTS ON LINEAR EQUATIONS OF THE SECOND ORDER

The most general linear operator of the second order is

$$L = a_0(x) \frac{d^2}{dx^2} + a_1(x) \frac{d}{dx} + a_2(x).$$

In the last section we required that all coefficients be infinitely differentiable; now we merely assume that $a_0(x)$, $a_1(x)$, $a_2(x)$ *are continuous*. Let $f(x)$ be piecewise continuous and let I be an interval on the x axis. We say that $u(x)$ is a solution (or classical solution) of

$$Lu = f, \qquad x \text{ in } I,$$

if u has a continuous derivative and a piecewise continuous second derivative, and if the functions Lu and f are equal at all points of continuity of f. (Classically, the notion of solution can be extended to the case where f is only integrable instead of piecewise continuous.)

Existence and Uniqueness Theorem

Theorem. *Let I be a closed interval in which $a_0(x) \neq 0$; let x_0 be a point in I, and let α and β be given numbers. The problem*

$$Lu = f, \quad x \text{ in } I; \qquad u(x_0) = \alpha, \quad u'(x_0) = \beta \tag{1.43}$$

has one and only one solution.

REMARKS.   The problem (1.43) is known as an initial-value problem (even though x_0 is not the left end point of the interval). The existence and uniqueness theorem will be proved in Exercise 3.10. We accept the theorem for the present but illustrate, by the following examples, the essential character of the assumption $a_0(x) \neq 0$. Consider

$$xy'' - y' = 0 \qquad \text{with } y(0) = 0, \quad y'(0) = 0.$$

The general solution for $x > 0$ is $A + Bx^2$. Imposing the initial conditions yields $y = Bx^2$, which violates the uniqueness portion of the above theorem. The difficulty is caused by the fact that $a_0(x) = x$ vanishes at a point in the interval (more precisely the trouble is that a_1/a_0 is discontinuous at a point in the interval). A point at which either a_1/a_0 or a_2/a_0 is discontinuous is known as a *singular point* of the differential equation. Solutions often become infinite at such points and the existence and uniqueness theorem may be violated. Consider, for instance, $xy'' + y' = 0$ with $y(0) = \alpha$, $y'(0) = \beta \neq 0$. For $x > 0$ the general solution of the differential equation is $A + B \log x$, and no choice of A and B enables us to satisfy the conditions at $x = 0$. In all that follows, it will be assumed that $a_0(x) \neq 0$ in I.

COROLLARY 1.   *The only solution of*

$$Lu = 0, \quad x \text{ in } I; \qquad u(x_0) = 0, \quad u'(x_0) = 0$$

is $u \equiv 0$ in I.

COROLLARY 2.   *If u is the solution of*

$$Lu = 0, \quad x \text{ in } I; \qquad u(x_0) = \alpha, \quad u'(x_0) = \beta,$$

then $v = \gamma u$ is the solution of

$$Lv = 0, \quad x \text{ in } I; \qquad v(x_0) = \gamma\alpha, \quad v'(x_0) = \gamma\beta.$$

Dependence and Independence; Wronskians

Consider n functions $f_1(x), \dots, f_n(x)$. These functions are said to be *dependent* over an interval I, if there exist constants $c_1, \dots, c_n$, not all zero, such that

$$c_1 f_1(x) + \cdots + c_n f_n(x) = 0 \qquad \text{for all } x \text{ in } I. \tag{1.44}$$

A set of n functions is therefore dependent if any one of them can be expressed as a linear combination of the others.

The set of n functions $f_1(x), \dots, f_n(x)$ is *independent* over I if (1.44) can only be satisfied by setting $c_1 = \cdots = c_n = 0$. Let $f_1(x), \dots, f_n(x)$ be functions which are $n - 1$ times differentiable. The *Wronskian* of $f_1, \dots, f_n$ is defined as the n by n determinant

$$W(f_1, \dots, f_n; x) = \begin{vmatrix} f_1 & f_2 & \cdots f_n \\ f_1' & f_2' & \cdots f_n' \\ \vdots & & \\ f_1^{(n-1)} & f_2^{(n-1)} & \cdots f_n^{(n-1)} \end{vmatrix}. \tag{1.45}$$

The discussion in this section requires only the concept of the Wronskian of two functions f and g, each of which is differentiable. From (1.45) we have

$$W(f, g; x) = \begin{vmatrix} f & g \\ f' & g' \end{vmatrix} = fg' - gf'. \tag{1.46}$$

If f and g are dependent over I, it is clear that their Wronskian vanishes for every x in I. The following example shows that the converse is not true. Let I be the interval $-1 \le x \le 1$, $f = x^2$, $g = x|x|$; then f and g are independent over I but $W(f, g; x)$ vanishes for every x in $-1 \le x \le 1$.

Abel's Formula for the Wronskian

Let u and v be any two solutions (independent or not) of $Lu = 0$. There exists a constant C such that

$$W(u, v; x) = Ce^{-m(x)} \qquad \text{where } \frac{dm}{dx} = \frac{a_1}{a_0}. \tag{1.47}$$

The proof is simple. From $vLu - uLv = 0$ it follows that

$$a_0(vu'' - uv'') + a_1(vu' - uv') = 0, \qquad \text{or} \qquad a_0(dW/dx) + a_1 W = 0.$$

Therefore,

$$W = C \exp\left[-\int (a_1/a_0)dx\right] = Ce^{-m(x)}.$$

Note that once $m(x)$ is chosen, C is unambiguously determined from u and v; furthermore, if W vanishes at any point x, it vanishes for all x.

Theorem. *Let u and v be solutions of $Lu = 0$; the necessary and sufficient condition for u and v to be dependent is that their Wronskian vanish at a single point x_0. (From the remark immediately preceding the theorem, W vanishes at one point if and only if $W \equiv 0$ or $C = 0$.)*

Proof. If u and v are dependent, it is obvious that $W \equiv 0$. If $W = 0$ at some point x_0, then

$$\begin{vmatrix} u(x_0) & v(x_0) \\ u'(x_0) & v'(x_0) \end{vmatrix} = 0.$$

From the theory of linear algebraic equations, we know that this is precisely the necessary and sufficient condition for the existence of a nontrivial solution (that is, c_1 and c_2 not both 0) to the set of equations

$$c_1 u(x_0) + c_2 v(x_0) = 0,$$

$$c_1 u'(x_0) + c_2 v'(x_0) = 0.$$

Let (c_1, c_2) be a nontrivial solution of this set of equations and let $U(x) = c_1 u(x) + c_2 v(x)$. It follows that $U(x_0) = 0$, and $U'(x_0) = 0$; furthermore,

$U(x)$, being a linear combination of two solutions of $Lu = 0$, is itself a solution of $Lu = 0$. By Corollary 1, $U \equiv 0$; hence u and v are dependent.

EXERCISES

1.35 The functions x^2 and $x|x|$ are independent over $-1 \le x \le 1$, yet their Wronskian is 0. Explain why this does not contradict the above theorem.

1.36 *The existence and uniqueness theorem for the equation of order n.* Let x_0 be a point in the interval I; let $\alpha_0, \ldots, \alpha_{n-1}$ be n given constants, and let L be the operator

$$L = a_0(x)\frac{d^n}{dx^n} + \cdots + a_{n-1}(x)\frac{d}{dx} + a_n(x),$$

where $a_0(x), \ldots, a_n(x)$ are continuous and $a_0(x) \ne 0$ over I. There exists one and only one solution of

$$Lu = f, \quad x \text{ in } I; \qquad u(x_0) = \alpha_0, \ldots, u^{(n-1)}(x_0) = \alpha_{n-1},$$

where f is a given piecewise continuous function. Assuming the validity of this theorem, derive the equivalent forms of Corollaries 1 and 2. Show that if $u_1(x), \ldots, u_n(x)$ are n solutions of $Lu = 0$, then

$$W(u_1, \ldots, u_n; x) = Ce^{-m(x)}, \qquad \text{where } m = \int \frac{a_1}{a_0}\, dx.$$

Show that the necessary and sufficient condition for the n solutions to be dependent is that W vanish at a single point x_0 (or equivalently that $W \equiv 0$, or $C = 0$).

The Homogeneous Differential Equation

Let $a_0(x) \ne 0$ over I and consider the homogeneous differential equation

$$Lu = a_0(x)\frac{d^2u}{dx^2} + a_1(x)\frac{du}{dx} + a_2(x)u = 0.$$

Theorem.   *There exist two solutions $u_1(x)$ and $u_2(x)$ of this equation which are independent over I. Every solution on the interval I can be written in the form $Au_1(x) + Bu_2(x)$ for some constants A, B.†*

---

† The independent solutions $u_1(x)$, $u_2(x)$, can be chosen in many different ways. As an example, the equation $(d^2u/dx^2) + u = 0$ has independent solutions $u_1(x) = \sin x$, $u_2(x) = \cos x$, and every solution is of the form $Au_1 + Bu_2$. If we are in a particularly perverse mood we can choose instead the two independent solutions $v_1 = \sin x + \cos x$, $v_2 = 3 \sin x - 7 \cos x$. Every solution of $(d^2u/dx^2) + u = 0$ can also be written $Cv_1 + Dv_2$.

Proof. Let x_0 be a point in I; let $u_1(x)$ be the one and only solution of $Lu = 0$, $u(x_0) = 1$, $u'(x_0) = 0$; let $u_2(x)$ be the one and only solution of $Lu = 0$, $u(x_0) = 0$, $u'(x_0) = 1$. These solutions are independent, since their Wronskian is not 0. If $u(x)$ is any solution of $Lu = 0$, we can write $u(x) = u(x_0)u_1(x) + u'(x_0)u_2(x)$, which is just the desired form.

Fundamental Solution

Any solution t of

$$Lt = a_0(x)\frac{d^2t}{dx^2} + a_1(x)\frac{dt}{dx} + a_2(x)t = \delta(x - \xi) \tag{1.48}$$

is known as a fundamental solution for L with pole at ξ. On the assumption that the coefficients $a_0(x)$, $a_1(x)$, $a_2(x)$ are infinitely differentiable, we have shown that (1.48) can be interpreted distributionally and always has a solution. Each solution $t(x \mid \xi)$ of (1.48) is a function which satisfies

$$Lt = 0, \qquad x < \xi \text{ and } x > \xi;$$

$$t \text{ continuous at } x = \xi; \tag{1.49}$$

$$\left.\frac{dt}{dx}\right|_{x=\xi+} - \left.\frac{dt}{dx}\right|_{x=\xi-} = \frac{1}{a_0(\xi)}.$$

If we now consider the case where the coefficients $a_0(x)$, $a_1(x)$, $a_2(x)$ are merely continuous instead of infinitely differentiable, the interpretation of (1.48) as a distributional equation no longer holds. Although it is possible to reformulate the theory of distributions on a new space of test functions which will permit the operations involved in (1.48), it will be more convenient to use (1.49) directly as the definition of a fundamental solution [but we will still use (1.48) for notational brevity, to stand for (1.49)].

It is easily seen that (1.49) always has solutions. Let $u(x)$ be a fixed solution of the homogeneous equation, and let $v_\xi(x)$ be a solution of the homogeneous equation still to be determined. We write

$$t(x \mid \xi) = \begin{cases} v_\xi(x), & x > \xi; \\ u(x), & x < \xi. \end{cases}$$

The matching conditions of (1.49) require

$$v_\xi(\xi) = u(\xi);$$

$$\left.\frac{dv_\xi(x)}{dx}\right|_{x=\xi} = u'(\xi) + \frac{1}{a_0(\xi)}.$$

From the existence and uniqueness theorem, $v_\xi(x)$ is then unambiguously determined. Thus, starting from any solution of the homogeneous equation for $x < \xi$, we have constructed a well-defined solution of $Lt = \delta(x - \xi)$. It is clear that the general solution of (1.49) is obtained by adding the general solution of the homogeneous equation to any particular solution of (1.49).

The usual superposition argument would lead one to believe that $w(x) = \int_{-\infty}^{\infty} t(x|\xi)f(\xi)d\xi$ furnishes a solution of the inhomogeneous equation $Lw = f$. This is indeed correct if $f(\xi)$ and $t(x|\xi)$ behave sufficiently well at $\xi = \pm\infty$ for the preceding integral to exist. In any event we observe that for any finite a and b, $z(x) = \int_{a}^{b} t(x|\xi)f(\xi)d\xi$ always exists and $Lz = \int_{a}^{b} (Lt)f(\xi)d\xi = \int_{a}^{b} \delta(x-\xi)f(\xi)d\xi$. Thus, $z(x) = \int_{a}^{b} t(x|\xi)f(\xi)d\xi$ is a solution of

$$Lz = \begin{cases} f(x), & a < x < b; \\ 0, & x < a, \quad x > b. \end{cases}$$

A proof of this statement is obtained by a procedure similar to that following (1.10).

One can circumvent the limitation to finite intervals by introducing the two fundamental solutions

$$t_1(x|\xi) = \begin{cases} v_\xi(x), & x > \xi; \\ 0, & x < \xi; \end{cases}$$

$$t_2(x|\xi) = \begin{cases} 0, & x > \xi; \\ -v_\xi(x), & x < \xi, \end{cases}$$

where $v_\xi(x)$ is the solution of the homogeneous equation satisfying the initial conditions

$$v_\xi(\xi) = 0, \qquad \frac{dv_\xi(x)}{dx}\bigg|_{x=\xi} = \frac{1}{a_0(\xi)}.$$

It follows that $z_1(x) = \int_{a}^{x} v_\xi(x)f(\xi)d\xi$ satisfies $Lz_1 = f$ for $x > a$ and that $z_2(x) = \int_{a}^{x} -v_\xi(x)f(\xi)d\xi$ satisfies $Lz_2 = f$ for $x < a$. Since $\int_{x}^{a} -v_\xi(x)f(\xi)d\xi = \int_{a}^{x} v_\xi(x)f(\xi)d\xi$, we conclude that $z(x) = \int_{a}^{x} v_\xi(x)f(\xi)d\xi$ satisfies $Lz = f$ *for all values of* x. Furthermore, $z'(x) = \int_{a}^{x} [dv_\xi(x)/dx]f(\xi)d\xi + v_x(x)f(x)$, so that $z'(a) = 0$ and $z(a) = 0$.

Theorem. *The one and only solution of the initial-value problem*

$$Lz = f, \quad -\infty < x < \infty; \qquad z(a) = 0, \quad z'(a) = 0$$

is given by

$$z(x) = \int_{a}^{x} v_\xi(x)f(\xi)d\xi. \tag{1.50}$$

where $v_\xi(x)$ *is the solution of the homogeneous equation satisfying the conditions*

$$v_\xi(\xi) = 0, \qquad \frac{dv_\xi(x)}{dx}\bigg|_{x=\xi} = \frac{1}{a_0(\xi)}.$$

The general solution of the inhomogeneous equation can be obtained by adding the general solution of the homogeneous equation to (1.50).

1.5 BOUNDARY VALUE PROBLEMS

In Section 1.1 we solved the boundary value problem

$$-Tu'' = f, \quad 0 < x < l; \qquad u(0) = 0, \quad u(l) = 0,$$

and found that there exists one and only one solution u corresponding to each piecewise continuous f. Our goal is to extend the results to an arbitrary linear differential equation of the second order with more general boundary conditions.

We shall consider the differential equation

$$Lu = a_0(x)u'' + a_1(x)u' + a_2(x)u = f(x), \qquad a < x < b,$$

where a_0, a_1, a_2 are continuous and f is piecewise continuous in $a \le x \le b$. We further require u to satisfy the two homogeneous boundary conditions $\qquad\qquad$ (1.51)

$$B_1(u) = 0: \alpha_{11}u(a) + \alpha_{12}u'(a) + \beta_{11}u(b) + \beta_{12}u'(b) = 0,$$

$$B_2(u) = 0: \alpha_{21}u(a) + \alpha_{22}u'(a) + \beta_{21}u(b) + \beta_{22}u'(b) = 0,$$

where the coefficients α_{ij}, β_{ij} are given real numbers.

To ensure that we really have two distinct boundary conditions, we shall assume that the given row vectors $(\alpha_{11}, \alpha_{12}, \beta_{11}, \beta_{12})$ and $(\alpha_{21}, \alpha_{22}, \beta_{21}, \beta_{22})$ are independent (that is, neither row vector is a constant multiple of the other).†

If $\beta_{11} = \beta_{12} = \alpha_{21} = \alpha_{22} = 0$, the conditions are *unmixed* or *pure boundary conditions* (one condition per end point):

$$\alpha_{11}u(a) + \alpha_{12}u'(a) = 0,$$
$$\beta_{21}u(b) + \beta_{22}u'(b) = 0. \qquad\qquad (1.52)$$

If $\alpha_{12} = \beta_{11} = \beta_{12} = \alpha_{21} = \beta_{21} = \beta_{22} = 0$, we have the *initial conditions*

$$u(a) = 0,$$
$$u'(a) = 0. \qquad\qquad (1.53)$$

Before analyzing the boundary value problem (1.51) by use of the Green's function, we make some preliminary observations.

---

† The boundary conditions (1.51) are suitable for the development of the mathematical theory; fortunately, they are also the ones that occur in most applications. The reason for having two instead of more or fewer conditions is fairly obvious; if we had fewer conditions the boundary value problem (1.51) would have more than one solution, whereas, with more conditions, the boundary value problem would usually have no solution. For similar reasons we exclude boundary conditions involving derivatives of order ≥ 2. As an illustration the differential equation $u'' = f(x)$ already determines u'' everywhere, so that u'' cannot be required to vanish at the end points (unless f happens to vanish there); higher derivatives of u (if they exist) are also determined from the differential equation by differentiation, so that it is in general inappropriate to specify such derivatives at the end points.

1. Any two solutions of (1.51) differ by a solution of the completely homogeneous system

$$Lu = 0, \quad a < x < b; \qquad B_1(u) = 0, \quad B_2(u) = 0. \qquad (1.54)$$

2. If (1.54) has only the trivial solution, it follows that (1.51) has at most one solution (we shall show below that the solution then actually exists). This is the usual situation.

3. If by chance the completely homogeneous system (1.54) has a non-trivial solution, then (1.51) either has no solution or else has many solutions. Consider, for instance, the completely homogeneous system

$$u'' = 0, \quad 0 < x < 1; \qquad u'(0) = 0, \quad u'(1) = 0,$$

which has the nontrivial solution $u = A$, where A is an arbitrary constant. The related inhomogeneous system

$$u'' = 1, \quad 0 < x < 1; \qquad u'(0) = 0, \quad u'(1) = 0$$

has no solution. [Indeed from the differential equation, $u = A + Bx + (x^2/2)$; the first boundary condition entails $B = 0$ and the second boundary condition cannot be satisfied.] On the other hand, the related inhomogeneous system

$$u'' = \cos \pi x, \quad 0 < x < 1; \qquad u'(0) = 0, \quad u'(1) = 0$$

has the infinite set of solutions $u(x) = A - (\cos \pi x/\pi^2)$. In a physical context, an explanation of the unusual behavior of these inhomogeneous systems was given in Exercise 1.2.

4. If v_1 is a solution of (1.51) corresponding to f_1, and v_2 is a solution corresponding to f_2, then $c_1 v_1 + c_2 v_2$ is a solution corresponding to $c_1 f_1 + c_2 f_2$. Indeed from the linearity of the differential operator, we have $L(c_1 v_1 + c_2 v_2) = c_1 L v_1 + c_2 L v_2 = c_1 f_1 + c_2 f_2$; since the boundary conditions are linear and homogeneous, $B_1(c_1 v_1 + c_2 v_2) = c_1 B_1(v_1) + c_2 B_1(v_2) = 0$, and similarly $B_2(c_1 v_1 + c_2 v_2) = 0$.

The Green's function $g(x \mid \xi)$ is the solution of the auxiliary problem

$$Lg = a_0(x)\frac{d^2 g}{dx^2} + a_1(x)\frac{dg}{dx} + a_2(x)g = \delta(x - \xi), \qquad (1.55)$$

$$a < x < b; \qquad \text{with } B_1(g) = 0, \qquad B_2(g) = 0.$$

The Green's function is a particular fundamental solution satisfying two prescribed boundary conditions. System (1.55) can be written in an equivalent form which does not involve the delta function,

$$Lg = 0, \quad a \le x < \xi \qquad \text{and} \qquad \xi < x \le b;$$

$$B_1(g) = 0, \qquad B_2(g) = 0;$$

$$g \text{ continuous at } x = \xi; \qquad (1.55a)$$

$$\left.\frac{dg}{dx}\right|_{x=\xi+} - \left.\frac{dg}{dx}\right|_{x=\xi-} = \frac{1}{a_0(\xi)}.$$

Theorem.   *If the completely homogeneous system* (1.54) *has only the trivial solution, the Green's function exists and is unique.*

The uniqueness is obvious, since the difference between two solutions of system (1.55) is a solution of the completely homogeneous system (1.54). By assumption, this latter system has only the trivial solution; hence, system (1.55) [or (1.55a)] can have at most one solution. We now proceed to show the existence of this solution by explicit construction.

1. *The Case of Unmixed Conditions* [see (1.52)]. Let $u_1(x)$ be a nontrivial solution of $Lu = 0$, satisfying the boundary condition at $x = a$, and let $u_2(x)$ be a nontrivial solution of $Lu = 0$, satisfying the boundary condition at $x = b$. It is clear that such solutions exist; in fact, we can take for u_1 the unique solution of $Lu = 0$ which satisfies the initial conditions $u(a) = \alpha_{12}, u'(a) = -\alpha_{11}$; since α_{11} and α_{12} are not both 0, $u_1(x)$ is not identically 0 and clearly u_1 satisfies the boundary condition at $x = a$. In a similar way we can show that $u_2(x)$ exists. We remark that u_1 and u_2 are independent functions, since the completely homogeneous system is required by assumption to have only the trivial solution.

The Green's function $g(x \mid \xi)$ is therefore of the form

$$g(x \mid \xi) = \begin{cases} Au_1(x), & a \le x < \xi; \\ Bu_2(x), & \xi < x \le b. \end{cases}$$

The continuity of g and the jump condition on dg/dx yield

$$Au_1(\xi) - Bu_2(\xi) = 0;$$

$$-Au_1'(\xi) + Bu_2'(\xi) = \frac{1}{a_0(\xi)}.$$

This inhomogeneous system of two linear algebraic equations in the two unknowns A and B will have a unique solution if and only if the determinant of the coefficients does not vanish. This determinant is recognized as the Wronskian of u_1 and u_2 evaluated at ξ. Since u_1 and u_2 are independent, their Wronskian cannot vanish anywhere, so that we can solve for A and B to obtain

$$A = \frac{u_2(\xi)}{a_0(\xi)W(u_1, u_2; \xi)}, \qquad B = \frac{u_1(\xi)}{a_0(\xi)W(u_1, u_2; \xi)}.$$

If we wish, we can write an alternative expression by using (1.47). The explicit form of the Green's function is

$$g(x \mid \xi) = \begin{cases} \dfrac{u_1(x)u_2(\xi)}{a_0(\xi)W(u_1, u_2; \xi)}, & a \le x < \xi; \\[4mm] \dfrac{u_1(\xi)u_2(x)}{a_0(\xi)W(u_1, u_2; \xi)}, & \xi < x \le b. \end{cases} \tag{1.56}$$

It is now easy to verify that $g(x \mid \xi)$ satisfies (1.55a).

2. *The Case of General Boundary Conditions* [see (1.51) and Exercise 1.53]. We content ourselves now with considering initial conditions; the completely homogeneous problem is *known* to have only the trivial solution, so that this property need not be assumed. We wish to construct the solution of the system

$$Lg = \delta(x - \xi), \quad a < x, \xi < \infty; \qquad g(a \mid \xi) = 0, \quad \frac{dg}{dx}(a \mid \xi) = 0. \qquad (1.57)$$

Hence

$$g(x \mid \xi) = \begin{cases} 0, & a < x < \xi; \\ Au_1(x) + Bu_2(x), & x > \xi, \end{cases}$$

where $u_1(x)$, $u_2(x)$ are two independent solutions of $Lu = 0$. The matching conditions at $x = \xi$ yield

$$Au_1(\xi) + Bu_2(\xi) = 0,$$

$$Au_1'(\xi) + Bu_2'(\xi) = \frac{1}{a_0(\xi)}.$$

Therefore,

$$A = -\frac{u_2(\xi)}{a_0(\xi)W(u_1, u_2; \xi)} \quad \text{and} \quad B = \frac{u_1(\xi)}{a_0(\xi)W(u_1, u_2; \xi)}.$$

Thus

$$g(x \mid \xi) = \begin{cases} 0, & a \le x < \xi; \\ \dfrac{u_1(\xi)u_2(x) - u_1(x)u_2(\xi)}{W(u_1, u_2; \xi)a_0(\xi)}, & x > \xi. \end{cases} \qquad (1.58)$$

We note that $[u_1(\xi)u_2(x) - u_1(x)u_2(\xi)]/W(u_1, u_2; \xi)a_0(\xi)$ is a solution of the homogeneous equation which vanishes at $x = \xi$ and has derivative $1/a_0(\xi)$ at $x = \xi$. Therefore this function is just the function $v_\xi(x)$ defined in (1.50). Hence

$$g(x \mid \xi) = \begin{cases} 0, & a \le x < \xi; \\ v_\xi(x), & x > \xi, \end{cases} \qquad (1.59)$$

where $Lv_\xi(x) = 0$ and $v_\xi(\xi) = 0$, $v_\xi'(\xi) = 1/a_0(\xi)$. If, in (1.57), both x and ξ are less than a, the problem is one of terminal conditions, and it is easy to show that

$$g(x \mid \xi) = \begin{cases} -v_\xi(x), & x < \xi; \\ 0, & \xi < x \le a. \end{cases} \qquad (1.59a)$$

The Green's function is used to solve inhomogeneous systems and to translate the eigenvalue problem into an eigenvalue integral equation. *The completely homogeneous system $Lu = 0$; $B_1(u) = 0$, $B_2(u) = 0$ is assumed to have* *only the trivial solution*, so that the preceding theorem guarantees the existence of $g(x \mid \xi)$.

(a) The system

$$Lu = f, \quad a < x < b; \qquad B_1(u) = 0, \quad B_2(u) = 0 \tag{1.60}$$

has the one and only solution

$$u(x) = \int_a^b g(x \mid \xi) f(\xi) d\xi. \tag{1.61}$$

Proof. Since g is a fundamental solution,

$$Lu = \int_a^b [Lg] f(\xi) d\xi = \int_a^b \delta(x - \xi) f(\xi) d\xi = \begin{cases} f(x), & a < x < b; \\ 0, & x < a, \quad x > b. \end{cases}$$

Furthermore,

$$B_1(u) = \int_a^b [B_1 g] f(\xi) d\xi = 0; \quad B_2(u) = \int_a^b [B_2 g] f(\xi) d\xi = 0.$$

One should also note that (1.61) depends continuously on f. Thus if the inhomogeneous term f is slightly changed then the solution u is only slightly changed. More precisely, consider the system (1.60) for f_1 and f_2 such that $|f_1(x) - f_2(x)| < \varepsilon, a < x < b$; then the corresponding solutions $u_1(x)$ and $u_2(x)$ satisfy

$$|u_1 - u_2| \leq \int_a^b |g(x \mid \xi)| \, |f_1(\xi) - f_2(\xi)| d\xi \leq M(b - a)\varepsilon,$$

where M is the maximum value of $|g|$ on the square $a \leq x, \xi \leq b$. (Since $|g|$ is continuous on this finite closed square it must be bounded.)

(b) Consider the completely inhomogeneous system (that is, inhomogeneous equation with inhomogeneous boundary conditions)

$$Lu = f, \quad a < x < b; \qquad B_1(u) = \alpha, \quad B_2(u) = \beta. \tag{1.62}$$

where α and β are given numbers. Let $u_1(x), u_2(x)$ be nontrivial solutions of the homogeneous equation satisfying the conditions $B_1(u_1) = 0$ and $B_2(u_2) = 0$, respectively. Since the completely homogeneous system has only the trivial solution, we must have $B_1(u_2) \neq 0, B_2(u_1) \neq 0$. We write the solution of (1.62) as

$$u(x) = \int_a^b g(x \mid \xi) f(\xi) d\xi + c_1 u_1(x) + c_2 u_2(x),$$

where $g(x \mid \xi)$ is the same Green's function used in (a) and c_1, c_2 are constants to be determined. Applying the boundary conditions in (1.62), we find

$$B_1(u) = \alpha = c_2 B_1(u_2);$$
$$B_2(u) = \beta = c_1 B_2(u_1).$$

Therefore,

$$u(x) = \int_a^b g(x \mid \xi) f(\xi) d\xi + \frac{\beta}{B_2(u_1)} u_1(x) + \frac{\alpha}{B_1(u_2)} u_2(x). \qquad (1.63)$$

It is easy to verify that (1.63) actually satisfies (1.62); further, since the difference of two solutions of (1.62) satisfies the completely homogeneous system (which has only the trivial solution), (1.63) is the only solution of (1.62). We also remark that the solution (1.63) depends continuously on f, α, and β.

(c) The eigenvalue problem

$$Lu = \lambda u, \quad a < x < b; \quad B_1(u) = 0, \quad B_2(u) = 0$$

is equivalent to the eigenvalue integral equation

$$u(x) = \lambda \int_a^b g(x \mid \xi) u(\xi) d\xi.$$

Adjoint, Symmetric, and Self-Adjoint Systems

Let $u(x)$ and $v(x)$ be twice-differentiable functions, but otherwise arbitrary. Consider

$$\int_a^b vLu \, dx = \int_a^b (va_0 u'' + va_1 u' + va_2 u) dx.$$

We integrate by parts, so as to transfer the differentiations from u to v; thus

$$\int_a^b vLu \, dx = \int_a^b u[(a_0 v)'' - (a_1 v)' + a_2 v] dx + [a_0(vu' - uv') + uv(a_1 - a_0')]_a^b.$$

The bracketed term in the integrand is a second-order differential operator acting on v; this operator is known as the *formal adjoint* of L and is denoted by L^* [see (1.36)]. Expanding the brackets, we find

$$L^* = a_0 \frac{d^2}{dx^2} + (2a_0' - a_1) \frac{d}{dx} + (a_0'' - a_1' + a_2).$$

The expression $L^* y = (a_0 y)'' - (a_1 y)' + a_2 y$

$$J(u,v) = a_0(vu' - uv') + (a_1 - a_0')(uv) \qquad (1.64)$$

is known in some circles as the bilinear concomitant (or conjunct) of u and v. Undaunted by this forbidding terminology, we note the following simple relation valid for all a and b:

$$\int_a^b (vLu - uL^*v) dx = J(u, v)]_a^b \qquad (1.65)$$

or, in differential form,

$$vLu - uL^*v = \frac{d}{dx} J(u, v). \qquad (1.66)$$

We refer to (1.65) as *Green's formula* and to (1.66) as *Lagrange's identity*. The differential operator L is said to be *formally self-adjoint* if $L^* = L$. The necessary and sufficient condition for an operator to be formally self-adjoint is

$$a_0'(x) = a_1(x).$$

A formally self-adjoint operator L can be written

$$L = \frac{d}{dx}\left[a_0(x)\frac{d}{dx}\right] + a_2(x),$$

and (1.64), (1.65), (1.66) are simplified to

$$J(u, v) = a_0(vu' - uv'), \tag{1.67}$$

$$\int_a^b (vLu - uLv)dx = J(u, v)]_a^b; \tag{1.68}$$

$$vLu - uLv = \frac{d}{dx}J(u, v). \tag{1.69}$$

The reader should observe that, if L is not formally self-adjoint, $vLu - uLv$ is not the derivative of an expression linear in each of the functions u, u', v, v'; this difficulty is overcome by using the formal adjoint L^*, which leads to (1.66).

Now suppose that u is required to satisfy two *given* homogeneous boundary conditions $B_1(u) = 0$, $B_2(u) = 0$, of the type (1.51), and let D be the set of all twice-differentiable functions which satisfy these boundary conditions.

We are interested in characterizing those functions v which will make the right side of (1.65) vanish whenever u is in D. We shall say that v belongs to D^* if it is twice-differentiable and if

$$J(u, v)]_a^b = 0,   \quad \text{for every } u \text{ in } D.$$

By inspection of (1.64) we can see that v will be in D^* if it satisfies two homogeneous boundary conditions (*the adjoint boundary conditions*) which are also of type (1.51) but possibly with different coefficients from those in $B_1(u) = 0$, $B_2(u) = 0$. These adjoint boundary conditions will be denoted by $B_1^*(v) = 0$, $B_2^*(v) = 0$.

As an example suppose that the original boundary conditions are $B_1(u) = u(a) = 0$, $B_2(u) = u'(b) = 0$. Then

$$J(u, v)]_a^b = \{[a_1(b) - a_0'(b)]v(b) - a_0(b)v'(b)\}u(b) - a_0(a)v(a)u'(a).$$

Since $u(b)$ and $u'(a)$ are arbitrary and both $a_0(a) \neq 0$ and $a_0(b) \neq 0$, $J(u, v)]_a^b$ will vanish if and only if

$$B_1^*(v) = v(a) = 0;$$

$$B_2^*(v) = v'(b) - \frac{[a_1(b) - a_0'(b)]}{a_0(b)}v(b) = 0,$$

and D^* is the set of all twice-differentiable functions which satisfy these two conditions. In our example then, the adjoint boundary conditions differ from the original ones and $D^* \neq D$. We note also that the adjoint boundary conditions depend on L; in fact, if L is formally self-adjoint then $a_1 = a_0'$ and the adjoint boundary conditions coincide with the original ones (that is, $D^* = D$). In Exercise 1.37 we characterize those boundary conditions for which $D^* = D$ if L is formally self-adjoint.

DEFINITION. The boundary-value problem or system

$$Lu = f, \quad a < x < b; \quad B_1(u) = 0, \quad B_2(u) = 0$$

is said to be *self-adjoint* if $L = L^*$ and $D = D^*$.

The Green's function $g(x \mid \xi)$ for an arbitrary operator L of the second order with homogeneous boundary conditions is the solution of

$$Lg = \delta(x - \xi), \quad a < x, \xi < b; \quad B_1(g) = 0, \quad B_2(g) = 0. \tag{1.70}$$

The *adjoint Green's function* $h(x \mid \xi)$ is defined as the solution of

$$L^*h = \delta(x - \xi), \quad a < x, \xi < b; \quad B_1^*(h) = 0, \quad B_2^*(h) = 0. \tag{1.71}$$

We now derive an exceedingly important relation between h and g. Take $\xi = \eta$ in (1.71), multiply the differential equation in (1.70) by $h(x \mid \eta)$ and the one in (1.71) by $g(x \mid \xi)$, subtract, and integrate from $x = a$ to $x = b$ to obtain

$$\int_a^b (hLg - gL^*h)dx = \int_a^b h(x \mid \eta)\delta(x - \xi)dx - \int_a^b g(x \mid \xi)\delta(x - \eta)dx.$$

Using Green's formula (1.65), we find

$$J(g, h)]_a^b = h(\xi \mid \eta) - g(\eta \mid \xi); \quad a < \xi, \eta < b.$$

Since h satisfies the adjoint boundary conditions, $J(g, h)]_a^b = 0$ and

$$h(x \mid \xi) = g(\xi \mid x); \quad a < \xi, x < b. \tag{1.72}$$

In particular, if the system (1.70) is self-adjoint, we have the symmetry property

$$g(x \mid \xi) = g(\xi \mid x); \quad a < \xi, x < b. \tag{1.73}$$

Consider next the completely inhomogeneous system

$$Lu = f, \quad a < x < b; \quad B_1(u) = \alpha, \quad B_2(u) = \beta. \tag{1.74}$$

We have found the solution in (1.63) but we now take a different approach which sheds additional light on the problem and which is more suitable for extension to partial differential equations. Multiply the differential equation in (1.74) by $h(x \mid \xi)$ and the differential equation in (1.71) by $u(x)$, subtract, and integrate from $x = a$ to $x = b$ to obtain, after appealing to Green's formula,

$$u(\xi) = \int_a^b h(x \mid \xi)f(x)dx - J(u, h)]_a^b.$$

If $\alpha = \beta = 0$ in (1.74), then $J(u, h)]_a^b = 0$ by the definition of adjoint boundary conditions; hence, by (1.72),

$$u(\xi) = \int_a^b h(x \mid \xi)f(x)dx = \int_a^b g(\xi \mid x)f(x)dx.$$

This is just the result (1.61) with a relabeling of the variables. If the boundary conditions in (1.74) are inhomogeneous, we obtain

$$u(\xi) = \int_a^b g(\xi \mid x)f(x)dx - J\{u(x), g(\xi \mid x)\}]_a^b. \qquad (1.75)$$

Now of course $J(u, g)]_a^b$ does not vanish but can be calculated explicitly in terms of g, α and β for each individual problem.

EXAMPLES

Example 1.   Suppose L is formally self-adjoint; that is $a_0' = a_1$.
(a) Abel's formula for the Wronskian (1.47) simplifies to

$$W(u, v; x) = \frac{C}{a_0(x)}. \qquad (1.76)$$

(b) If the boundary conditions are unmixed [see (1.52)], one easily sees that the system is self-adjoint and the Green's function (1.56) becomes

$$g(x \mid \xi) = \begin{cases} \dfrac{u_1(x)u_2(\xi)}{C}, & a < x < \xi; \\[4mm] \dfrac{u_1(\xi)u_2(x)}{C}, & \xi < x < b, \end{cases} \qquad (1.77)$$

where $u_1(x)$ satisfies the boundary condition at $x = a$, $u_2(x)$ satisfies the boundary condition at $x = b$, and C is defined from $W(u_1, u_2; x) = C/a_0(x)$. As expected from (1.74), $g(x \mid \xi)$ is a symmetric function of its arguments. Of course, to construct g, we have assumed that the completely homogeneous system has only the trivial solution. The solution of the boundary value problem

$$Lu = f, \quad a < x < b; \qquad B_1(u) = 0, \quad B_2(u) = 0$$

is

$$u(x) = \int_a^b g(x \mid \xi)f(\xi)d\xi = \frac{u_2(x)}{C} \int_a^x u_1(\xi)f(\xi)d\xi + \frac{u_1(x)}{C} \int_x^b u_2(\xi)f(\xi)d\xi.$$

Example 2.   Consider the operator $L = d^2/dx^2$ with $u(0) = 0$, $(du/dx)(l) = 0$. The completely homogeneous system has only the trivial solution; hence the Green's function can be constructed; indeed, we have

$$g(x \mid \xi) = \begin{cases} Ax, & 0 < x < \xi; \\ B, & \xi < x < l. \end{cases}$$

Continuity at $x = \xi$ yields $B = A\xi$; the jump condition in the first derivative gives $A = -1$. Thus

$$g(x \mid \xi) = \begin{cases} -x, & 0 \leq x < \xi; \\ -\xi, & \xi < x \leq l. \end{cases}$$

This result can also be obtained by using (1.77) with $u_1(x) = x$, $u_2(x) = 1$, $a_0(x) = 1$; then $W(u_1, u_2; x) = u_1 u_2' - u_2 u_1' = -1$, and $C = -1$.

Example 3.   Let L be an arbitrary linear operator of the second order with the associated initial conditions

$$u(0) = 0, \qquad u'(0) = 0.$$

Introduce an interval from 0 to l (l has no physical significance; it is used only to apply our principles). Then

$$J(u, v)]_0^l = a_0(vu' - uv') + uv(a_1 - a_0')]_0^l$$

$$= a_0(l)[v(l)u'(l) - u(l)v'(l)] + u(l)v(l)[a_1(l) - a_0'(l)].$$

Since $u(l)$ and $u'(l)$ are arbitrary, $J(u, v)]_0^l$ will vanish for all u if and only if $v(l) = 0$ and $v'(l) = 0$. Thus, the adjoint boundary conditions are

$$v(l) = 0, \qquad v'(l) = 0.$$

Therefore, even if $L = L^*$, the original system is not self-adjoint (initial-value problems are never self-adjoint!). Even so, we have no difficulty in solving the system

$$Lu = f, \quad 0 < x < l; \qquad u(0) = 0, \quad u'(0) = 0.$$

In fact, using (1.59) and (1.61), we find

$$u(x) = \int_0^x v_\xi(x) f(\xi) d\xi, \qquad 0 < x < l,$$

where $v_\xi(x)$ is the one and only solution of the homogeneous equation which satisfies $v_\xi(\xi) = 0$, $v_\xi'(\xi) = 1/a_0(\xi)$. We observe that our result is in fact true for any $x > 0$, since nothing prevents us from taking l as large as we please. The answer of course coincides with the formula (1.50), which was obtained previously.

Consider next the system

$$Lu = f, \quad 0 < x < \infty; \qquad u(0) = \alpha, \quad u'(0) = \beta, \tag{1.78}$$

which by inspection has the solution

$$u(x) = \int_0^x v_\xi(x) f(\xi) d\xi + \alpha u_1(x) + \beta u_2(x),$$

where u_1 and u_2 are the solutions of the homogeneous equation satisfying, respectively, the initial conditions

$$u_1(0) = 1, \qquad u_1'(0) = 0;$$

$$u_2(0) = 0, \qquad u_2'(0) = 1.$$

If L is formally self-adjoint, then $W(u_1, u_2; \xi)a_0(\xi)$ is constant (1.76), and since $W(u_1, u_2; 0) = 1$, this constant is just $a_0(0)$. Thus by (1.58) and (1.59),

$$v_\xi(x) = [u_1(\xi)u_2(x) - u_1(x)u_2(\xi)]a_0^{-1}(0).$$

The solution of (1.78) therefore becomes

$$u(x) = \int_0^x [u_1(\xi)u_2(x) - u_1(x)u_2(\xi)]a_0^{-1}(0)f(\xi)d\xi + \alpha u_1(x) + \beta u_2(x). \qquad (1.79)$$

This solution can also be obtained from (1.75) by introducing the artificial right end point $x = l$. The calculations are left to the reader.

Example 4.   Let the thermal conductivity in a rod of unit length be a function $k(x)$ which is continuously differentiable and positive, $0 \le x \le 1$. Appendix A shows that the steady temperature u is governed by the equation

$$-\frac{d}{dx}\left(k\frac{du}{dx}\right) = f(x),$$

where $f(x)$ is the density of heat generated by applied heat sources along the rod. If the ends are kept at 0 temperature and a unit source is located at $x = \xi$, the temperature in the rod satisfies the system

$$-\frac{d}{dx}\left(k\frac{dg}{dx}\right) = \delta(x - \xi), \quad 0 < x, \xi < 1; \qquad g(0\,|\,\xi) = g(1\,|\,\xi) = 0.$$

The solutions of the homogeneous equation which respectively satisfy the left and right end-boundary conditions are

$$u_1(x) = \int_0^x k^{-1}(\alpha)d\alpha, \qquad u_2(x) = \int_x^1 k^{-1}(\alpha)d\alpha,$$

so that

$$W(u_1, u_2; x) = -\frac{1}{k(x)}u_1(x) - \frac{1}{k(x)}u_2(x) = -\frac{1}{k(x)}\int_0^1 k^{-1}(\alpha)d\alpha.$$

From (1.77) (with $a_0 = -k$), we find

$$g(x\,|\,\xi) = \left[\int_0^1 k^{-1}(\alpha)d\alpha\right]^{-1}\begin{cases}u_1(x)u_2(\xi), & 0 < x < \xi; \\ u_2(x)u_1(\xi), & \xi < x < 1.\end{cases}$$

Example 5.   *Bessel's equation of order zero.*   The differential operator $(d/dx)[x(d/dx)] + x$ is known as the *Bessel operator* of order 0. To avoid the singular point at $x = 0$, let $0 < a < b$, and consider the problem

$$Lg = \frac{d}{dx}\left(x\frac{dg}{dx}\right) + xg = \delta(x - \xi), \qquad a < x, \xi < b,$$

with the boundary conditions

$$g = 0 \qquad \text{at } x = a \quad \text{and} \quad x = b.$$

This problem occurs in the study of heat flow in a cylindrical shell. The system is self-adjoint; two independent solutions of the homogeneous equation are the functions $J_0(x)$ and $N_0(x)$ discussed in Appendix B. We define two other independent solutions of the homogeneous equation by

$$Z_0^{(1)}(x) = J_0(x)N_0(a) - N_0(x)J_0(a);$$
$$Z_0^{(2)}(x) = J_0(x)N_0(b) - N_0(x)J_0(b).$$

Since $Z_0^{(1)}(x)$ satisfies the boundary condition at $x = a$, and $Z_0^{(2)}(x)$ satisfies the condition at $x = b$, we have, from (1.77),

$$g(x \mid \xi) = \begin{cases} \dfrac{Z_0^{(1)}(x)Z_0^{(2)}(\xi)}{C}, & a < x < \xi; \\[2mm] \dfrac{Z_0^{(1)}(\xi)Z_0^{(2)}(x)}{C}, & \xi < x < b. \end{cases}$$

Since $W[J_0, N_0; x] = 2/\pi x$ [see (B.7)], it follows that

$$W[Z_0^{(1)}, Z_0^{(2)}; x] = \frac{2}{\pi x}[J_0(a)N_0(b) - N_0(a)J_0(b)].$$

In our case $a_0(x) = x$, and, therefore,

$$C = \frac{2}{\pi}[J_0(a)N_0(b) - N_0(a)J_0(b)].$$

The preceding calculation of $g(x \mid \xi)$ is based on the assumption that the completely homogeneous system has only the trivial solution (that is, $C \neq 0$). Although this is true for most choices of a and b, there exist exceptional values [for instance, if a and b are both roots of $J_0(x)$] for which the construction of g is not possible.

Example 6.   The terms *symmetric*, *Hermitian*, and *self-adjoint* are used interchangeably in much of the physics literature. In the mathematical literature "symmetric" and "Hermitian" are used synonymously but "self-adjoint" is a horse of quite a different color.

Consider the differential operator $L = (d/dx)[a_0(d/dx)] + a_2$, which we have called formally self-adjoint. Suppose we have *any number* of homogeneous linear boundary conditions associated with L [these conditions do not have to be of the form (1.51)] and let D be the set of all twice-differentiable functions satisfying these boundary conditions. The operator L defined on the domain D is *symmetric* if, for all u and v in D, we have

$$J(u, v)]_a^b = a_0(vu' - uv')]_a^b = 0; \quad \text{hence} \int_a^b vLu\ dx = \int_a^b uLv\ dx.$$

The difference between this and self-adjointness is best illustrated by an example. Consider d^2/dx^2 with $u(0) = u'(0) = u(1) = u'(1) = 0$. We obviously have too " many " conditions, yet the system is *symmetric* (but *not* self-adjoint). To find the adjoint boundary conditions we must determine all functions $v(x)$ such that $J(u, v)]_a^b = 0$, for every u with $u(0) = u'(0) = u(1) = u'(1) = 0$. Any twice-differentiable function $v(x)$ satisfying no further conditions will do the trick. Thus D^* does not coincide with D and the system is *not* self-adjoint. To get a full appreciation of the distinction, the reader should study Chapter 2.

EXERCISES

1.37 Let $L = L^*$, and let the boundary conditions be of type (1.51); show that the necessary and sufficient condition for the system (1.51) to be self-adjoint is $a_0(a)p_{34} = a_0(b)p_{12}$, where

$$p_{12} = \begin{vmatrix} \alpha_{11} & \alpha_{12} \\ \alpha_{21} & \alpha_{22} \end{vmatrix}, \quad p_{34} = \begin{vmatrix} \beta_{11} & \beta_{12} \\ \beta_{21} & \beta_{22} \end{vmatrix}.$$

These equations are obviously satisfied if the boundary conditions are unmixed. [The self-adjointness of this problem was already pointed out in Example 1(b).]

As another special case, show that the " periodic " boundary conditions $u(a) = u(b)$ and $a_0(a)u'(a) = a_0(b)u'(b)$ lead to a self-adjoint system when associated with a formally self-adjoint operator.

1.38 Let $L = (d^2/dx^2) + 4(d/dx) - 3$; then $L^* = (d^2/dx^2) - 4(d/dx) - 3$, and $J(u, v) = vu' - uv' + 4uv$. If we are given the boundary conditions $u'(a) + 4u(a) = 0$ and $u'(b) + 4u(b) = 0$, show that the adjoint boundary conditions are $v'(a) = 0$ and $v'(b) = 0$.

1.39 For an nth-order linear differential operator, the concepts of self-adjointness and adjoint operators are defined in a manner similar to that used for second-order operators. Find the formal adjoint of such an nth-order operator. Show that an operator of odd order cannot be formally self-adjoint.

Consider $L = d^4/dx^4$ and the four boundary conditions $u(0) = 0$, $u(1) = 0$, $u'(0) = 0$, $u'(1) = 0$. Show that this system is self-adjoint.

Let $L = d/dx$ with the boundary condition $u(0) = \alpha u(1)$. Find L^* and D^*.

1.40 Prove that, if L is a second-order operator, there exists $s(x)$ so that $L_1 = sL$ is formally self-adjoint.

1.41 Show that $(L^*)^* = L$ and $(D^*)^* = D$, for systems of type (1.51).

1.42 Let $L = (d^2/dx^2) - 2(d/dx) + 2$, with the boundary conditions $u(0) = 0$, $(du/dx)(\pi/4) = 0$. Show that the completely homogeneous system has only the trivial solution. Construct $g(x|\xi)$. Determine L^* and the adjoint boundary conditions; construct the adjoint Green's function from basic considerations. By comparing the explicit forms, show that $h(x|\xi) = g(\xi|x)$.

1.43 Construct the Green's function for $L = (d^2/dx^2) + k^2$, where $k^2 > 0$, with the boundary conditions $u(0) = 0$, $u(1) = 0$. What are the values of k^2 for which the construction is impossible?

1.44 Find the Green's function of $L = d^2/dx^2$, subject to the conditions $u'(0) = u(1)$, $u'(1) = 0$. Find L^* and the adjoint boundary conditions; construct the adjoint Green's function from basic considerations. Show explicitly that $g(x|\xi) = h(\xi|x)$.

1.45 Find the Green's function of $L = (d/dx)[(x + 1)(d/dx)]$, with the conditions $u(0) = 0$, $u(1) = 0$.

1.46 *Bessel's equation of order v.* Let $0 < a < b$, and consider the equation

$$\frac{d}{dx}\left(x\frac{dg}{dx}\right) + \left(x - \frac{v^2}{x}\right)g = \delta(x - \xi); \qquad a < x, \xi < b,$$

with the boundary conditions

$$g = 0 \qquad \text{at } x = a \quad \text{and} \quad x = b.$$

Find $g(x|\xi)$ by using the results in Appendix B and the ideas in Example 5. Is the construction always possible?

1.47 Consult Example 5 to find the solution of the system

$$\frac{d}{dx}\left(x\frac{du}{dx}\right) + xu = f(x); \qquad u(a) = \alpha, \quad u(b) = \beta.$$

1.48 Find the Green's function of $L = (d/dx)[x(d/dx)]$ with the conditions $u(0)$ finite, $u(1) = 0$. A general discussion of singular problems of this type is found in Chapter 4.

1.49 Consider the differential expression d^4/dx^4 with the four boundary conditions $u(0) = u'(1) = u(1) = u'(1) = 0$. Find the Green's function for this system. [You must show first that $g(x|\xi)$, $(d/dx)g$, $(d^2/dx^2)g$ are continuous at $x = \xi$, and

$$(d^3/dx^3)g(x|\xi)|_{x=\xi+} - (d^3/dx^3)g(x|\xi)|_{x=\xi-} = 1.]$$

1.50 *Extension of superposition principle.* Let θ be a parameter, and consider the system

$$Lu = f(x, \theta); \qquad B_1(u) = 0, \quad B_2(u) = 0.$$

The solution u will of course depend on θ and is written $u(x, \theta)$. Show that the solution of

$$Lv = \frac{\partial f}{\partial \theta}; \qquad B_1(v) = 0, \quad B_2(v) = 0$$

is given by $v(x, \theta) = (\partial u/\partial \theta)(x, \theta)$.

1.51 *Static deflections of a beam.* If a transverse pressure $f(x)$ is applied to a beam, the differential equation for the deflection is $EI(d^4u/dx^4) = f(x)$, where E and I are known physical constants. The beam is clamped at its ends; therefore, $u(0) = u'(0) = u(l) = u'(l) = 0$.

If a concentrated unit force is applied at $x = \xi$, then $f(x) = \delta(x - \xi)$, and the corresponding deflection is $g(x|\xi)$.

Show that a concentrated unit moment (equivalent to a dipole) can be translated into a symbolic pressure $(d/dx)\delta(x - \xi)$. By Exercise 1.50, the corresponding deflection is $-(d/d\xi)g(x|\xi)$.

Show that the deflection corresponding to a continuous moment distribution $m(x)$ is the same as the deflection due to the pressure distribution dm/dx.

1.52 Electrical engineers refer to the causal fundamental solution as the *impulse response.* If the independent variable is the time, the impulse response $g(t|\tau)$ satisfies

$$Lg = \delta(t - \tau); \qquad g \equiv 0 \quad \text{for } t < \tau.$$

For $\tau > 0$, we can equally well characterize g by the initial-value problem

$$Lg = \delta(t - \tau); \qquad g(0|\tau) = 0, \quad \frac{dg}{dt}(0|\tau) = 0.$$

The function $g(t|\tau)$ is given by (1.59). The solution of

$$Lu = f(t), \quad t > 0; \qquad u(0) = u'(0) = 0 \tag{1.80}$$

is

$$u = \int_0^t g(t|\tau)f(\tau)d\tau. \tag{1.81}$$

One can also express the solution of (1.80) in terms of the *step response* $Z(t|\tau)$, which is defined from

$$LZ = H(t - \tau) = \begin{cases} 0, & t < \tau; \\ 1, & t > \tau; \end{cases}$$

$Z(0 | \tau) = 0$; $(dZ/dt)(0 | \tau) = 0$. It is clear, of course, that $Z(t | \tau) \equiv 0$ for $t < \tau$. From the relation $\partial H(t - \tau)/\partial t = -\partial H(t - \tau)/\partial \tau = \delta(t - \tau)$ and from Exercise 1.50, it follows that

$$g(t | \tau) = -\frac{\partial Z(t | \tau)}{\partial \tau}.$$

Substituting in (1.81), we obtain

$$u(t) = -\int_0^t \frac{\partial Z}{\partial \tau} f(\tau) d\tau = \int_0^t Z(t | \tau) f(\tau) d\tau - Z(t | \tau) f(\tau)]_{\tau=0}^{\tau=t}.$$

Since $Z(\tau | \tau) = 0$,

$$u(t) = Z(t | 0) f(0) + \int_0^t Z(t | \tau) f(\tau) d\tau. \tag{1.82}$$

The form (1.82) of the solution is sometimes more convenient than (1.81).

1.53 Consider the second-order operator L with the most general boundary conditions of type (1.51). Assume that the completely homogeneous system has only the 0 solution. Construct the Green's function $g(x | \xi)$ as the sum of the causal fundamental solution and some solution of the homogeneous equation.

[Let $g(x | \xi) = t(x | \xi) + Au_1(x) + Bu_2(x)$, where $u_1(x)$ satisfies the first boundary condition and $u_2(x)$ the second; determine A and B by imposing the boundary conditions on g.]

1.6 ALTERNATIVE THEOREMS AND THE MODIFIED GREEN'S FUNCTION

We have already pointed out at the beginning of Section 1.5 that the uniqueness and existence theorems do not necessarily hold for boundary value problems. The difficulty encountered is similar to one that arises in the solution of the linear algebraic equations discussed below.

Systems of n Linear Algebraic Equations in n Unknowns

Let A be an n by n matrix whose elements a_{ij} are real. The *rank* of A is the order of its largest nonvanishing subdeterminant. If rank $A = n$, then det $A \neq 0$, and no row of A is a linear combination of the other rows; that is, there are no interdependencies among the rows of A. If rank $A = n - k$, then det $A = 0$, and there are k interdependencies among the rows of A.

We shall consider three vector equations associated with the matrix A:

(1) The homogeneous equation: $Au = 0$, or $\sum_{j=1}^{n} a_{ij} u_j = 0$, $i = 1, \ldots, n$.

(2) The inhomogeneous equation: $Ay = f$, or $\sum_{j=1}^{n} a_{ij} y_j = f_i$, $i = 1, \ldots, n$.

(3) The adjoint homogeneous equation: $A^*v = 0$, or $\sum_{j=1}^{n} a_{ij}^* v_j = 0$, $i = 1, \ldots, n$.

Here A^* is the adjoint or transposed matrix which is obtained by interchanging the rows and columns of A; thus $a_{ij}^* = a_{ji}$.

We denote the inner product (also known as dot product or scalar product) of two arbitrary vectors u and v by $\langle u, v \rangle$. By definition $\langle u, v \rangle = \sum_{i=1}^{n} u_i v_i$. The vectors u and v are orthogonal if and only if $\langle u, v \rangle = 0$.

RESULTS. (a) If $\det A \neq 0$, rank $A =$ rank $A^* = n$. The only solution of (1) and of (3) is the vector identically 0, that is, the vector whose n components are 0. We say that (1) and (3) have only the trivial solution. Then the one and only solution of (2) is $y = A^{-1}f$, where A^{-1} is the inverse matrix of A.

(b) If $\det A = 0$, rank $A =$ rank $A^* = n - k$, where $k(\leq n)$ depends on A. There are k linearly independent solutions of (1), say $u^{(1)}, \ldots, u^{(k)}$. Any solution of (1) may be written $\sum_{i=1}^{k} c_i u^{(i)}$. System (3) also has k solutions, say $v^{(1)}, \ldots, v^{(k)}$. Any solution of (3) may be written $\sum_{i=1}^{k} d_i v^{(i)}$. The inhomogeneous equation (2) will usually *not* have any solution. This should be clear intuitively, because there are k interdependencies in the rows of A, and, unless these are reflected in f, no solution will exist.

A necessary and sufficient condition for the existence of a solution to (2) is that f be orthogonal to *every* solution of (3), that is, f must satisfy certain *consistency conditions*. This is equivalent to stating that f should be orthogonal to each of the k vectors, $v^{(1)}, v^{(2)}, \ldots, v^{(k)}$. Thus k consistency conditions must be satisfied by f for a solution of (2) to exist.

REMARKS. If $\det A \neq 0$, the consistency conditions are automatically satisfied, since $v \equiv 0$.

If $\det A = 0$, and f is orthogonal to the k linearly independent solutions $v^{(1)}, \ldots, v^{(k)}$ of system (3), then (2) will have an infinite number of solutions given by $y = y_p + \sum_{i=1}^{k} c_i u^{(i)}$, where y_p is any particular solution of (2).

The proof of the necessity of the consistency condition is easy. Take the inner product of (2) by v. We have

$$\langle v, f \rangle = \langle v, Ay \rangle = \sum_{\substack{i=1 \\ j=1}}^{n} v_i a_{ij} y_j = \langle y, A^*v \rangle.$$

It follows that $\langle v, f \rangle = \sum_{i=1}^{n} v_i f_i = 0$, for every solution v of (3).

The sufficiency proof is more complicated and will not be taken up here (see Chapter 2).

EXAMPLE

Consider the inhomogeneous equation

$$Ay = f: \begin{cases} y_1 + y_2 + y_3 = 1; \\ 2y_1 - y_2 + y_3 = 3; \\ y_1 - 2y_2 = 1. \end{cases}$$

For a solution to exist, $f = (1, 3, 1)$ must be orthogonal to each v which is a solution of

$$A^* v = 0: \begin{cases} v_1 + 2v_2 + v_3 = 0; \\ v_1 - v_2 - 2v_3 = 0; \\ v_1 + v_2 = 0. \end{cases}$$

We have

$$\det A^* = \begin{vmatrix} 1 & 2 & 1 \\ 1 & -1 & -2 \\ 1 & 1 & 0 \end{vmatrix} = 0.$$

Since $\begin{vmatrix} 1 & 2 \\ 1 & -1 \end{vmatrix} \neq 0$, rank $A^* =$ rank $A = 2$.

We solve $A^* v = 0$ to obtain $v_1 = -v_2$, $-2v_2 = 2v_3$. Thus $v_1 = -v_2 = v_3$ is the general solution of $A^* v = 0$; this can be written in the form $c(1, -1, 1)$. The consistency requirement is that f be orthogonal to $(1, -1, 1)$, but, since $(1, 3, 1) \cdot (1, -1, 1) = -1 \neq 0$, the inhomogeneous equation has *no* solution.

Linear Integral Equations of the Second Kind

Let λ be a fixed, arbitrary number, $\lambda \neq 0$. Consider the following three equations:

(1) $\lambda \int_a^b k(x, \xi) u(\xi)\, d\xi - u(x) = 0$, the homogeneous equation.

(2) $\lambda \int_a^b k(x, \xi) y(\xi)\, d\xi - y(x) = f(x)$, the inhomogeneous equation.

(3) $\lambda \int_a^b k(\xi, x) v(\xi)\, d\xi - v(x) = 0$, the adjoint homogeneous equation.

Theorem.   (a) *If* (1) *has only the trivial solution,* (3) *has only the trivial solution, and* (2) *has one and only one solution.*

(b) *If* (1) *has nontrivial solutions,* (3) *has nontrivial solutions, and* (2) *has no solution unless* $\int_a^b f(x)v(x)dx$ *vanishes for every v which is a solution of* (3).

This alternative theorem is proved in Chapter 3.

Linear Differential Equations of the Second Order

Alternative theorems similar to the ones above hold for differential equations. The difficulty that occasionally arises in the solution of the inhomogeneous problem can be related to the physical phenomenon known as *resonance*.

Suppose we consider the *forced* vibration of a string with fixed end points under the applied pressure $f(x, t)$, where x is the space coordinate and t the time coordinate. The deflection $u(x,t)$ satisfies the partial differential equation (see Appendix A),

$$T \frac{\partial^2 u}{\partial x^2} = \rho \frac{\partial^2 u}{\partial t^2} - f(x, t); \qquad u(0, t) = u(l, t) = 0. \tag{1.83}$$

For simplicity, the tension T in the string and the mass density ρ are both taken to be 1.

Suppose in addition that $f(x, t) = F(x)e^{-i\omega t}$, the impressed frequency of the load being a *given* positive real number ω. Then it is reasonable to assume (after transient effects have died out) that (1.83) will admit a solution $u(x, t) = X(x)e^{-i\omega t}$. Let us see whether such a solution is possible. Substituting $u = X(x)e^{-i\omega t}$ in (1.83) we obtain

$$-\frac{d^2 X}{dx^2} - \omega^2 X = F(x); \qquad X(0) = X(l) = 0.$$

This is an ordinary differential equation for X, the space part of the solution (the time dependence is $e^{-i\omega t}$). Letting $-(d^2/dx^2) - \omega^2 = L_\omega$, the inhomogeneous equation may be written

$$L_\omega X = F(x); \qquad X(0) = X(l) = 0. \tag{1.84}$$

Note that for any ω, the system consisting of L_ω and the boundary conditions is self-adjoint. It is important to find out under what circumstances (1.84) possesses a solution and whether this solution is unique. It is easy to show that there are cases (unusual, to be sure) when (1.84) does *not* have any solutions. Indeed, suppose ω is an exceptional number for which the system

$$L_\omega Z = 0, \qquad Z(0) = Z(l) = 0 \tag{1.85}$$

has a nontrivial solution $Z_\omega(x)$. Then, multiplying (1.84) by Z_ω and (1.85) by X, subtracting and integrating, we obtain

$$\int_0^l (Z_\omega'' X - X'' Z_\omega)dx = \int_0^l Z_\omega(x)F(x)dx.$$

The left side is just $(XZ_\omega' - Z_\omega X')]_0^l$. This vanishes by the boundary conditions on X and Z_ω.

Thus, for (1.84) to have a solution, it is *necessary that*

$$\int_0^l Z_\omega(x)F(x)dx = 0. \tag{1.86}$$

This is a severe restriction on $F(x)$ unless $Z_\omega(x) = 0$. When is $Z_\omega(x) \neq 0$? When does (1.85) have nontrivial solutions? The answer is: when ω is one of the natural frequencies of the system. System (1.85) is exactly the one satisfied by the amplitude of the *free* vibrations of the string. The solutions of (1.85) are easily found. If $\omega^2 \neq \pi^2/l^2, 4\pi^2/l^2, 9\pi^2/l^2, \ldots$, the only solution of (1.85) is $Z_\omega(x) = 0$. If $\omega^2 = k^2\pi^2/l^2$, with k an integer, then

$$Z_\omega(x) = c \sin (k\pi x/l).$$

It can be shown that condition (1.86) is also *sufficient* for the existence of a solution to (1.84). These results are contained in the following *alternative theorem*.

Theorem. *If* $\omega \neq \pi/l, 2\pi/l, 3\pi/l, \ldots$, *then* (1.85) *has only the trivial solution and* (1.84) *has* one and only one *solution.*

If $\omega = k\pi/l$ *for some fixed integer k, then* (1.84) *will have* no *solution, unless $F(x)$ obeys the* consistency condition

$$\int_0^l F(x) \sin \frac{k\pi x}{l}\, dx = 0.$$

In physical terms: If the impressed frequency ω is not a natural frequency, (1.84) has a solution and (1.83) has a particular solution which vibrates with the impressed frequency ω. If $\omega = k\pi/l$, we say that the impressed frequency is in *resonance* with the natural frequency $k\pi/l$, and (1.84) has no solution (unless the consistency condition is satisfied), which in turn implies that (1.83) does *not* have a particular solution which vibrates at the frequency ω; we expect instead that (1.83) will have a solution which grows in time.

It is instructive to solve (1.83) exactly, with $f(x, t) = F(x)e^{-i\omega t}$. Suppose for simplicity that the initial deflection and velocity of the string are 0. We want to solve

$$\frac{\partial^2 u}{\partial x^2} = \frac{\partial^2 u}{\partial t^2} - F(x)e^{-i\omega t}; \qquad u(0, t) = u(l, t) = 0; \qquad u(x, 0) = \frac{\partial u}{\partial t}(x, 0) = 0.$$

$$(1.87)$$

For any $t > 0$, we can expand $u(x, t)$ in a sine series whose coefficients will depend on t,

$$u(x, t) = \sum_{k=1}^{\infty} a_k(t) \sin \frac{k\pi x}{l}, \qquad (1.88)$$

where

$$a_k(t) = \frac{2}{l} \int_0^l u(x, t) \sin \frac{k\pi x}{l}\, dx.$$

To determine $a_k(t)$ we could substitute the series (1.88) in (1.87) and differentiate term by term. To circumvent the question of the legitimacy of term-by-term differentiation, we shall resort to a slightly different procedure. Let us multiply (1.87) by $\sin(k\pi x/l)$ and integrate from 0 to l (this is known as taking the finite sine transform). Setting

$$F_k = \frac{2}{l} \int_0^l F(x) \sin \frac{k\pi x}{l} \, dx,$$

we obtain

$$\frac{2}{l} \int_0^l \frac{\partial^2 u}{\partial x^2} \sin \frac{k\pi x}{l} \, dx = a_k''(t) - F_k e^{-i\omega t}.$$

Integrating by parts twice and using the boundary conditions, we find

$$a_k'' + \frac{k^2 \pi^2}{l^2} a_k = F_k e^{-i\omega t}; \qquad a_k(0) = a_k'(0) = 0.$$

Thus $a_k(t)$ is the solution of an initial-value problem for an ordinary differential equation. By (1.79), the unique solution is

$$a_k(t) = \frac{lF_k}{k\pi} \int_0^t \sin \frac{k\pi}{l} (t - \tau) \, e^{-i\omega \tau} \, d\tau; \qquad k = 1, 2, \ldots .$$

If ω is not a natural frequency, we find

$$a_k = \frac{F_k}{2\alpha_k} \left[e^{-i\omega t} \left(\frac{2\alpha_k}{\alpha_k^2 - \omega^2} \right) - \frac{e^{-i\alpha_k t}}{\alpha_k - \omega} - \frac{e^{i\alpha_k t}}{\alpha_k + \omega} \right],$$

where we have set

$$\alpha_k = \frac{k\pi}{l}.$$

If ω is a natural frequency, say $\omega = n\pi/l$, the result for a_k is the same when $k \neq n$; on the other hand, for $k = n$, we have

$$a_n(t) = \frac{F_n}{2i\omega} \left[\frac{\sin \omega t}{\omega} - t e^{-i\omega t} \right].$$

Therefore, if ω coincides with a natural frequency, (1.88) will have one term which increases in time unless $F_n = 0$. If $F_n = 0$ [that is,

$$\int_0^l F(x) \sin(n\pi x/l) dx = 0],$$

$F(x)$ does no work with respect to the mode $\sin(n\pi x/l)$, so that this mode is not excited and the solution (1.88) does not grow in time.

We now investigate alternative theorems for general differential equations of the second order. Consider the related systems:

(1) The homogeneous system: $Lu = 0, a < x < b$; $B_1(u) = 0, B_2(u) = 0$.
(2) The inhomogeneous system: $Ly = f, a < x < b$; $B_1(y) = 0, B_2(y) = 0$.
(3) The adjoint homogeneous system: $L^* v = 0, \quad a < x < b$; $B_1^*(v) = 0$, $B_2^*(v) = 0$.

Here L, B_1, B_2, f are given and L^*, B_1^*, B_2^* are easily calculated by the methods of the preceding section.

Theorem.   (a) *If* (1) *has only the trivial solution* $u(x) = 0$ *in* $a \le x \le b$, *then* (3) *has only the trivial solution, and* (2) *has one and only one solution.*

(b) *If* (1) *has nontrivial solutions,* (3) *will have nontrivial solutions* [*usually different from those of* (1)], *and* (2) *has no solution unless the "consistency condition"* $\int_a^b f(x)v(x)dx = 0$ *is satisfied for every function* $v(x)$ *which is a solution of* (3).

REMARKS.   If (3) has only the trivial solution, the consistency condition is automatically satisfied whatever f is, and there is no contradiction between parts (a) and (b).

If (1) has nontrivial solutions of the form $cu_1(x)$, (3) will have nontrivial solutions of the form $cv_1(x)$. If $\int_a^b fv_1\, dx = 0$, then (2) will have an infinite number of solutions: $y(x) = y_p(x) + cu_1(x)$, where $y_p(x)$ is any particular solution of (2).

If (1) has two linearly independent solutions $u_1(x)$ and $u_2(x)$, then (3) will have two linearly independent solutions $v_1(x)$ and $v_2(x)$. If $\int_a^b fv_1\, dx = \int_a^b fv_2\, dx = 0$, then (2) will have an infinite number of solutions: $y(x) = y_p(x) + c_1u_1(x) + c_2u_2(x)$, where c_1 and c_2 are arbitrary constants and $y_p(x)$ is any particular solution of (2).

From the theory of differential equations, system (1) cannot have more than two linearly independent solutions.

Proof of the Necessity of the Consistency Condition.   Multiply (2) by v and (3) by y, subtract, and integrate from a to b to obtain

$$\int_a^b (vLy - yL^*v)dx = \int_a^b f(x)v(x)dx.$$

The left side reduces to $J(y, v)]_a^b$, which is 0 by the boundary conditions. Therefore we must have $\int_a^b f(x)v(x)dx = 0$, for every $v(x)$ which satisfies (3). The sufficiency will be proved as a corollary of the alternative theorems on integral equations (see Chapter 3).

EXAMPLES

Example 1.   Consider the system

$$-\frac{d^2u}{dx^2} = 0, \quad 0 < x < l; \qquad \text{with } \frac{du}{dx}(0) = 0, \quad \frac{du}{dx}(l) = 0.$$

This system is self-adjoint, so (3) coincides with (1). There is a nontrivial solution of the homogeneous equation—$u_1 = $ constant. Consider the system

$$-\frac{d^2y}{dx^2} = f(x), \quad 0 < x < l; \qquad \text{with } \frac{dy}{dx}(0) = 0, \quad \frac{dy}{dx}(l) = 0.$$

This corresponds to heat conduction in a rod whose ends and lateral surface are insulated. Since the sources along the rod generate heat at a rate $f(x)$ per unit length per unit time, a solution is possible only if $\int_0^l f(x)dx = 0$, that is, if the net heat added per unit time is 0. If this condition is violated, it is physically clear that the temperature would rise (or decline) with time and no steady-state solution could exist.

Suppose $\int_0^l f(x)dx = 0$. To be specific, let $f(x) = \sin(2\pi x/l)$. We can solve the differential equation $-d^2y/dx^2 = \sin(2\pi x/l)$ to obtain $y(x) = A + Bx + (l^2/4\pi^2)\sin(2\pi x/l)$. The boundary condition at the left end yields $B = -l/2\pi$; from the boundary condition at the right end, $B + (l^2/4\pi^2)(2\pi/l)\cos 2\pi = 0$, which is satisfied by $B = -l/2\pi$; furthermore, A is arbitrary. Therefore, the general solution of the system is $y(x) = A + (l^2/4\pi^2)\sin(2\pi x/l) - (l/2\pi)x$. It is easy to check that this satisfies all the conditions on the problem.

It is apparent that the alternative theorem does not tell us how to obtain the solution; it merely predicts the existence or nonexistence of solutions.

Example 2.   Consider the inhomogeneous system

$$y'' + 2y' + 5y = f(x), \quad 0 < x < \pi; \qquad y(0) = 0, \quad y(\pi) = 0.$$

The corresponding homogeneous system has the nontrivial solution $e^{-x}\sin 2x$. The adjoint homogeneous system is

$$v'' - 2v' + 5v = 0, \quad 0 < x < \pi; \qquad v(0) = 0, \quad v(\pi) = 0,$$

which, by direct calculation, can be shown to have the nontrivial solution $e^x\sin 2x$. The original inhomogeneous system will therefore have solutions if and only if

$$\int_0^\pi f(x)e^x\sin 2x \, dx = 0,$$

and, if this consistency condition is satisfied,

$$y = y_p + Ae^{-x}\sin 2x,$$

where y_p is any particular solution of the inhomogeneous system [which can be obtained explicitly by (1.50) or by the method outlined below].

The Modified Green's Function

We have seen that the self-adjoint system $-d^2u/dx^2 = 0, 0 \le x \le l$, with $u'(0) = u'(l) = 0$, has the nontrivial solution $u = $ constant.

This means that the system

$$-\frac{d^2y}{dx^2} = f(x); \qquad y'(0) = y'(l) = 0 \tag{1.89}$$

has a solution if and only if $\int_0^l f(x)dx = 0$. It follows that the ordinary Green's function cannot be constructed for this problem. The system

$$-\frac{d^2g}{dx^2} = \delta(x - \xi); \qquad \frac{dg}{dx}\bigg|_{x=0} = \frac{dg}{dx}\bigg|_{x=l} = 0 \qquad (1.90)$$

has no solution, since $\int_0^l \delta(x - \xi)dx \neq 0$.

There is a simple physical interpretation of this difficulty. We know that (1.90) represents the steady-state temperature in a *completely* insulated rod when a steady heat source is present at the point $x = \xi$ along the rod. These conditions are contradictory, since the temperature would surely rise indefinitely in the interior of such a rod, owing to the presence of the steady source.

If we insist upon constructing something like a Green's function [a function that will help us solve system (1.90) when this system has a solution, that is, when $\int_0^l f(x)dx = 0$], the remedy is rather simple. We introduce an additional source *density* of strength $-1/l$ in the rod. Thus the net heat input per unit time in the rod for this new problem is

$$\int_0^l \left[\delta(x - \xi) - \frac{1}{l}\right]dx = 0.$$

The *modified* Green's function satisfies

$$-\frac{d^2g_M}{dx^2} = \delta(x - \xi) - \frac{1}{l}; \qquad \frac{dg_M}{dx}\bigg|_0 = \frac{dg_M}{dx}\bigg|_l = 0. \qquad (1.91)$$

Since the consistency condition is satisfied, this system has a solution (determined only up to an additive constant). For $x \neq \xi$, $-g_M'' = -1/l$, so that

$$g_M(x \mid \xi) = \begin{cases} A + Bx + \dfrac{x^2}{2l}, & 0 \leq x < \xi; \\[2mm] C + Dx + \dfrac{x^2}{2l}, & \xi < x \leq l. \end{cases}$$

The boundary conditions yield $B = 0$, $D = -1$. Continuity at $x = \xi$ implies $A + (\xi^2/2l) = C - \xi + (\xi^2/2l)$, or $C = A + \xi$. The jump condition on dg_M/dx at $x = \xi$ gives $1 - (\xi/l) + (\xi/l) = 1$, which is automatically satisfied. Therefore,

$$g_M(x \mid \xi) = \begin{cases} A + \dfrac{x^2}{2l}, & 0 \leq x < \xi; \\[2mm] A + \xi - x + \dfrac{x^2}{2l}, & \xi < x \leq l. \end{cases} \qquad (1.92)$$

As was expected, an arbitrary constant A appears in the solution. It is often convenient to choose a particular modified Green's function which is a symmetric function of x and ξ. To accomplish this, consider $g_M(x\,|\,\xi_1)$ and $g_M(x\,|\,\xi_2)$, which satisfy the systems

$$-\frac{d^2 g_M(x\,|\,\xi_1)}{dx^2} = \delta(x - \xi_1) - \frac{1}{l}; \qquad \frac{dg_M}{dx}\bigg|_{x=0} = \frac{dg_M}{dx}\bigg|_{x=l} = 0$$

and

$$-\frac{d^2 g_M(x\,|\,\xi_2)}{dx^2} = \delta(x - \xi_2) - \frac{1}{l}; \qquad \frac{dg_M}{dx}\bigg|_{x=0} = \frac{dg_M}{dx}\bigg|_{x=l} = 0,$$

respectively. Combining these equations in the usual way, we obtain

$$g_M(\xi_1\,|\,\xi_2) - g_M(\xi_2\,|\,\xi_1) - \frac{1}{l}\int_0^l g_M(x\,|\,\xi_2)dx + \frac{1}{l}\int_0^l g_M(x\,|\,\xi_1)dx = 0.$$

If we impose the condition $\int_0^l g_M(x\,|\,\xi)dx = 0$ for every ξ, then $g_M(x\,|\,\xi)$ will be symmetric. In our particular case this condition yields

$$\int_0^\xi \left(A + \frac{x^2}{2l}\right)dx + \int_\xi^l \left(A + \xi - x + \frac{x^2}{2l}\right)dx = 0$$

or

$$A = \frac{1}{l}\left(\frac{l^2}{3} + \frac{\xi^2}{2} - \xi l\right).$$

The *symmetric* modified Green's function is given by

$$g_M(x\,|\,\xi) = \begin{cases} \dfrac{l}{3} - \xi + \dfrac{x^2 + \xi^2}{2l}, & 0 \le x < \xi; \\[2mm] \dfrac{l}{3} - x + \dfrac{x^2 + \xi^2}{2l}, & \xi < x \le l. \end{cases}$$

This result could have been obtained by inspecting (1.92) and making a judicious choice of A.

The modified Green's function can be used to solve the system

$$-\frac{d^2 y}{dx^2} = f(x); \qquad \frac{dy}{dx}(0) = \frac{dy}{dx}(l) = 0, \qquad (1.93)$$

where $f(x)$ satisfies $\int_0^l f(x)dx = 0$ [no solution exists unless $\int_0^l f(x)dx = 0$].

Multiply (1.93) by $g_M(x\,|\,\xi)$, (1.91) by $y(x)$, subtract, and integrate to obtain

$$-\int_0^l (g_M y'' - y g_M'')dx = \int_0^l g_M(x\,|\,\xi)f(x)dx - y(\xi) + \frac{1}{l}\int_0^l y(x)dx.$$

Therefore, after imposing the boundary conditions,

$$y(\xi) = \text{constant} + \int_0^l g_M(x\,|\,\xi) f(x)\,dx,$$

where $g_M(x\,|\,\xi)$ is any solution of (1.91). If we choose $g_M(x\,|\,\xi)$ to be the symmetric solution of (1.91) then $y(\xi) = \text{constant} + \int_0^l g_M(\xi\,|\,x) f(x)\,dx$, or

$$y(x) = \text{constant} + \int_0^l g_M(x\,|\,\xi) f(\xi)\,d\xi.$$

Consider now the problem of a general self-adjoint system. We assume that all the nontrivial solutions of the homogeneous system $Lu = 0$; $B_1(u) = B_2(u) = 0$, are of the form $Cu_1(x)$, where $u_1(x)$ is a normalized solution; that is,

$$\int_a^b u_1^2\,dx = 1.$$

The *modified Green's function* satisfies

$$Lg_M(x\,|\,\xi) = \delta(x - \xi) - u_1(x)u_1(\xi); \qquad B_1(g) = B_2(g) = 0. \qquad (1.94)$$

This system has a solution because $\int_a^b [\delta(x - \xi) - u_1(x)u_1(\xi)]u_1(x)\,dx = 0$. The construction is entirely similar to that for the ordinary Green's function described in Section 1.5, but the modified Green's function is not uniquely determined. We can add $Cu_1(x)$ to a Green's function without violating any of the requirements on it. The reader can verify that the modified Green's function will by symmetric if

$$\int_a^b g_M(x\,|\,\xi)u_1(x)\,dx = 0.$$

The modified Green's function enables us to solve the inhomogeneous system

$$Ly = f(x); \qquad B_1(y) = B_2(y) = 0.$$

We require $\int_a^b f(x)u_1(x)\,dx = 0$, for otherwise no solution exists. By the usual procedure we obtain

$$\int_a^b (g_M Ly - y Lg_M)\,dx = \int_a^b g_M(x\,|\,\xi) f(x)\,dx - y(\xi) + \int_a^b y(x)u_1(x)u_1(\xi)\,dx.$$

The left side vanishes by the boundary conditions and, therefore,

$$y(\xi) = \int_a^b g_M(x\,|\,\xi) f(x)\,dx + Cu_1(\xi).$$

If we use the symmetric modified Green's function, the above result can be written

$$y(x) = \int_a^b g_M(x \mid \xi) f(\xi) d\xi + C u_1(x).$$

The above arguments can be modified in a suitable manner when there exist two linearly independent solutions of the homogeneous equation (see Exercise 1.55).

EXERCISES

1.54 Show that a sufficient condition for the modified Green's function to be symmetric is

$$\int_a^b g_M(x \mid \xi) u_1(x) dx = 0.$$

Show that there are problems where this condition is not necessary.

1.55 Develop the theory of modified Green's functions in the case of a self-adjoint system where the completely homogeneous system has two linearly independent solutions $u_1(x)$ and $u_2(x)$ (hence every solution of the homogeneous equation satisfies the boundary conditions).

1.56 Consider steady-state heat conduction in an insulated thin ring of constant cross section. Let x be a coordinate along the center line of the ring, where x ranges from 0 to l. The equation governing the temperature distribution $u(x)$ in the ring is $-kA(d^2u/dx^2) = f(x)$; $0 < x < l$.

Although, at first glance, there appear to be no boundary conditions associated with the system, further thought shows that the temperature and its derivative must have the same value at $x = 0$ and $x = l$. Therefore, $u(0) = u(l)$, $(du/dx)(0) = (du/dx)(l)$. The completely homogeneous system has the nontrivial solution $u = $ constant. Find the modified Green's function for this problem. Use this Green's function to solve

$$-\frac{d^2y}{dx^2} = f(x); \qquad y(0) = y(l), \quad y'(0) = y'(l),$$

when $\int_a^b f(x) dx = 0$.

1.57 Find the modified Green's function for the system $L = d^2/dx^2$ with $y(0) = -y(1)$, $y'(0) = y'(1)$. This system is not self-adjoint.

1.58 Apply the result of Exercise 1.54 to find the modified Green's function for the system $L = (d^2/dx^2) + 1$ with $y(0) = y(2\pi)$, $y'(0) = y'(2\pi)$.

1.59 (a) Find the consistency condition for the system

$$-\frac{d^2y}{dx^2} = f(x); \qquad y'(0) = \alpha, \quad y'(1) = \beta.$$

(b) Find the consistency conditions for the system

$$\frac{d^2y}{dx^2} + y = f(x); \qquad y(0) - y(2\pi) = \alpha, \quad y'(0) - y'(2\pi) = \beta.$$

SUGGESTED READINGS FOR CHAPTER 1

The letters E, I, and A indicate elementary, intermediate, and advanced books, respectively.

Ordinary Differential Equations
(E) Agnew, R. P., *Differential Equations*, McGraw-Hill, New York, 1960.
(I) Birkhoff, G., and G. C. Rota, *Ordinary Differential Equations*, Ginn, Boston, 1962.
(A) Coddington, E. A., and N. Levinson, *Theory of Ordinary Differential Equations*, McGraw-Hill, New York, 1955.
(I) Indritz, J., *Methods in Analysis*, Macmillan, New York, 1963.
(I) Yosida, K., *Lectures on Differential and Integral Equations*, Interscience, New York, 1960.

Green's Functions
(A) Coddington, E. A., and N. Levinson, *Theory of Ordinary Differential Equations*, McGraw-Hill, New York, 1955.
(I) Courant, R., and D. Hilbert, *Methods of Mathematical Physics*, Vol. I, Interscience, New York, 1953.
(I) Friedman, B., *Principles and Techniques of Applied Mathematics*, Wiley, New York, 1956.
(I) Yosida, K., *Lectures on Differential and Integral Equations*, Interscience, New York, 1960.

Theory of Distributions
(A) Bremermann, H. J., *Distributions, Complex Variables, and Fourier Transforms*, Addison-Wesley, Reading, 1965.
(I) Erdélyi, A., *Operational Calculus and Generalized Functions*, Holt, Rinehart and Winston, New York, 1962.
(I) Gelfand, I. M., and G. E. Shilov, *Generalized Functions*, Vol. I, Academic Press, New York, 1964.
(I) Schwartz, L., *Théorie des Distributions*, Vol. I, Hermann, Paris, 1950.
(I) Zemanian, A. H., *Distribution Theory and Transform Analysis*, McGraw-Hill, New York, 1965.

Chapter 2

INTRODUCTION TO
LINEAR SPACES

2.1 FUNCTIONS AND TRANSFORMATIONS

Real Function of a Real Variable

DEFINITION. If to each real number x, there is a rule f which assigns a real number y, we say that f is a real-valued function of the real variable x, and write $y = f(x)$. For emphasis one refers to f as a single-valued function, which means that the number y is *unambiguously* determined from x.

The concept of a function can be dramatized by the use of the "black box" so dear to electrical engineers (see Figure 2.1). A real number x (the input or

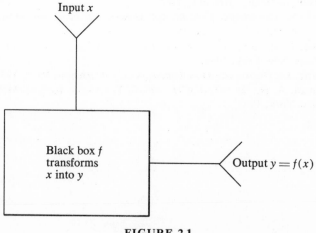

Input x

Black box f
transforms
x into y

Output $y = f(x)$

FIGURE 2.1

independent variable) is fed into the box f. The box transforms x into the real number y (the output or dependent variable). Strictly speaking then, the function f is the box itself, whereas $f(x)$ is the value of the function at x, that is, the value of the output corresponding to the input x. Despite the conceptual distinction between f and $f(x)$, we shall often lapse into the classical usage of giving the name *function* to both f and $f(x)$.

In some cases we can even represent the effect of a black box by a simple formula valid for every input x; for instance, $y = x^3$, $y = x \sin x$, $y = 1/(x^2 + 1)$, ... The formula or recipe may be quite complicated, or there may be different formulas for different inputs x. For instance,

$$y = f(x) = \begin{cases} x^2, & x \geq 0; \\ -x, & x < 0 \end{cases}$$

is *one* function, even though there are two different formulas for different values of x. The familiar graph can also be used to illustrate the relation between x and y. In terms of Cartesian coordinates in the plane, we plot the ordered pairs $\{x, f(x)\}$. Since f is unambiguously determined from x, each vertical line intersects the graph only once. The technical ease or difficulty of drawing the graph in no way affects its conceptual value.

For a particular black box f, it may happen that *not all* real numbers x are suitable as inputs. For reasons of convenience or necessity, we may wish to restrict the inputs x. The admissible inputs form the *domain* of f. The domain of f is therefore a subset of the real numbers; in some cases the domain of f will be the set of all real numbers. Strictly speaking, a formula such as $y = 1/(x^2 + 1)$ represents different functions when different domains of definition are considered. For instance, $1/(x^2 + 1)$ defined for all real x is not the same function as $1/(x^2 + 1)$ defined for $x \geq 0$.

As x runs through the admissible input values, y will run through the output or image values. These values of y form a subset of the real numbers known as the *range* of f. A real number belongs to the range of f if it can be written in the form $f(x)$ for some x in the domain of f.

EXAMPLES

Example 1. $y = f(x) = 1/(x^2 + 1)$ with domain f: $-\infty < x < \infty$; the range of f consists of all real numbers $0 < y \leq 1$.

Example 2. $y = g(x) = 1/(x^2 + 1)$ with domain g: $0 \leq x \leq 2$; the range of g consists of all real numbers $\frac{1}{5} \leq y \leq 1$.

DEFINITION. If to each y in the range of f, there corresponds *exactly* one x in the domain of f, we say that the function f (or transformation, or mapping) is *one-to-one*.

EXAMPLES

Example 1. $y = f(x) = 1/(x^2 + 1)$ with domain f: $0 \leq x \leq \infty$, is one-to-one.

Example 2. $y = g(x) = 1/(x^2 + 1)$ with domain $g: -\infty < x < \infty$, is *not* one-to-one.

One-to-one transformations can be inverted. Suppose a function f is one-to-one, then to each y in the range of f corresponds one and only one x in the domain of f. We can therefore think of an inverse function $f^{-1}(y)$ which assigns to y the value of x for which $f(x) = y$. The domain of f^{-1} is the range of f, and the range of f^{-1} is the domain of f. Thus, each horizontal line will intersect the graph of $f(x)$ no more than once. In Example (1) we have $x = f^{-1}(y) = [(1 - y)/y]^{1/2}$, where the nonnegative square root is understood.

General Transformations

We are now ready to look at more sophisticated boxes. Instead of being numbers, the inputs and outputs may be elements of sets of a completely arbitrary nature. Let X and Y be two arbitrary sets; a function F is said to be defined on X and to assume its values in Y if to each element x belonging to X there corresponds one and only one element y in Y. We write $y = F(x)$ or $y = Fx$, and speak of F as a *function, transformation, mapping,* or *operator.*† The variety of terminology may confuse the newcomer to mathematics, but it has the advantage of relieving the boredom of the professional; moreover in those problems where the elements of the sets X and/or Y are themselves functions, it will be convenient to call F a transformation.

Again we illustrate the idea of function or transformation by a black box (see Figure 2.2). The transformation F is single-valued, since the output is unambiguously determined from the input. The set of admissible inputs is

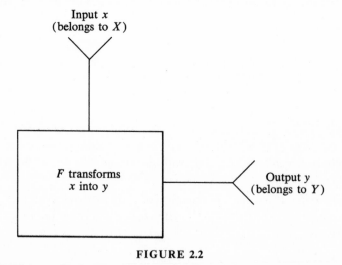

FIGURE 2.2

† If the set y is a set of real (complex) numbers, the term *real* (complex) *functional* is often used for F.

known as the *domain* of F and is written D_F (this is merely another term for the set X).

The set of all outputs corresponding to admissible inputs is the *range* of F and is denoted by R_F. In the definition of a transformation, it is not necessary for every y in Y to be a possible output. Thus the range of F is a subset of Y and consists of all elements y which are of the form Fx for some x in the domain of F. If the range of F coincides with Y, the transformation is said to be *onto* Y; in the general case where the range of F may not coincide with Y, the transformation is said to be *into* Y.

The transformation F is one-to-one if to each y belonging to R_F there is exactly one x in D_F such that $Fx = y$. In this case the inverse transformation F^{-1} is defined.

EXAMPLES OF TRANSFORMATIONS

Example 1.   If x is a real number and y is a real number we are back to the concept of a real function of a real variable. Instead of writing $y = Fx$, we write $y = f(x)$.

Example 2.   If x is an n-tuple of real numbers $(x_1, \ldots, x_n)$, that is, a point in n-dimensional space, and y is a real number, we say that y is a function of the n variables $x_1, \ldots, x_n$, and write $y = f(x_1, \ldots, x_n)$ instead of $y = Fx$.

Example 3.   If x is an n-tuple of real numbers and y is an m-tuple of real numbers, we have a transformation from an n-dimensional space to an m-dimensional space. We can write $y = Fx$, or else $y_1 = f_1(x_1, \ldots, x_n), \ldots, y_m = f_m(x_1, \ldots, x_n)$. Thus we can think of the transformation as a single box or as m boxes of the type described in (2).

Example 4.   Let X be an appropriate set of real functions $x(t)$, $a \le t \le b$, for which the definitions below make sense. The inputs are themselves functions, and each function is regarded as an individual element of X. We shall consider a number of different possibilities for the set of outputs.

(a) The output y is a real number. We usually call y a functional; for example; $y = \int_a^b x^3(t)\, dt$, $y = x(a)$, ...

(b) The output y is a function of t, $a \le t \le b$.

   (i) $y(t) = f_0(t) x(t)$, where $f_0(t)$ is a *fixed* function of t, $a \le t \le b$.

   (ii) $y(t) = Fx = dx/dt$. The natural domain D_F of definition of this transformation is the set of all differentiable functions in $a \le t \le b$. If the domain of F is so chosen, its range will include some non-differentiable functions $y(t)$, and therefore the range does not coincide with the domain.

   (iii) $y(t) = dx/dt$ defined over the set D_F consisting of all differentiable functions, $a \le t \le b$, with the additional restriction $x(a) = 0$. This is a different transformation from that in (ii), since the domains are different.

To make further progress in the study of transformations, it will be necessary to restrict the nature of X, Y, and F. The sets X and Y, as they occur in most physical applications, are endowed with both algebraic and metric structures. The algebraic structure of X (and of Y) will usually be that of a linear space. Roughly speaking, this means that the sum of two admissible inputs is an admissible input and that every admissible input may be scaled up (or down) by multiplication by a real number. The definition and some elementary properties of linear spaces are given in Section 2.2. In addition, X and Y will be provided with a metric (or topological) structure; this means that we can measure the "distance" between two inputs and that this numerical function has properties akin to those of the distance between points in ordinary three-dimensional Euclidean space. A set with this metric structure is known as a metric space (see Section 2.3). Mathematicians have occasion to study metric spaces which have no algebraic structure and linear spaces with no metric structure; in the applications which we have in mind, the two structures will both be present. The various restrictions that may be imposed on the transformation F are treated in detail in Section 2.4.

2.2 LINEAR SPACES (ALSO KNOWN AS VECTOR SPACES)

DEFINITION. A collection of elements (called *vectors*) $x, y, z, \ldots$ will be known as a *real vector space* $\mathscr{A}^{(r)}$ if the following axioms are satisfied.

1. To every pair of vectors x and y there corresponds a vector $x + y$, known as the sum of x and y, with the properties
   (a) $x + y = y + x$.
   (b) $x + (y + w) = (x + y) + w$ (we write $x + y + w$ for the triple sum).
   (c) There exists a *unique* vector 0 such that $x + 0 = x$ for every x.
   (d) To every x, there exists a unique vector labeled $-x$ such that $x + (-x) = 0$.

2. To every vector x and every *real number* α, there corresponds a vector αx such that
   (a) $\alpha(\beta x) = (\alpha\beta)x$.
   (b) $(\alpha + \beta)x = \alpha x + \beta x$.
   (c) $\alpha(x + y) = \alpha x + \alpha y$.
   (d) $1x = x$.

DEFINITION. A complex vector space $\mathscr{A}^{(c)}$ is a collection of elements satisfying (1) and (2) above, but where multiplication by complex numbers α is now allowed in (2).

We use the same symbol 0 for both the zero vector and the number zero, hoping no confusion arises. We use the same $+$ sign for vector addition and addition of numbers, even though the operations are conceptually quite different. We also write $x + (-y) = x - y$. The superscripts (c) and (r) are used for complex and real vector spaces, respectively. If no superscript is used in a statement about vector spaces, the statement is true for both real and complex spaces.

EXERCISE

1.1 (a) Given x and y there exists one and only one vector z such that $x = y + z$ and $z = x - y$.

    (b) Show that $0x = 0$.

    (c) Show that $(-1)x = -x$.

Dependence and Independence of Vectors

DEFINITION.   Let $\mathscr{A}^{(c)}$ be a complex vector space.

1. A vector x is said to be a linear combination of $x_1, \ldots, x_k$ if there exist complex numbers $\alpha_1, \ldots, \alpha_k$ such that $x = \sum_{i=1}^{k} \alpha_i x_i$.

2. k vectors $x_1, \ldots, x_k$ belonging to $\mathscr{A}^{(c)}$ are said to be *dependent* (or form a dependent set), if there exist complex numbers $\alpha_1, \ldots, \alpha_k$, *not all zero*, such that

$$\alpha_1 x_1 + \cdots + \alpha_k x_k = 0. \tag{2.1}$$

3. If (2.1) can be satisfied only for $\alpha_1 = \cdots = \alpha_k = 0$, the vectors are *independent*.

REMARKS.   1. If we are dealing with a real vector space, the definitions are changed only in that the numbers $\alpha_1, \ldots, \alpha_k$ are *real* numbers.

2. If $x_1, \ldots, x_k$ are dependent, at least one vector is a linear combination of the others.

3. If 0 belongs to a set of vectors, the set is dependent.

4. If $x_1, \ldots, x_k$ is a dependent set, so is any set which includes $x_1, \ldots, x_k$.

5. In trying to define independence for an infinite set of vectors, one is tempted to use (2.1) directly for an infinite sum of vectors. Unfortunately such a sum is not defined in a general linear space. To discuss infinite sums, one needs the notion of convergence which, in turn is based on the concept of distance between vectors (See Section 2.3).

Dimension of a Vector Space

DEFINITION.   The vector space $\mathscr{A}$ is *n-dimensional* if it possesses a set of n independent vectors, but every set of $n + 1$ vectors is a dependent set.

DEFINITION.   If for every positive integer k, we can find k independent vectors in $\mathscr{A}$, $\mathscr{A}$ is *∞-dimensional*.

DEFINITION.   A finite set of vectors $e_1, \ldots, e_k$ is said to be a basis for a vector space $\mathscr{A}$, if

    (a) The vectors $e_1, \ldots, e_k$ are independent.

(b) Every vector x in $\mathscr{A}$ can be written as a linear combination of the basis vectors; that is,

$$x = \xi_1 e_1 + \cdots + \xi_k e_k. \tag{2.2}$$

Theorem. *The representation (2.2) is unique.*

Proof. Otherwise we would also have $x = \eta_1 e_1 + \cdots + \eta_k e_k$ and by subtraction

$$0 = (\eta_1 - \xi_1)e_1 + \cdots + (\eta_k - \xi_k)e_k.$$

Since the vectors $e_1, \ldots, e_k$ are independent, we infer $\eta_1 = \xi_1, \ldots, \eta_k = \xi_k$, and hence the representation (2.2) is unique.

Theorem. *If $\mathscr{A}$ is n-dimensional, any set of n independent vectors $e_1, \ldots, e_n$ forms a basis.*

Proof. If x is any vector in $\mathscr{A}$, the set $x, e_1, \ldots, e_n$ is dependent and the equation

$$\alpha x + \alpha_1 e_1 + \cdots + \alpha_n e_n = 0$$

is satisfied for constants $\alpha, \alpha_1, \ldots, \alpha_n$ not all 0. Since the set $e_1, \ldots, e_n$ is independent, we must have $\alpha \neq 0$, and $x = -(\alpha_1/\alpha)e_1 - \cdots - (\alpha_n/\alpha)e_n$. Therefore, every vector x can be expressed as a linear combination of $e_1, \ldots, e_n$.

EXAMPLES OF VECTOR SPACES

Example 1. **(a)** In elementary algebra, one frequently encounters the space $\mathscr{E}_n^{(r)}$ of all ordered n-tuples of real numbers. (This space appears in a natural way in the solution of n linear equations in n unknowns.) Let $x = (\xi_1, \ldots, \xi_n)$ and $y = (\eta_1, \ldots, \eta_n)$ be any two elements of $\mathscr{E}_n^{(r)}$, and introduce the following definitions:

$$x + y = (\xi_1 + \eta_1, \ldots, \xi_n + \eta_n);$$

$$\alpha x = (\alpha\xi_1, \ldots, \alpha\xi_n);$$

$$0 = (0, \ldots, 0);$$

$$-x = (-\xi_1, \ldots, -\xi_n).$$

With these definitions $\mathscr{E}_n^{(r)}$ is readily seen to be a real vector space. The vectors $e_1 = (1, 0, \ldots, 0), \ldots, e_n = (0, 0, \ldots, 0, 1)$ form a basis in the space $\mathscr{E}_n^{(r)}$, which is therefore n-dimensional. Note that there are many other bases in $\mathscr{E}_n^{(r)}$, for instance, $e_1' = (1, 0, 0, \ldots, 0), e_2' = (1, 1, 0, \ldots, 0, 0), \ldots, e_n' = (1, 1, \ldots, 1)$.

(b) $\mathscr{E}_n^{(c)}$ is the space of all ordered n-tuples of complex numbers. The same definitions as in **(a)** are used, but multiplication by complex numbers α is allowed. $\mathscr{E}_n^{(c)}$ is a complex vector space of dimension n. Again $e_1 = (1, 0, \ldots, 0), \ldots, e_n = (0, 0, \ldots, 0, 1)$ form a basis in $\mathscr{E}_n^{(c)}$.

Example 2. (a) Let $f_1(t), \ldots, f_n(t)$ be any n given real functions defined in $a \le t \le b$, where a and b are arbitrary but fixed. Consider all functions $f(t)$ of the form

$$f(t) = \alpha_1 f_1(t) + \cdots + \alpha_n f_n(t),$$

where $\alpha_1, \ldots, \alpha_n$ are real numbers.

The space of all such functions $f(t)$ is a real linear space, under the usual rules for addition of functions and multiplication of functions by real numbers. The function which is identically zero in $a \le t \le b$ belongs to the space and plays the role of the 0 element. If the functions $f_1(t), \ldots, f_n(t)$ are independent over $a \le t \le b$, the dimension of the space is n; otherwise the dimension is smaller than n.

(b) A special case of (a) is P_n, the space of all polynomials of degree less than n. By choosing $f_1(t) = 1, f_2(t) = t, \ldots, f_n(t) = t^{n-1}$, we obtain P_n. The dimension of P_n is n. There are many possible bases in P_n. The simplest is probably $e_1 = f_1(t) = 1, e_2 = f_2(t) = t, \ldots, e_n = f_n(t) = t^{n-1}$.

Example 3. The spaces below are all ∞-dimensional.

(a) The space of all real (or complex)-valued functions $x(t)$ defined in $a \le t \le b$ is a linear space with the usual definition of addition of functions and multiplication of functions by real (or complex) numbers.

(b) The space of all real (or complex)-valued continuous functions $x(t)$ in $a \le t \le b$ is a linear space.

(c) The space of all real-valued functions $x(t)$ for which $\int_a^b x^2(t)dt$ exists is a real linear space. All that has to be shown is that if $\int_a^b x^2\, dt$ and $\int_a^b y^2\, dt$ both exist, so does $\int_a^b (x + y)^2\, dt$. This follows from the Schwarz inequality (2.7) in the next section.

(d) The space of all complex-valued functions $x(t)$ for which $\int_a^b |x|^2\, dt = \int_a^b x\bar{x}\, dt$ exists is a complex linear space.

Example 4. The space of all real (or complex)-valued functions $x(t_1, \ldots, t_k)$ defined over a region V in the k variables $t_1, \ldots, t_k$ is a linear space. The space is ∞-dimensional.

2.3   METRIC SPACES, NORMED LINEAR SPACES, AND INNER PRODUCT SPACES

Metric Spaces

The vectors encountered so far possess algebraic properties similar to those of ordinary three-dimensional vectors—vectors can be added and multiplied by scalars subject to the rules of a linear space—but the familiar notions of length and direction have not yet made their apperance. We wish to endow vector spaces of higher dimension with as rich a structure as the one available to us in three-dimensional vector analysis. To the algebraic structure already introduced, we must superimpose a metric structure. We start by investigating some properties of metric spaces.

DEFINITION.   A collection of elements (called *points*) $x, y, z, \ldots$ will be known as a *metric space* if to each pair of elements x, y corresponds a real number $d(x, y)$ satisfying the properties

(1) $d(x, y) = d(y, x)$;

(2) (a) $d(x, y) \geq 0$,   (b) $d(x, y) = 0$ if and only if $x = y$;   (2,3)

(3) $d(x, z) \leq d(x, y) + d(y, z)$.

REMARKS.   1. The elements of metric space need not be vectors; there may not exist any way of adding elements nor any way of multiplying them by scalars.

2. The function $d(x, y)$ is called the *metric* (or *distance function*). The first two properties under (2.3) are obviously desirable for any function which professes to play the role of a distance. The third property— *the triangle inequality*—is analogous to the Euclidean proposition that one side of a triangle is no longer than the sum of the other two sides.

Consider a sequence $\{x_k\}$ of elements of a metric space. To say that x_k converges to x means that $d(x_k, x)$ approaches 0 as k approaches ∞. Since $d(x_k, x)$ is a sequence of real numbers, the notion of convergence in a metric space is reduced to the familiar notion of convergence of a sequence of real numbers. We are therefore led to the following definition of convergence.

DEFINITION.   We write $\lim_{k \to \infty} x_k = x$ (or $x_k \to x$, or x_k *converges* to x) if to each $\varepsilon > 0$ there exists an index N such that

$$d(x, x_k) \leq \varepsilon \qquad \text{whenever } k > N.$$

Often we deal with a sequence whose elements get close to each other but where it is not known that the elements converge to a fixed element.

DEFINITION.   A sequence $\{x_k\}$ is a *Cauchy sequence* if to each $\varepsilon > 0$ there exists N such that

$$d(x_m, x_p) \leq \varepsilon \qquad \text{whenever } m, p > N.$$

If $\{x_k\}$ is a Cauchy sequence, we shall write

$$\lim_{m, p \to \infty} d(x_m, x_p) = 0.$$

Theorem.   *If a sequence $\{x_k\}$ converges, it is a Cauchy sequence.*

Proof.   Let x be the limit of the sequence. By the triangle inequality $d(x_m, x_p) \leq d(x_m, x) + d(x_p, x)$. By assumption $x_k \to x$, therefore, there exists N such that $d(x_n, x) \leq \varepsilon/2$ whenever $n > N$. Hence if m and p are both larger than N, $d(x_m, x_p) \leq \varepsilon$, and the sequence $\{x_k\}$ is a Cauchy sequence.

It might appear at first that the converse is also true. If the points of a sequence get close to each other, they should get close to some fixed point x. This will be true if the limit x has not been carelessly excluded from the space.

DEFINITION. A metric space is *complete* if every Cauchy sequence is a convergent sequence. If a metric space is not complete, there is a simple way to add elements to the space to make it complete.

EXAMPLE

The space of rational numbers with the metric $d(x, y) = |x - y|$ is a metric space. But it is not complete, as the following example shows. Consider the sequence of rational numbers

$$x_1 = 1, x_2 = 1 + \frac{1}{1!}, \ldots, x_n = 1 + \frac{1}{1!} + \frac{1}{2!} + \cdots + \frac{1}{(n-1)!}, \ldots.$$

For $p > m \geq 1$, we have

$$|x_p - x_m| = \frac{1}{m!} + \frac{1}{(m+1)!} + \cdots + \frac{1}{(p-1)!}$$

$$= \frac{1}{m!} \left\{ 1 + \frac{1}{m+1} + \frac{1}{(m+1)(m+2)} \right.$$

$$\left. + \cdots + \frac{1}{(m+1)(m+2)\cdots(p-1)} \right\}$$

$$\leq \frac{1}{m!} \left\{ 1 + \frac{1}{2} + \frac{1}{4} + \cdots \right\} = \frac{2}{m!}.$$

By choosing m sufficiently large, the right side can be made arbitrarily small; hence to every $\varepsilon > 0$ there exists N such that

$$|x_m - x_p| < \varepsilon \qquad \text{whenever } m, p > N.$$

This sequence is therefore a Cauchy sequence of rational numbers; yet it does not converge in the space of rational numbers. In fact, suppose that $x_k \to x = p/q$, where p and q are integers and q is a fixed integer which can obviously be chosen larger than 2. By the definition of convergence, there exists N such that

$$\left| \frac{p}{q} - \left(1 + \cdots + \frac{1}{k!} \right) \right| < \frac{1}{4q!}, \qquad \text{whenever } k > N.$$

Since the sequence x_k is strictly increasing, we actually have

$$0 < \frac{p}{q} - \left(1 + \cdots + \frac{1}{k!} \right) < \frac{1}{4q!}, \qquad k > N.$$

Multiplying through by $q!$ and rearranging, we find

$$0 < \text{integer} < \frac{1}{4} + \frac{q!}{(q+1)!} + \cdots + \frac{q!}{k!}.$$

Now, since $q > 2$,

$$\frac{q!}{(q+1)!} + \cdots + \frac{q!}{k!} < \frac{1}{q+1} + \cdots + \frac{1}{(q+1)(q+2)\cdots k} < \frac{1}{3} + \frac{1}{3^2} + \cdots = \frac{1}{2}.$$

Thus

$$0 < \text{integer} < \tfrac{3}{4},$$

which is a contradiction, so that x_k cannot converge to a rational limit. Of course, if the sequence is viewed in the space of real numbers, it converges to the irrational limit e.

The difficulty lies in the space of rational numbers, which is full of gaps invisible to the naked eye. One of the standard ways of defining the space of real numbers is to add to the space of rational numbers all "limits" of Cauchy sequences of rational numbers. Every time we are faced with a Cauchy sequence of rational numbers which does not have a rational limit, we create a new abstract element (an irrational number), which plays the role of the limit. The set of all rational numbers plus these new abstract elements forms the space of real numbers. One can properly ask whether a Cauchy sequence of elements taken from this new space necessarily converges to an element of the space. The answer is affirmative, and a proof can be found in any book on real variables.

EXAMPLES OF METRIC SPACES

Example 1. The space of real numbers becomes a metric space with the definition

$$d(x, y) = |x - y|.$$

The properties (2.3) are easily verified. Furthermore, the space is complete (as indicated in the preceding paragraphs).

Example 2. The space of complex numbers becomes a metric space with the definition

$$d(x, y) = |x - y|.$$

The properties (2.3) are readily established. We show that the space is complete. Indeed, let $\{x_k\}$ be a Cauchy sequence of complex numbers. We write $x_k = s_k + it_k$, with s_k, t_k real. To every $\varepsilon > 0$ there exists N such that $|x_p - x_m| = [(s_p - s_m)^2 + (t_p - t_m)^2]^{1/2} \leq \varepsilon$ whenever $m, p > N$. Thus $|s_p - s_m| \leq \varepsilon$ and $|t_p - t_m| \leq \varepsilon$ whenever $m, p > N$. From Example 1, it follows that $s_k \to s$ and $t_k \to t$, and therefore $s_k + it_k \to s + it$, and the space of complex numbers is complete.

Example 3. Consider the space $\mathscr{E}_n^{(r)}$ of n-tuples of real numbers. Let $x = (\xi_1, \ldots, \xi_n)$ and $(\eta_1, \ldots, \eta_n)$ be any two points in this space. We define

$$d(x, y) = [(\xi_1 - \eta_1)^2 + \cdots + (\xi_n - \eta_n)^2]^{1/2}.$$

It is easily seen that $d(x, y)$ satisfies properties (1) and (2) of (2.3); property (3) follows from the Schwarz inequality [see (2.17)]. Thus $\mathscr{E}_n^{(r)}$ is now a metric space; furthermore it is complete. Indeed, let $x_k = (\xi_1^{(k)}, \ldots, \xi_n^{(k)})$ be a Cauchy sequence in $\mathscr{E}_n^{(r)}$; then for any $\varepsilon > 0$ there exists N such that

$$d(x_p, x_m) = \{[\xi_1^{(p)} - \xi_1^{(m)}]^2 + \cdots + [\xi_n^{(p)} - \xi_n^{(m)}]^2\}^{1/2} \le \varepsilon$$

whenever $m, p > N$. This implies that

$$|\xi_1^{(p)} - \xi_1^{(m)}| \le \varepsilon, \ldots, |\xi_n^{(p)} - \xi_n^{(m)}| \le \varepsilon$$

whenever $m, p > N$. From Example 1 it follows that each of the sequences $\xi_1^{(k)}, \ldots, \xi_n^{(k)}$ must converge as $k \to \infty$. Let $\lim_{k \to \infty} \xi_i^{(k)} = \xi_i$; then $\lim_{k \to \infty} x_k = (\xi_1, \ldots, \xi_n)$ and the space $\mathscr{E}_n^{(r)}$ is complete.

Example 4. Consider the space $\mathscr{E}_n^{(c)}$ of n-tuples of complex numbers. Let $x = (\xi_1, \ldots, \xi_n)$ and $y = (\eta_1, \ldots, \eta_n)$ be any two points of this space. With the definition

$$d(x, y) = [|\xi_1 - \eta_1|^2 + \cdots + |\xi_n - \eta_n|^2]^{1/2},$$

the space $\mathscr{E}_n^{(c)}$ becomes a complete metric space.

Example 5. Consider the space $C(a, b)$ of all real-valued continuous functions $x(t)$ defined in $a \le t \le b$, with

$$d_1(x, y) = \max_{a \le t \le b} |x(t) - y(t)|.$$

The conditions (2.3) can be verified for $d_1(x, y)$. Let $x_k(t)$ be a Cauchy sequence of functions in $C(a, b)$; that is, $\lim_{m, p \to \infty} \max_{a \le t \le b} |x_p(t) - x_m(t)| = 0$. This is just the Cauchy definition of uniform convergence; hence there exists a function $x(t)$ such that $x_k(t)$ approaches $x(t)$ uniformly over $a \le t \le b$. From real variable theory it is known that a uniformly convergent sequence of continuous functions converges to a continuous function. Thus a Cauchy sequence of elements from $C(a, b)$ converges to an element in $C(a, b)$, and $C(a, b)$ is therefore *complete*.

Example 6. The space of all real-valued continuous functions $x(t)$ defined on the finite interval $a \le t \le b$. We use a different metric than in Example 5. Let

$$d_2(x, y) = \left\{ \int_a^b [x(t) - y(t)]^2 \, dt \right\}^{1/2}.$$

All the conditions (2.3) are satisfied by this metric [again one must appeal to the Schwarz inequality, this time in the form (2.20)]. This space is *not complete*.

Consider the sequence of continuous functions

$$x_k(t) = \frac{1}{2} + \frac{1}{\pi} \arctan kt, \qquad -1 \le t \le 1.$$

These functions were sketched in Figure 1.10. It is clear from the sketch that $x_k(t)$ is a Cauchy sequence; that is, $\displaystyle\lim_{m,p \to \infty} \int_{-1}^{1} \{x_p(t) - x_m(t)\}^2 \, dt = 0$. The limit $x_k(t)$ in the sense of ordinary convergence is the *discontinuous* function

$$y(t) = \begin{cases} 1, & 0 < t \le 1; \\ \frac{1}{2}, & t = 0; \\ 0, & -1 \le t < 0. \end{cases}$$

One easily verifies that

$$\lim_{k \to \infty} d_2(x_k, y) = \lim_{k \to \infty} \left[\int_{-1}^{1} \{x_k(t) - y(t)\}^2 \, dt \right]^{1/2} = 0.$$

There is no continuous function $x(t)$ for which $d_2(x, y) = 0$; hence there is no continuous function $x(t)$ for which $\displaystyle\lim_{k \to \infty} d_2(x_k, x) = 0$.

Example 7. The space $\mathscr{L}_2^{(r)}(a, b)$. The difficulty with Example 6 is that the space of continuous functions is not extensive enough to accommodate the metric $\left[\int_a^b (x - y)^2 \, dt \right]^{1/2}$, just as the space of rational numbers is not extensive enough to accommodate the metric $|x - y|$.

We must try to fill the "gaps" in the space of continuous functions by adjoining to this space all abstract limits of Cauchy sequences (one such limit is the discontinuous function of Example 6). This procedure of completion follows the same conceptual pattern as the procedure which enables us to go from rational numbers to real numbers. The mathematical details are outside the scope of this book, and we merely describe the results.

The space of real-valued continuous functions defined in $a \le t \le b$ with metric $d(x, y) = \left[\int_a^b \{x - y\}^2 \, dt \right]^{1/2}$ becomes, upon completion, the space $\mathscr{L}_2^{(r)}(a, b)$ of all functions which are square-integrable in the Lebesgue sense.

The notion of Lebesgue integration is essential to modern mathematical analysis, and the reader is hereby encouraged to familiarize himself with this subject. The five salient facts about Lebesgue integrals described below will suffice for our purposes.

(a) If $x(t)$ is Riemann-integrable, it is also Lebesgue-integrable to the same value. There are functions which are Lebesgue-integrable but not Riemann-integrable. When an integral sign is used without further qualification, the Lebesgue integral is understood.

(b) If $x(t)$, $y(t)$ are Lebesgue-integrable, so are $cx(t)$ and $x(t) + y(t)$.

(c) If $x(t)$, $y(t)$ are square-integrable in the Lebesgue sense (that is, the

Lebesgue integrals $\int_a^b x^2 \, dt$ and $\int_a^b y^2 \, dt$ exist), then xy is Lebesgue-integrable and $x + y$ is square-integrable. Furthermore, if the interval (a, b) is finite x and $|x|$ are Lebesgue-integrable.

(d) Two functions $x_1(t)$, $x_2(t)$ are said to be *equal almost everywhere* on $a \leq t \leq b$ if $\int_a^b \{x_1(t) - x_2(t)\}^2 \, dt = 0$. To fulfill requirement (2b) of (2.3) we must regard x_1 and x_2 as the *same element* of $\mathscr{L}_2^{(r)}(a, b)$.

(e) *The Lebesgue convergence theorem.* Let $x_n(t)$ be a sequence of functions, integrable over (a, b), which approaches a limit $x(t)$ except possibly over a set of measure 0. If there exists an integrable function $f(t)$ such that, for all sufficiently large n, $|x_n(t)| \leq f(t)$, then $x(t)$ is integrable and

$$\lim_{n \to \infty} \int_a^b x_n(t)dt = \int_a^b x(t)dt.$$

REMARKS.   1. A set S of real numbers is said to be of *measure* 0, if, for each $\varepsilon > 0$, the set can be covered by a finite or infinite number of open intervals whose total length does not exceed ε. Every countable set $\{x_n\}$ is of measure 0, since the element x_n can be enclosed in an open interval of length $\varepsilon/2^n$ and the whole set is then covered by open intervals of total length ε.

2. The Lebesgue convergence theorem is much more powerful than the elementary theorem on term-by-term integration, which assumes uniform convergence of $x_n(t)$ to $x(t)$ over a finite interval [see, for instance, Exercise 2.25, parts (b), (c) and (e)]. Moreover, the Lebesgue theorem is applicable to infinite intervals.

Normed Linear Spaces

We now return to linear spaces. We want to define a notion of length or norm for the vectors of a linear space.

DEFINITION.   A *normed linear space* is a linear space in which a real valued function $\|x\|$ (known as the *norm* of x) is defined, with the properties

(1) (a) $\|x\| \geq 0$,   (b) $\|x\| = 0$ if and only if $x = \mathbf{0}$;

(2) $\|\alpha x\| = |\alpha| \, \|x\|$;   (2.4)

(3) $\|x_1 + x_2\| \leq \|x_1\| + \|x_2\|$.

REMARKS.   1. The reader should understand the significance of the three properties of the norm and verify that they hold for ordinary three-dimensional vectors.

2. A normed linear space is *automatically* a metric space if we define the metric by

$$d(x, y) = \|x - y\|.$$ (2.5)

Indeed by property 2 above we have $d(x, y) = d(y, x)$. From property 1 we have $d(x, y) \geq 0$ with the equality holding only if $x = y$. Using property 3 with $x_1 = x - y$ and $x_2 = y - z$, we have $d(x, z) \leq d(x, y) + d(y, z)$. All the conditions (2.3) are satisfied, so that $d(x, y)$ is a suitable metric known as the *natural metric generated by the norm*. We can recover $\|x\|$ from the natural metric $d(x, y)$ by observing that $\|x\| = d(x, 0)$.

3. A normed linear space may be viewed either as a linear space, a metric space, or both; hence we may refer to its elements interchangeably as *vectors* or *points*. This is a familiar situation in ordinary three-dimensional geometry. Here the space consists of points with the usual Euclidean distance. On the other hand, a fixed origin having been chosen, each point is the terminal point of a well-defined vector emanating from that origin. Thus we can identify points and vectors. The distance $d(x, y)$ between two points is indeed the length of the difference of the two vectors (that is, $\|x - y\|$); in particular $d(x, 0) = \|x\|$, so that the distance of a point to the origin is the length of the vector.

4. A linear space can be endowed with a metric which may not be the natural metric generated by any norm. As an example consider the space of real numbers, which is of course a linear space. Let us define $d(x, y)$ by

$$d(x, y) = 0 \qquad \text{if } x = y;$$

$$d(x, y) = 1 \qquad \text{if } x \neq y.$$

All the conditions (2.3) are trivially verified. If there existed a norm which generated this metric, we would have

$$\|x\| = d(x, 0) = \begin{cases} 0, & x = 0; \\ 1, & x \neq 0. \end{cases}$$

This clearly violates condition (2) of (2.4); hence the above metric is not generated by any norm.

5. Suppose a metric $d(x, y)$ is given on a linear space. What conditions must d obey so that the space becomes a normed linear space? The answer is simple; we must have

$$d(\alpha x, \alpha y) = |\alpha| d(x, y), \qquad \text{for all } x, y, \text{ and } \alpha.$$

We can then define $\|x - y\| = d(x, y)$, and we easily check that the conditions (2.4) are satisfied.

DEFINITION. A normed linear space which is complete in its natural metric is called a *Banach space*.

EXAMPLE

Consider the seven examples of metric spaces that were presented earlier. In each case the space is also a linear space. In each case the metric satisfies $d(cx, cy) = |c| d(x, y)$, so that we can use $d(x, 0)$ as $\|x\|$. Thus all these spaces are normed linear spaces, and with the exception of Example 6 they are all Banach spaces.

Inner Product Spaces

A normed linear space provides us with a way of measuring the length of a vector. We want to refine the structure further, so that we shall also have available a notion of angle between vectors (in particular, we want to be able to tell whether or not two vectors are perpendicular). By analogy with ordinary three-dimensional vectors, we shall derive these notions from an inner product (also known as a scalar or dot product).

DEFINITION. An *inner product* $\langle x, y \rangle$ on a *real* linear space $\mathscr{A}^{(r)}$ is a *real*-valued function of ordered pairs of vectors x, y with the properties

$$\langle x, y \rangle = \langle y, x \rangle;$$
$$\langle \alpha x, y \rangle = \alpha \langle x, y \rangle;$$
$$\langle x_1 + x_2, y \rangle = \langle x_1, y \rangle + \langle x_2, y \rangle;$$
$$\langle x, x \rangle \geq 0, \quad \text{with } \langle x, x \rangle = 0 \text{ if and only if } x = 0.$$

(2.6)

Theorem (*The Schwarz Inequality*). *For any two vectors x and y, we have*

$$\langle x, y \rangle^2 \leq \langle x, x \rangle \langle y, y \rangle. \tag{2.7}$$

Proof. It follows from (2.6) that, for any real number α,

$$0 \leq \langle x + \alpha y, x + \alpha y \rangle = \alpha^2 \langle y, y \rangle + 2\alpha \langle x, y \rangle + \langle x, x \rangle.$$

The right side is a nonnegative quadratic in α, so that its discriminant is non-positive; therefore,

$$\langle x, y \rangle^2 - \langle x, x \rangle \langle y, y \rangle \leq 0,$$

which is the desired inequality.

Letting $\langle x, x \rangle^{1/2}$ and $\langle y, y \rangle^{1/2}$ stand for nonnegative square roots, we have

$$|\langle x, y \rangle| \leq \langle x, x \rangle^{1/2} \langle y, y \rangle^{1/2}. \tag{2.7a}$$

The reader should prove that the equality in (2.7) or in (2.7a) occurs if and only if x and y are dependent.

Using (2.7a),

$$\langle x + y, x + y \rangle = \langle x, x \rangle + \langle y, y \rangle + 2\langle x, y \rangle$$
$$\leq \langle x, x \rangle + \langle y, y \rangle + 2\langle x, x \rangle^{1/2} \langle y, y \rangle^{1/2}$$
$$= [\langle x, x \rangle^{1/2} + \langle y, y \rangle^{1/2}]^2.$$

Hence

$$\langle x + y, x + y \rangle^{1/2} \leq \langle x, x \rangle^{1/2} + \langle y, y \rangle^{1/2}. \tag{2.7b}$$

It is now clear that the quantity $\langle x, x \rangle^{1/2}$ is a norm on our linear space.

From (2.6) and (2.7b) one verifies that $\langle x, x \rangle^{1/2}$ satisfies the conditions (2.4) on $\|x\|$. Thus an inner product space has a *natural norm* defined by

$$\|x\| = \langle x, x \rangle^{1/2}. \tag{2.8}$$

Since a norm generates a natural metric, we have

$$d(x, y) = \|x - y\| = \langle x - y, x - y \rangle^{1/2}. \tag{2.9}$$

We now rewrite the Schwarz inequality (2.7a) in the more attractive form

$$|\langle x, y \rangle| \le \|x\| \, \|y\|. \tag{2.10}$$

DEFINITION. Two vectors x and y are said to be *orthogonal* (or perpendicular) if $\langle x, y \rangle = 0$. A set of vectors, each pair of which is orthogonal, is called an *orthogonal set*.

If two vectors x and y satisfy $\langle x, y \rangle = 0$, we have $\langle x + y, x + y \rangle = \langle x, x \rangle + \langle y, y \rangle$ or $\|x + y\|^2 = \|x\|^2 + \|y\|^2$, so that the Pythagorean theorem holds. This justifies the use of the word orthogonal for the property $\langle x, y \rangle = 0$.

One obtains without difficulty the proposition: *An orthogonal set of nonzero vectors is independent.*

DEFINITION. The set of vectors αy, where $y \ne 0$ and α runs through all real numbers, is called the *line* generated by y. The set of vectors αy, where $y \ne 0$ and $\alpha \ge 0$, is called the *positive half-line* generated by y.

There are two unit vectors (that is, vectors of unit length) lying on the line generated by y, $y/\|y\|$ and $-y/\|y\|$.

DEFINITION. The projection of x on the line generated by y is the vector $x_p = \langle x, e \rangle e$, where e is either unit vector lying on the line (either choice of e yields the same vector, x_p).

This projection x_p may be written in terms of y,

$$x_p = \frac{\langle x, y \rangle}{\|y\|^2} \, y. \tag{2.11}$$

Given a vector x and a vector $y \ne 0$, x can be decomposed in one and only one way as the sum of two vectors, the first lying on the line generated by y and the second perpendicular to this line (see Figure 2.3). We have specifically,

$$x = x_p + z, \qquad x_p = \frac{\langle x, y \rangle}{\|y\|^2} \, y, \qquad z = x - \frac{\langle x, y \rangle}{\|y\|^2} \, y, \qquad \langle z, y \rangle = 0. \tag{2.12}$$

The above decomposition is unique. If $x_p' + z'$ were another such decomposition, then we would have $0 = (x_p - x_p') + (z - z')$, where $x_p - x_p'$ is proportional to y and $z - z'$ is orthogonal to y; since the vectors $x_p - x_p'$ and $z - z'$ are orthogonal, they are either independent or else at least one of them must be zero. They cannot be independent, since their sum vanishes; therefore one of them is 0, hence the other must also be 0. This states that $x_p = x_p'$ and

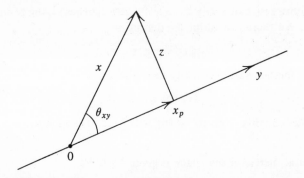

FIGURE 2.3

$z = z'$, and the decomposition is unique. The angle $\theta_{xy}(0 \leq \theta_{xy} \leq \pi)$ between x and y is defined as the angle between the positive half-lines generated by x and y. If e is the unit vector on the same half-line as y, that is, $e = y/\|y\|$, then (see Figure 2.3)

$$\cos \theta_{xy} = \frac{\langle x, e \rangle}{\|x\|} = \frac{\langle x, y \rangle}{\|x\| \, \|y\|}.$$

From the Schwarz inequality (2.10) we conclude that the right side is between -1 and 1, so that this formula defines a real angle between 0 and π.

We now try to define an inner product for a complex vector space. For the inner product to generate a norm, we must preserve the property $\langle x, x \rangle > 0$ for all $x \neq 0$. This will force us to change some of the other definitions in (2.6); otherwise, $\langle ix, ix \rangle = i\langle x, ix \rangle = i\langle ix, x \rangle = -1\langle x, x \rangle$, and it would be impossible to have $\langle x, x \rangle > 0$ for all $x \neq 0$. The remedy is simple: We change the first property in (2.6) and substitute $\langle x, y \rangle = \overline{\langle y, x \rangle}$.

DEFINITION.   An *inner product* $\langle x, y \rangle$ on a *complex* linear space is a *complex-valued* function of ordered pairs x, y with the properties

$$\langle x, y \rangle = \overline{\langle y, x \rangle};$$

$$\langle \alpha x, y \rangle = \alpha \langle x, y \rangle; \qquad\qquad (2.13)$$

$$\langle x_1 + x_2, y \rangle = \langle x_1, y \rangle + \langle x_2, y \rangle;$$

$$\langle x, x \rangle \geq 0, \qquad \text{with } \langle x, x \rangle = 0 \text{ if and only if } x = 0.$$

A complex linear space provided with the above inner product is called a *complex inner product space*. From the first two properties, we infer

$$\langle x, \alpha y \rangle = \bar{\alpha} \langle x, y \rangle.$$

We can again prove the Schwarz inequality

$$|\langle x, y \rangle| \leq \langle x, x \rangle^{1/2} \langle y, y \rangle^{1/2}. \qquad\qquad (2.14)$$

The real, nonnegative quantity $\langle x, x \rangle^{1/2}$ again satisfies all the conditions (2.4) on a norm. We therefore adopt the definition

$$\|x\| = \langle x, x \rangle^{1/2}, \tag{2.15}$$

and rewrite the Schwarz inequality in the form

$$|\langle x, y \rangle| \le \|x\| \, \|y\|. \tag{2.16}$$

Again the equality sign in (2.16) will hold if and only if x and y are dependent.

The natural metric in the space is given by (2.9).

DEFINITION. An inner product space which is complete in its natural metric is called a *Hilbert space*.

EXAMPLES OF INNER PRODUCT SPACES

Example 1. (a) Any n-dimensional real inner product space is called a *real Euclidean n-space* and is denoted by $E_n^{(r)}$. Any such space is complete; the simplest proof is based on the existence of an orthonormal basis in $E_n^{(r)}$ (see Exercise 2.11).

(b) A concrete example of **(a)** is the space of n-tuples of real numbers (see Example 1 of vector spaces) which can be seen to be an inner product space if we define

$$\langle x, y \rangle = \xi_1 \eta_1 + \cdots + \xi_n \eta_n.$$

We have

$$\|x\| = (\xi_1^2 + \cdots + \xi_n^2)^{1/2}$$

and

$$d(x, y) = \|x - y\| = [(\xi_1 - \eta_1)^2 + \cdots + (\xi_n - \eta_n)^2]^{1/2}.$$

The Schwarz inequality becomes

$$\left[\sum_{k=1}^{n} \xi_k \eta_k \right]^2 \le \left[\sum_{k=1}^{n} \xi_k^2 \right] \left[\sum_{k=1}^{n} \eta_k^2 \right]. \tag{2.17}$$

This space has already been shown to be complete (see Example 3 of metric spaces), and is therefore a Hilbert space.

(c) Another concrete example of **(a)** is the linear space P_n of real polynomials $x = x(t)$ of degree less than n defined over an interval $a \le t \le b$, with the inner product defined as

$$\langle x, y \rangle = \int_a^b x(t) y(t) dt.$$

Example 2. (a) Any n-dimensional complex inner product space is called a *complex Euclidean n-space* and is denoted by $E_n^{(c)}$. For a proof of completeness see Exercise 2.12.

(b) A concrete example of **(a)** is the space of n-tuples of complex numbers with the definition

$$\langle x, y \rangle = \sum_{k=1}^{n} \xi_k \bar{\eta}_k.$$

The conditions (2.13) are easily verified, and

$$\|x\| = \left[\sum_{k=1}^{n} \xi_k \bar{\xi}_k \right]^{1/2} = \left[\sum_{k=1}^{n} |\xi_k|^2 \right]^{1/2},$$

$$d(x, y) = \|x - y\| = \left[\sum_{k=1}^{n} |\xi_k - \eta_k|^2 \right]^{1/2}.$$

The Schwarz inequality (2.16) becomes

$$\left| \sum_{k=1}^{n} \xi_k \bar{\eta}_k \right|^2 \leq \left[\sum_{k=1}^{n} |\xi_k|^2 \right] \left[\sum_{k=1}^{n} |\eta_k|^2 \right]. \tag{2.18}$$

Example 3. The Hilbert space $\mathscr{L}_2^{(r)}(a, b)$. Consider the space $\mathscr{L}_2^{(r)}(a, b)$ of all real-valued functions $x(t)$ defined on $a \leq t \leq b$, for which the Lebesgue integral $\int_a^b x^2 \, dt$ exists. We introduce an inner product:

$$\langle x, y \rangle = \int_a^b xy \, dt. \tag{2.19}$$

Using the properties of the Lebesgue integral (Example 7 of metric spaces), one sees that (2.19) is indeed an acceptable inner product.

The corresponding norm is

$$\|x\| = \left[\int_a^b x^2(t) dt \right]^{1/2},$$

which generates the metric

$$d(x, y) = \|x - y\| = \left[\int_a^b (x - y)^2 \, dt \right]^{1/2}.$$

The Schwarz inequality becomes

$$\left| \int_a^b x(t)y(t)dt \right| \leq \left[\int_a^b x^2(t)dt \right]^{1/2} \left[\int_a^b y^2(t)dt \right]^{1/2}. \tag{2.20}$$

It has already been pointed out, without proof, that this space is complete. Thus $\mathscr{L}_2^{(r)}(a, b)$ is a Hilbert space.

Example 4. The Hilbert space $\mathscr{L}_2^{(c)}(a, b)$. Consider the space $\mathscr{L}_2^{(c)}(a, b)$ of all complex-valued functions $x(t)$ defined on $a \leq t \leq b$, for which the Lebesgue integral $\int_a^b |x|^2 \, dt$ exists. It can be shown that the following definition yields a suitable inner product,

$$\langle x, y \rangle = \int_a^b x\bar{y} \, dt. \tag{2.21}$$

The natural norm and metric are

$$\|x\| = \left[\int_a^b |x|^2 \, dt \right]^{1/2} ; \qquad d(x, y) = \|x - y\| = \left[\int_a^b |x - y|^2 \, dt \right]^{1/2}.$$

The Schwarz inequality becomes

$$\left| \int_a^b x\bar{y} \, dt \right| \leq \left[\int_a^b |x|^2 \, dt \right]^{1/2} \left[\int_a^b |y|^2 \, dt \right]^{1/2}. \tag{2.22}$$

We state, without proof, that $\mathscr{L}_2^{(c)}(a, b)$ is complete, hence is a Hilbert space.

Example 5. Let V be a region in the k-dimensional space $\mathscr{E}_k^{(r)}$. Consider the space $\mathscr{L}_2^{(c)}(V)$ of all complex-valued functions $x(t_1, \ldots, t_k)$ defined on V, for which

$$\int_V \cdots \int |x(t_1, \ldots, t_k)|^2 \, dt_1 \cdots dt_k$$

exists in the Lebesgue sense (Lebesgue integration can be defined in any finite number of dimensions). If the inner product is defined as

$$\langle x, y \rangle = \int_V \cdots \int x\bar{y} \, dt_1 \cdots dt_k,$$

this space becomes a Hilbert space.

EXERCISES

2.2 Show that $\mathscr{E}_n^{(c)}$ with the inner product $\xi_1\bar{\eta}_1 + \cdots + \xi_n\bar{\eta}_n$ is complete.

2.3 Consider $\mathscr{E}_n^{(r)}$ with the norm

$$\|x\| = \max \{|\xi_1|, \ldots, |\xi_n|\}.$$

Show that this a complete normed linear space.

2.4 The quadratic form $Q = \sum_{i,j=1}^n a_{ij}\theta_i\bar{\theta}_j$ is positive definite if Q is real and positive whenever the complex numbers $\theta_1, \ldots, \theta_n$ are not all 0. Show that Q can be used to define an inner product and a norm on $\mathscr{E}_n^{(c)}$. Show that the space is complete.

2.5 Let $s(t)$ be continuous, real, and positive in $a \leq t \leq b$. Consider the space of all complex-valued functions $x(t)$ for which $\int_a^b s(t)x(t)\bar{x}(t)dt < \infty$. Show that this is a linear space. With the inner product

$$\langle x, y \rangle = \int_a^b s(t)x(t)\bar{y}(t)dt,$$

the space becomes a complete inner product space, that is, a Hilbert space.

2.6 (a) Show that in any inner product space,

$$\|x + y\|^2 + \|x - y\|^2 = 2\|x\|^2 + 2\|y\|^2, \quad \text{for all } x \text{ and } y. \quad (2.23)$$

Interpret this equation geometrically and justify the name *parallelogram law*.

(b) Show that in any inner product space,

$$\langle x, y \rangle + \langle y, x \rangle = \tfrac{1}{2}[\|x + y\|^2 - \|x - y\|^2],$$

and that for a complex inner product space,

$$\langle x, y \rangle - \langle y, x \rangle = \frac{i}{2} [\|x + iy\|^2 - \|x - iy\|^2].$$

Consequently in a complex inner product space,

$$\langle x, y \rangle = \tfrac{1}{4}[\|x + y\|^2 - \|x - y\|^2 + i\|x + iy\|^2 - i\|x - iy\|^2], \quad (2.24)$$

and in a real inner product space,

$$\langle x, y \rangle = \tfrac{1}{4}[\|x + y\|^2 - \|x - y\|^2]. \quad (2.25)$$

We see from (2.24) and (2.25) that in an inner product space a knowledge of the norm unambiguously determines the inner product.

Thus, in any normed linear space (real or complex), *there can exist at most one inner product which generates the norm.*

2.7 Consider a real Banach space *whose norm satisfies* (2.23). Define the real-valued function $f(x, y)$ from

$$f(x, y) = \tfrac{1}{4}[\|x + y\|^2 - \|x - y\|^2].$$

(a) Show that $f(x, y)$ is a continuous function of the vector y.
(b) Show that for any integer k, $f(kx, y) = kf(x, y)$; hence that for any real number $\alpha, f(\alpha x, y) = \alpha f(x, y)$.
(c) Show that $f(x_1 + x_2, y) = f(x_1, y) + f(x_2, y)$.
In the light of these properties $f(x, y)$ is an acceptable inner product in the space [we note that $f(x, x) = \|x\|^2$]. By the remark following (2.25), it is the only possible inner product which generates the given norm. Thus, *the necessary and sufficient condition for a real Banach space to be a Hilbert space is that the norm satisfies the parallelogram law* (2.23). Moreover, if this condition is satisfied, the inner product can be calculated from the norm by (2.25).

2.8. Using the result of Exercise 2.7, show that Example 5 (under metric spaces) is not a Hilbert space even though it is a Banach space. Reach the same conclusion for Exercise 2.3.

2.9 Consider the space of real numbers with the proposed metric $d_k(x,y) = |x^k - y^k|$, where k is a given odd integer.
  (a) Show that the conditions (2.3) are satisfied.
  (b) Why can we not choose k even?
  (c) Show that the space is complete.
  (d) A normed linear space is obtained if and only if $k = 1$.

Additional Properties of Metric Spaces

Let $\mathscr{A}$ be a metric space, and let S be a set of points in $\mathscr{A}$. The *closure* of S is the set $\bar{S}$ consisting of the limits of all sequences which can be constructed from points of S. It is clear that $\bar{S}$ contains all the points of S; indeed, if x is a point S, the sequence $\{x, x, \ldots\}$ has limit x, and hence x belongs to $\bar{S}$. If S is the set of real numbers x for which $0 < x < 1$, then $\bar{S}$ is the set $0 \le x \le 1$; this shows that $\bar{S}$ may contain points other than those of S. A set S is *closed* if $S = \bar{S}$. A set S is *compact* if each sequence of points in S contains a convergent subsequence. Every finite set is compact. The set of all integers is not compact, since the sequence $\{1, 2, 3, \ldots\}$ has no convergent subsequence.†

Dense Sets

Let $\mathscr{A}$ be a metric space, and let S and T be two sets in $\mathscr{A}$, S being included in $T (S \subset T)$. We say that S is *dense* in T if, to every element f in T and to every $\varepsilon > 0$, we can find an element e in S such that $d(e, f) < \varepsilon$. In geometric terms, this means that to any element in T we can find an arbitrarily close element in S. The concept of denseness clearly depends on the metric used.

Suppose now that S, T and U are three sets of points in $\mathscr{A}$. If S is dense in T, and T is dense in U, then S is dense in U.

EXAMPLES

Example 1.   Let $\mathscr{A}$ be the real line with $d(x, y) = |x - y|$, let $T = \mathscr{A}$, and let S be the set of rational numbers. S is dense in T: Given any *real* number f and any $\varepsilon > 0$, we can find a rational number e such that $|f - e| < \varepsilon$.

---

† Given the sequence $s_1, s_2, \ldots, s_n, \ldots$ and a sequence of positive integers $k_1, k_2, \ldots, k_n, \ldots$ with $k_{n-1} < k_n$, the sequence $s_{k_1}, s_{k_2}, \ldots, s_{k_n}, \ldots$ is said to be a subsequence of $s_1, s_2, \ldots, s_n, \ldots$. Thus $1, 5, 9, 13, \ldots$ is a subsequence of $1, 3, 5, 7, \ldots$, but $1, 1, 1, \ldots$ is not a subsequence of $1, 3, 5, 7, \ldots$.

Example 2. (a) *Weierstrass approximation theorem*. This theorem (proved in Exercise 1.17) states that any continuous function can be uniformly approximated by polynomials on a finite, closed interval: To each $x(t)$ continuous on $a \leq t \leq b$, and to each $\varepsilon > 0$, there exists a polynomial $p(t)$ such that $|x(t) - p(t)| < \varepsilon$ for *all* t simultaneously in $a \leq t \leq b$. We can intepret this theorem in the terminology of metric spaces. Consider the space $\mathscr{A}$ of all functions $x(t)$ continuous on $a \leq t \leq b$ with the metric $d(x, y) = \max_{a \leq t \leq b} |x - y|$. The set of polynomials is a subset of $\mathscr{A}$; the Weierstrass theorem states that this set is dense in $\mathscr{A}$.

Although the Weierstrass approximation theorem was proved for real-valued continuous functions using approximating polynomials with real coefficients, it is easily extended to complex-valued continuous functions with approximating polynomials having complex coefficients. A further extension can be made to continuous functions of any finite number of variables.

(b) Consider the set T of complex-valued continuous functions on the finite interval $a \leq t \leq b$, with metric $d(x, y) = \left[\int_a^b |x - y|^2 \, dt\right]^{1/2}$. The set S of all complex-valued polynomials is clearly a subset of T. We claim that S is dense in T. Given $x(t)$ and $\varepsilon > 0$, we must find a polynomial $p(t)$ such that $d(x, p) < \varepsilon$. We have

$$d(x, p) = \left[\int_a^b |x - p|^2 \, dt\right]^{1/2} \leq (b - a)^{1/2} \left\{\max_{a \leq t \leq b} |x - p|^2\right\}^{1/2}.$$

By the Weierstrass theorem, we can find $p(t)$ such that $|x(t) - p(t)| < \varepsilon/(b-a)^{1/2}$ on $a \leq t \leq b$; hence $d(x, p) < \varepsilon$, as desired.

(c) Consider the space $\mathscr{L}_2^{(c)}(a, b)$ of complex-valued functions $x(t)$ such that $\int_a^b |x|^2 \, dt < \infty$. We use the natural metric $d(x, y) = \left[\int_a^b |x - y|^2 \, dt\right]^{1/2}$. The set T in part **(b)** is a subset of $\mathscr{L}_2$; it can be shown that T is dense in $\mathscr{L}_2$. Given any $x(t)$ in $\mathscr{L}_2$ and any $\varepsilon > 0$, there exists a *continuous* function $c(t)$ such that $d(x, c) < \varepsilon$.

(d) Since continuous functions are dense in $\mathscr{L}_2$ and polynomials are dense in the set of continuous functions, polynomials are dense in $\mathscr{L}_2$. To each $x(t)$ in $\mathscr{L}_2$ and to each $\varepsilon > 0$, there exists a polynomial $p(t)$ such that $d(x, p) < \varepsilon$.

Example 3. The gist of Example 2 is that functions in $\mathscr{L}_2$, wild as they may be, can be approximated in the mean by well-behaved functions such as continuous functions or even polynomials. We could now develop a hierarchy of theorems using more and more pleasant approximating functions. We content ourselves with a few examples.

(a) Let $t_1, \ldots, t_m$ be fixed points in $a \leq t \leq b$. The set of continuous functions which vanish at all the points $t_1, \ldots, t_m$ is dense in $\mathscr{L}_2$.

(b) The set of functions which vanish in some neighborhood of $t = a$ is dense in $\mathscr{L}_2^{(c)}(a, b)$.

(c) The set of differentiable functions is dense in $\mathscr{L}_2$.

(d) Let m and n be fixed. The set of all n times differentiable functions which assume the values $\alpha_1, \ldots, \alpha_m$ at the points $t_1, \ldots, t_m$ is dense in $\mathscr{L}_2$.

(e) The set of all test functions (see Exercise 1.21) is dense in $\mathscr{L}_2(a, b)$.

2.4 PROPERTIES OF A SEPARABLE HILBERT SPACE

We recall that a Hilbert space $\mathscr{A}$ is a *linear space* on which an *inner product* is defined, the space being *complete* in the metric generated by the inner product. We shall impose an additional requirement which, loosely speaking, restricts the "number" of elements in the space. The Hilbert space $\mathscr{A}$ is *separable* if there exists a *countable* set of elements $(f_1, \ldots, f_n, \ldots)$ whose finite linear combinations are dense in $\mathscr{A}$.† Thus, given f in $\mathscr{A}$ and $\varepsilon > 0$, there exist an index N and constants $\alpha_1, \ldots, \alpha_N$ such that $\|f - \sum_{k=i}^{N} \alpha_k f_k\| < \varepsilon$.

A set such as $(f_1, \ldots, f_n, \ldots)$ is called a *spanning set*. If S stands for the set of all finite linear combinations of a spanning set, we have $\bar{S} = \mathscr{A}$.

Any finite-dimensional Hilbert space E_n is separable; in fact there exists a set of n vectors $(f_1, \ldots, f_n)$ such that each vector in E_n has the representation $f = \sum_{k=1}^{n} \xi_k f_k$, which certainly implies separability. In Example 2(d) at the end of the last section, we showed that the set $(1, t, t^2, \ldots)$, which is clearly countable, is a spanning set for $\mathscr{L}_2(a, b)$, where a and b are finite. The spaces $\mathscr{L}_2(a, \infty)$, $\mathscr{L}_2(-\infty, b)$, and $\mathscr{L}_2(-\infty, \infty)$ are also separable, but the previous arguments must be modified, since polynomials are no longer elements in the space (see Exercise 2.22). The space $\mathscr{L}_2(V)$ of square-integrable functions of k independent variables $t_1, \ldots, t_k$ is also separable. The spaces listed above are the only ones which will appear in the applications we have in mind, and we therefore *consider only separable Hilbert spaces from here on*.

Parts of the next few pages will be divided into two columns. Statements pertinent to $E_n^{(c)}$ will be in the left column, those devoted to $\mathscr{L}_2^{(c)}$ in the right column; general results valid for any separable Hilbert space are written across the two columns.

EXERCISE

2.10 Let $\mathscr{A}$ be a complete metric space and S a subset of $\mathscr{A}$. The complement of the set $\bar{S}$ (with respect to $\mathscr{A}$) is called the *exterior* of S. Show that the union of S and its exterior is dense in $\mathscr{A}$.

† A set is countable if its elements can be placed in one-to-one correspondence with the positive integers or with some subset of the positive integers. Every set containing a finite number of elements is therefore countable; a well-known result of real-variable theory states that the rational numbers form a countable set but the real numbers do not.

$$\underline{E_n^{(c)}} \qquad\qquad \text{Function space} - \underline{\mathscr{L}_2^{(c)}(a, b)}$$

Description

An abstract, complex, n-dimensional linear space with inner product $\langle x, y \rangle$ satisfying properties (2.13).

(A concrete example of this kind of space is $\mathscr{E}_n^{(c)}$, whose elements x are n-tuples of complex numbers).

A concrete, complex, ∞-dimensional linear space whose elements x are complex-valued functions $x(t)$ defined on $a \le t \le b$ with $\int_a^b |x|^2 \, dt < \infty$. The inner product is $\langle x, y \rangle = \int_a^b x\bar{y} \, dt$.

Norm

$$\|x\| = \langle x, x \rangle^{1/2}.$$

$$\|x\| = \langle x, x \rangle^{1/2} = \left[\int_a^b |x|^2 \, dt \right]^{1/2}.$$

Metric

$$d(x, y) = \|x - y\| = \langle x - y, x - y \rangle^{1/2}.$$

$$d(x, y) = \|x - y\| = \langle x - y, x - y \rangle^{1/2}$$
$$= \left[\int_a^b |x - y|^2 \, dt \right]^{1/2}.$$

The space $E_n^{(c)}$ is complete (see Exercise 2.11).

The space $\mathscr{L}_2^{(c)}(a, b)$ is complete (proof omitted).

Schwarz inequality

$$|\langle x, y \rangle| \le \|x\| \, \|y\|.$$

$$\left| \int_a^b x\bar{y} \, dt \right| \le \left[\int_a^b |x|^2 \, dt \right]^{1/2} \left[\int_a^b |y|^2 \, dt \right]^{1/2}.$$

Convergence of sequences

A sequence of vectors $x_1, x_2, \ldots, x_k, \ldots$ is said to converge to x if $\lim_{k \to \infty} \|x - x_k\| = 0$. Thus, the notion of convergence of a sequence of vectors has been reduced to the convergence of a sequence of numbers. We use the notation $x_k \to x$ or $\lim_{k \to \infty} x_k = x$. A sequence is said to be a Cauchy sequence if $\lim_{m,n \to \infty} \|x_m - x_n\| = 0$. Every convergent sequence is a Cauchy sequence, and every Cauchy sequence converges (since the spaces are complete). The following theorem is easily verified. If $x_k \to x$ and $y_k \to y$, then $\alpha x_k + \beta y_k \to \alpha x + \beta y$. By reapplying this theorem we can extend it to any *finite sum of terms*.

In functional notation $x_k \to x$ if and only if

$$\lim_{k \to \infty} \left[\int_a^b |x_k(t) - x(t)|^2 \, dt \right]^{1/2} = 0.$$

[or what is equivalent, if and only if

$$\lim_{k \to \infty} \int_a^b |x_k(t) - x(t)|^2 \, dt = 0.]$$

This definition of convergence in function space is traditionally known as *convergence in the mean*. We use this terminology only when we want to emphasize the distinction among modes of convergence; otherwise, we just call it *convergence*.

The connection among various modes of convergence in function space is the subject of Exercises 2.13 and 2.25.

Convergence of series

A series $u_1 + u_2 + \cdots + u_k + \cdots$ is said to converge to x if and only if the sequence of partial sums $x_k = \sum_{i=1}^{k} u_i$ converges to x. Thus $\sum_{k=1}^{\infty} u_k = x$ if and only if $\lim_{k \to \infty} \left\| \sum_{i=1}^{k} u_i - x \right\| = 0$.

Continuity of inner product

If $x_n \to x$ and h is any vector, then $\langle x_n, h \rangle \to \langle x, h \rangle$. We must show that $\langle x_n, h \rangle - \langle x, h \rangle \to 0$, or that $\langle x_n - x, h \rangle \to 0$. The Schwarz inequality yields $|\langle x_n - x, h \rangle|^2 \le \|x_n - x\|^2 \|h\|^2$, and since $\|x_n - x\| \to 0$ by assumption, the desired result follows.

If $x_n \to x$, $\langle x_n, h \rangle \to \langle x, h \rangle$ for any h.

If $x_n \to x$,
$$\int_a^b x_n(t)\overline{h}(t)dt \to \int_a^b x(t)\overline{h}(t)dt$$
for any h.

If $\langle x_n, h \rangle \to \langle x, h \rangle$ for every h, then $x_n \to x$.

If $\langle x_n, h \rangle \to \langle x, h \rangle$ for every h, it does *not* follow that $x_n \to x$ (see Exercise 2.21).

Dependence and Independence of Vectors

A finite or countably infinite set of vectors $x_1, \ldots, x_k, \ldots$ is said to be *independent* if $\alpha_1 x_1 + \cdots + \alpha_k x_k + \cdots = 0$ implies $\alpha_1 = \cdots = \alpha_k = \cdots = 0$. If a set of vectors is independent, no vector is a linear combination of the others.

There are n independent vectors in $E_n^{(c)}$, but every set of $n+1$ vectors is dependent. (This is an axiom for $E_n^{(c)}$.)

There exists an infinite set of independent vectors in $\mathscr{L}_2$. For instance, the set $x_0 = 1$, $x_1 = t$, $x_2 = t^2, \ldots, x_k = t^k, \ldots$ is an independent set containing an infinite number of elements.

Basis

A finite or countably infinite set of vectors $e_1, \ldots, e_k, \ldots$ is a basis for a space if (1) the vectors are independent, (2) each vector x in the space can be written as a linear combination of a finite or infinite number of basis vectors.

It follows easily that the representation is unique.

Every set of n independent vectors is a basis in $E_n^{(c)}$, and every basis consists of n independent vectors. Given a basis $\{e_1, \ldots, e_n\}$, each vector x has a unique representation $x = \xi_1 e_1 + \cdots + \xi_n e_n$. The coefficients $\xi_1, \ldots, \xi_n$ are known as the coordinates of x in the basis $\{e_1, \ldots, e_n\}$.

A basis in $\mathscr{L}_2$ must have a countably infinite number of independent elements, but a set consisting of a countably infinite number of independent elements does not necessarily form a basis. Given a basis $\{e_1, \ldots, e_k, \ldots\}$, each vector x has a unique representation $x = \sum_{k=1}^{\infty} \xi_k e_k$, where $\{\xi_k\}$ are the coordinates of x in the basis.

It is obviously desirable for a set of vectors to form a basis in a Hilbert space $\mathscr{A}$; one can then express any vector in $\mathscr{A}$ as a finite or infinite series in terms of the basis vectors. We now distinguish between the concepts of a basis and of a spanning set consisting of independent vectors.

A set of vectors $(f_1 \ldots, f_n, \ldots)$ is a spanning set if each vector x in $\mathscr{A}$ can be approximated, to any preassigned degree of accuracy, by a finite linear combination of the vectors in the set: To each x and $\varepsilon > 0$, there exist $N > 0$ and constants $\alpha_1, \ldots, \alpha_N$ such that $\left\| x - \sum_{k=1}^{N} \alpha_k f_k \right\| < \varepsilon$. As we reduce ε, that is, require greater accuracy in the approximation, we expect to have to increase the index N, but it may also be necessary to change previously found coefficients $\alpha_1, \ldots, \alpha_N$; hence there might *not* exist a *fixed* sequence of constants $\xi_1, \ldots, \xi_n, \ldots$ with the property $x = \sum_{k=1}^{\infty} \xi_k f_k$, as would be required if the set $\{f_k\}$ were a basis. As was already pointed out in the last section, the independent set $f_0 = 1, f_1 = t, f_2 = t^2, \ldots$ is a spanning set for $\mathscr{L}_2(-1, 1)$ but is not a basis, since there are many functions (for instance, $|t|$) which belong to $\mathscr{L}_2(-1, 1)$ and yet cannot be expanded in a series $\sum_{k=0}^{\infty} \xi_k t^k$. Let us examine the problem more closely; if $x(t)$ is continuous, the Weierstrass approximation theorem guarantees the existence of a polynomial $p^{(k)}(t)$ such that $\|x(t) - p^{(k)}(t)\| < 1/k$. We can easily construct an infinite series $q^{(1)}(t) + q^{(2)}(t) + \cdots$ which has $p^{(k)}(t)$ for its sequence of partial sums; it suffices to choose $q^{(k)}(t) = p^{(k)}(t) - p^{(k-1)}(t)$. The infinite series $\sum_{k=1}^{\infty} q^{(k)}(t)$ clearly converges to $x(t)$, and each $q^{(k)}(t)$ is a polynomial; yet *this is not a power series* $\sum_{j=0}^{\infty} \xi_j t^j$. To transform $\sum_{k=1}^{\infty} q^{(k)}(t)$ into a power series we would first collect all the constants in the various $q^{(k)}(t)$ and bring them to the front; next we collect all terms in t and make this sum the second term, etc. Such drastic rearrangements of series are not always permissible, and the series $\sum_{k=1}^{\infty} q^{(k)}(t)$ is not usually equivalent to a power series.

We shall encounter a very similar phenomenon when dealing with expansions in Legendre polynomials $P_k(t)$. It will be shown that the continuous (but nondifferentiable) function $x(t) = |t|$ can be expanded in a series $\sum\limits_{k=0}^{\infty} \alpha_k P_k(t)$ in $-1 \le t \le 1$; yet $|t|$ can not be expanded in a power series $\sum\limits_{j=0}^{\infty} \xi_j t^j$. Again, we are not permitted to collect the terms in the Legendre expansion to rearrange it in a power series (see Exercise 2.23).

So far we have been emphasizing the differences between the concepts of a basis and of a spanning set. The reader will be encouraged to find out that there are similarities; we will show that for sets consisting of orthogonal elements, the two concepts are identical. Moreover, a process will be described through which an orthogonal spanning set can be constructed from an arbitrary spanning set.

Orthogonality

Two vectors x, y are *orthogonal* or *perpendicular* if $\langle x, y \rangle = 0$. A finite or infinite set of vectors $\{\varphi_1, \ldots, \varphi_k, \ldots\}$ is said to be an *orthogonal set* if $\langle \varphi_i, \varphi_j \rangle = 0$, $i \ne j$. A *proper orthogonal* set is an orthogonal set none of whose elements is the zero vector. A proper orthogonal set is an independent set. In $E_n^{(c)}$ a proper orthogonal set contains at most n elements. A set is orthonormal if

$$\langle \varphi_i, \varphi_j \rangle = \begin{cases} 0, & i \ne j; \\ 1, & i = j. \end{cases}$$

Individual vectors for which $\|x\| = 1$ are said to be *normalized*.

Linear Manifolds

In ordinary three-dimensional Euclidean space $E_3^{(r)}$, we can find subsets, known as *linear manifolds*, which are themselves linear spaces. These linear manifolds are just the lines and planes containing the origin. The concept can be extended to an arbitrary linear space $\mathscr{A}$. A set M in $\mathscr{A}$ is said to be a linear manifold if, whenever x and y belong to M, so does $\alpha x + \beta y$ for arbitrary complex α and β; thus 0 always belongs to M, and it is clear that M is itself a linear space (with the same definitions of vector addition and multiplication by scalars used in $\mathscr{A}$).

A particularly important role is played by closed linear manifolds, that is, linear manifolds which are closed sets; the reason is that if $\mathscr{A}$ is a Hilbert space and M a closed linear manifold in $\mathscr{A}$, then M is itself a Hilbert space. Indeed if $\{x_k\}$ is a Cauchy sequence in M, it must have a limit x in $\mathscr{A}$ because $\mathscr{A}$ is complete; x must also belong to M since M is closed; it follows therefore that M is a complete inner product space, hence a Hilbert space.

EXAMPLES OF LINEAR MANIFOLDS

Example 1. Let $(x_1, \ldots, x_k)$ be a set of k independent vectors in the Hilbert space $\mathscr{A}(k \leq \dim \mathscr{A})$. Define M to be the set of all linear combinations of these k vectors; M is clearly a linear manifold in $\mathscr{A}$ with dimension k; M is known as the linear manifold *generated* by $(x_1, \ldots, x_k)$ and can be viewed geometrically as a k-dimensional hyperplane through the origin. Since M is a k-dimensional linear space, it must be complete (see Exercise 2.11), and therefore closed. It follows that every linear manifold in a finite-dimensional space is necessarily closed.

Example 2. Let $(x_1, \ldots, x_k \ldots)$ be an infinite set of independent vectors in $\mathscr{L}_2$. Consider the set S of all linear combinations of a *finite* number of the $\{x_k\}$. This set S is a linear manifold but is *not* closed. The closure $\bar{S}$ of S is itself a linear manifold. To show how different S and $\bar{S}$ can be, let us take a concrete example in $\mathscr{L}_2(a, b)$. Let $x_k(t) = t^{k-1}$; then S is the set of all polynomials; on the other hand, the closure of S is the set $\bar{S}$ of all elements which can be approximated by polynomials; thus $\bar{S}$ is the whole space $\mathscr{L}_2(a, b)$.

Example 3. The set S of all continuous functions in $\mathscr{L}_2(a, b)$ is a linear manifold; S is not closed but $\bar{S}$ is the whole space $\mathscr{L}_2(a, b)$.

Example 4. Let M be a linear manifold (closed or not) in $\mathscr{A}$; consider the set $M^\perp$ of all vectors which are orthogonal to every vector in M. The set $M^\perp$ is a linear manifold; furthermore, $M^\perp$ is closed. Indeed, let $x^{(k)}$ be a sequence of vectors in $M^\perp$ with $\lim_{k \to \infty} x^{(k)} = x$; we have $\langle x^{(k)}, f \rangle = 0$, for every f in M, and by continuity of the inner product $\langle x^{(k)}, f \rangle \to \langle x, f \rangle$; hence $\langle x, f \rangle = 0$ for every f in M, and x is in $M^\perp$. This proves that $M^\perp$ is closed. One can show with little difficulty that $(M^\perp)^\perp = \bar{M}$, so that if M is itself closed, $(M^\perp)^\perp = M$. In this latter case M and $M^\perp$ are known as *orthogonal complements*.

Projections

The simplest linear manifold is the line generated by a single nonzero vector φ_1 (which is taken as a unit vector). Each vector x in $\mathscr{A}$ can be decomposed, in a unique manner, as a sum $x_p + z$, where x_p is proportional to φ_1 and z is perpendicular to φ_1. We exhibit the vectors x_p and z: $x_p = \langle x, \varphi_1 \rangle \varphi_1$, $z = x - \langle x, \varphi_1 \rangle \varphi_1$. The reader will have no trouble in showing that the decomposition is unique. The vector x_p is the *projection* of x on the line generated by φ_1 (see Figure 2.3).

Suppose now that M is an arbitrary closed linear manifold in $\mathscr{A}$, and let $M^\perp$ be its orthogonal complement. If x is an arbitrary vector in $\mathscr{A}$, it can again be decomposed, in a unique manner, as a sum $x_p + z$, where x_p is in M and z is in $M^\perp$; x_p is known as the *projection* of x on the manifold M and z is the projection of x on $M^\perp$. We defer the proof of this theorem until the section on best approximations.

Theorem (*Riesz-Fischer Theorem*). *Let* $\{\varphi_1, \ldots, \varphi_n, \ldots\}$ *be an infinite orthonormal set in* $\mathscr{L}_2^{(c)}(a, b)$ *and let* $\{a_n\}$ *be a sequence of complex numbers.*

(a) *If* $\sum\limits_{n=1}^{\infty} |a_n|^2$ *diverges, then* $\sum\limits_{n=1}^{\infty} a_n \varphi_n$ *diverges.*

(b) *If* $\sum\limits_{n=1}^{\infty} |a_n|^2$ *converges, then* $\sum\limits_{n=1}^{\infty} a_n \varphi_n$ *converges to some element* g *in* $\mathscr{L}_2^{(c)}(a, b)$ *and* $a_n = \langle g, \varphi_n \rangle$.

Proof. Suppose $\sum\limits_{n=1}^{\infty} a_n \varphi_n$ converges; then to each $\varepsilon > 0$ there exists N such that for m and $p > N$ we have

$$\left\| \sum_{n=m+1}^{p} a_n \varphi_n \right\|^2 < \varepsilon.$$

This implies $\sum\limits_{n=m+1}^{p} |a_n|^2 < \varepsilon$, so that $\sum\limits_{n=1}^{\infty} |a_n|^2$ converges, which proves part (a).

To prove (b) consider the sequence $x_k = \sum\limits_{n=1}^{k} a_n \varphi_n$; then

$$\|x_p - x_m\|^2 = \left\| \sum_{n=m+1}^{p} a_n \varphi_n \right\|^2 = \sum_{n=m+1}^{p} |a_n|^2.$$

Since, by assumption, $\sum\limits_{n=1}^{\infty} |a_n|^2$ converges, we know that for m and p sufficiently large, $\sum\limits_{n=m+1}^{p} |a_n|^2 < \varepsilon$, and hence $\|x_p - x_m\|^2 < \varepsilon$, so that x_k is a Cauchy sequence. The space $\mathscr{L}_2^{(c)}(a, b)$ being complete, x_k must therefore converge to an element in the space, say g. If $m \geq k$, we have

$$\langle x_m, \varphi_k \rangle = \left\langle \sum_{n=1}^{m} a_n \varphi_n, \varphi_k \right\rangle = a_k.$$

Since $x_m \to x$, the continuity of the inner product entails

$$a_k = \lim_{m \to \infty} \langle x_m, \varphi_k \rangle = \langle g, \varphi_k \rangle.$$

Construction of an Orthonormal Set from an Independent Set (Gram-Schmidt Procedure)

We are given $k(\leq n)$ independent vectors $\{e_1, \ldots, e_k\}$. We wish to construct an orthonormal set $\{\varphi_1, \ldots, \varphi_k\}$ each of whose elements is a linear combination of the members of the set

Starting from a finite or infinite independent set $\{e_1, \ldots, e_k, \ldots\}$ we construct an orthonormal set $\{\varphi_1, \ldots, \varphi_k, \ldots\}$ by the method described on the left.

$\{e_1, \ldots, e_k\}$. This can be done in many ways, but we describe a method based on simple geometric considerations; the method has the further advantage that φ_i is a linear combination of only the first i elements $e_1, \ldots, e_i$; that is, $\varphi_i = \sum_{j=1}^{i} a_{ij} e_j$. This construction proceeds as follows: let $\varphi_1 = e_1 / \langle e_1, e_1 \rangle^{1/2}$; to obtain φ_2 we first remove from e_2 its projection on φ_1, which yields $g_2 = e_2 - \langle e_2, \varphi_1 \rangle \varphi_1$. The vector g_2 is a linear combination of e_1 and e_2 and is orthogonal to φ_1; to obtain φ_2, we normalize g_2:

$$\varphi_2 = \frac{g_2}{\langle g_2, g_2 \rangle^{1/2}}.$$

In a similar way,

$$g_3 = e_3 - \langle e_3, \varphi_2 \rangle \varphi_2 - \langle e_3, \varphi_1 \rangle \varphi_1;$$

$$\varphi_3 = \frac{g_3}{\langle g_3, g_3 \rangle^{1/2}}.$$

$$\vdots$$

$$g_k = e_k - \sum_{i=1}^{k-1} \langle e_k, \varphi_i \rangle \varphi_i;$$

$$\varphi_k = \frac{g_k}{\langle g_k, g_k \rangle^{1/2}}.$$

The only thing that could impede the construction is to have $\langle g_i, g_i \rangle = 0$ at some stage; that is, $g_i = 0$. This is impossible, since g_i is a linear combination of the independent vectors $e_1, \ldots, e_i$ with at least one coefficient (the one belonging to e_i) different from 0.

Note that $\{e_1, \ldots, e_k\}$, $\{g_1, \ldots, g_k\}$, $\{\varphi_1, \ldots, \varphi_k\}$ all generate the same linear manifold.

In functional notation, we have

$$g_k(t) = e_k(t) - \varphi_{k-1}(t) \int_a^b e_k(t) \bar{\varphi}_{k-1}(t) dt$$

$$\cdots - \varphi_1(t) \int_a^b e_k(t) \bar{\varphi}_1(t) dt;$$

$$\varphi_k(t) = \frac{g_k(t)}{\left[\int_a^b |g_k(t)|^2 dt \right]^{1/2}}, \qquad k = 1, 2, \ldots.$$

The procedure is frequently used without the final step of normalization from $g_k(t)$ to $\varphi_k(t)$. The set $\{g_1, \ldots, g_k, \ldots\}$ is clearly a proper orthogonal set.

Example. Consider the interval

$$-1 \le t \le 1,$$

and the independent set

$$e_0 = 1, e_1 = t, \ldots, e_k = t^k, \ldots.$$

Using the Gram-Schmidt procedure *without* normalization, but requiring instead that all elements take on the value 1 at $t = 1$, we obtain the orthogonal set of *Legendre polynomials:*

$$\begin{aligned}
\psi_0(t) &= 1, \\
\psi_1(t) &= t, \\
\psi_2(t) &= \tfrac{1}{2}(3t^2 - 1), \\
\psi_3(t) &= \tfrac{1}{2}(5t^3 - 3t), \\
&\vdots
\end{aligned}$$

Orthonormal Basis

A basis consisting of orthonormal vectors is known as an *orthonormal basis*; if the vectors are merely orthogonal, so is the basis.

Given a basis $\{e_1, \ldots, e_n\}$, we can construct an orthonormal set $\{\varphi_1, \ldots, \varphi_n\}$ by the Gram-Schmidt procedure. This new set is independent and has n elements and is therefore an orthonormal basis for $E_n^{(c)}$.

The computation of the coordinates of a vector in an orthonormal basis is particularly simple. Let $x = \xi_1\varphi_1 + \cdots + \xi_n\varphi_n$; the inner product of both sides with φ_k yields

$$\xi_k = \langle x, \varphi_k \rangle = \overline{\langle \varphi_k, x \rangle}.$$

Thus $x = \sum_{k=1}^{n} \langle x, \varphi_k \rangle \varphi_k$ and x is the sum of its projections along n mutually perpendicular axes.†

If x and y are two vectors with coordinates $\{\xi_k\}$ and $\{\eta_k\}$, respectively, we have

$$\langle x, y \rangle = \sum_{k=1}^{n} \xi_k \bar{\eta}_k$$

and

$$\langle x, x \rangle = \|x\|^2 = \sum_{k=1}^{n} |\xi_k|^2.$$

Given a basis or merely an independent spanning set $\{e_1, \ldots, e_k, \ldots\}$, we can construct an orthonormal set by the Gram-Schmidt procedure. In the next section on best approximation, we show that this orthonormal set is a basis.

Given an orthonormal basis $\{\varphi_1, \ldots, \varphi_k, \ldots\}$ and a vector x, we have the unique representation $x = \sum_{i=1}^{\infty} \xi_i\varphi_i$; that is, $x = \lim_{m \to \infty} \sum_{i=1}^{m} \xi_i\varphi_i$. Consider

$$x_m = \sum_{i=1}^{m} \xi_i\varphi_i$$

for sufficiently large m. Take the inner product with respect to the fixed element φ_k $(k \leq m)$; then

$$\langle x_m, \varphi_k \rangle = \xi_k.$$

Since $x_m \to x$, it follows by the continuity of the inner product that

$$\xi_k = \langle x, \varphi_k \rangle = \overline{\langle \varphi_k, x \rangle}.$$

If x and y are two vectors with coordinates $\{\xi_k\}$ and $\{\eta_k\}$, respectively, we have

$$\langle x, y \rangle = \sum_{k=1}^{\infty} \xi_k \bar{\eta}_k$$

and

$$\langle x, x \rangle = \|x\|^2 = \sum_{k=1}^{\infty} |\xi_k|^2.$$

Best Approximation (Least Squares)

We want to approximate an arbitrary vector x in terms of a linear combination of the independent set $\{e_1, \ldots, e_k\}$, where $k \leq n$ if x is a vector in E_n and k is an arbitrary integer if x is in $\mathscr{L}_2$. By the best approximation we mean the linear combination $\sum_{i=1}^{k} b_i e_i$ which is closest to x, that is, for which $\left\| x - \sum_{i=1}^{k} b_i e_i \right\|$ is smallest. We first construct an orthonormal set $\{\varphi_1, \ldots, \varphi_k\}$ from $\{e_1, \ldots, e_k\}$ by the Gram-Schmidt procedure. Since these two sets generate the same linear manifold, we may as well determine the linear combination $\sum_{i=1}^{k} a_i\varphi_i$ which is

† If a basis $\{e_1, \ldots, e_n\}$ of nonorthogonal vectors is used, we have the representation $x = \sum_{k=1}^{n} \zeta_k e_k$, but ζ_k is *not* given by $\langle x, e_k \rangle$. Thus the coordinates of x in an oblique coordinate system are not equal to the projections on the coordinate axes.

closest to x. (The reason for this approach is that the coefficients $\{a_i\}$ are more easily calculated than the coefficients $\{b_i\}$.) We wish to choose $a_1, \ldots, a_k$ so as to minimize $\left\| x - \sum_{i=1}^{k} a_i \varphi_i \right\|$, or, what is equivalent, to minimize $\left\| x - \sum_{i=1}^{k} a_i \varphi_i \right\|^2$.

For any $a_1, \ldots, a_k$, we have

$$\left\| x - \sum_{i=1}^{k} a_i \varphi_i \right\|^2 = \|x\|^2 + \sum_{i=1}^{k} a_i \bar{a}_i - \sum_{i=1}^{k} a_i \langle \varphi_i, x \rangle - \sum_{i=1}^{k} \bar{a}_i \overline{\langle \varphi_i, x \rangle}$$

$$= \|x\|^2 + \sum_{i=1}^{k} |\langle x, \varphi_i \rangle - a_i|^2 - \sum_{i=1}^{k} |\langle x, \varphi_i \rangle|^2.$$

It is clear that the minimum is obtained by choosing $a_i = \langle x, \varphi_i \rangle$. These optimal values of the coefficients are known as the *Fourier coefficients* of x with respect to the orthonormal set $\{\varphi_i\}$; they will be denoted by c_i; thus $c_i = \langle x, \varphi_i \rangle$, $i = 1, \ldots, k$. The uniquely determined best approximation to x is the *Fourier sum* $\sum_{i=1}^{k} c_i \varphi_i = \sum_{i=1}^{k} \langle x, \varphi_i \rangle \varphi_i$. Geometrically this is the projection of x on the linear manifold generated by $\{\varphi_1, \ldots, \varphi_k\}$ or, if one prefers, the sum of the projections of x along the individual axes defined by $\varphi_1, \ldots, \varphi_k$. Of course one cannot expect that the best approximation is perfect! As a matter of fact the square of the distance between x and its projection is

$$\left\| x - \sum_{i=1}^{k} \langle x, \varphi_i \rangle \varphi_i \right\|^2 = \|x\|^2 - \sum_{i=1}^{k} |\langle x, \varphi_i \rangle|^2.$$

Since the quantity on the left is nonnegative, we have *Bessel's inequality*,

$$\|x\|^2 \geq \sum_{i=1}^{k} |\langle x, \varphi_i \rangle|^2.$$

The following feature of the Fourier sum $\sum_{i=1}^{k} c_i \varphi_i$ should be noted: If we decide to add another vector φ_{k+1} to our orthonormal approximating set of vectors, the best approximation now becomes $\sum_{i=1}^{k+1} \langle x, \varphi_i \rangle \varphi_i$. Thus we have merely added one term to the expansion, *without changing* previously computed coefficients. (This leads to the possibility of a series expansion if an infinite orthonormal set is used in $\mathscr{L}_2$.) If we had used independent, but not orthogonal vectors $e_1, \ldots, e_k$ to approximate x, the addition of a new vector e_{k+1} to the approximating set might entail a recomputation of the previously found coefficients.

At this juncture, let us consider $E_n^{(c)}$ and $\mathscr{L}_2^{(c)}(a, b)$ separately. The approximating set for $E_n^{(c)}$ consists of $k(\leq n)$ orthonormal vectors, whereas for $\mathscr{L}_2^{(c)}(a, b)$ one can envisage either a finite or infinite orthonormal approximating set.

Given an orthonormal set $\{\varphi_1, \ldots, \varphi_k\}$, with $k \leq n$, we associate with each vector x in $E_n^{(c)}$ the expansion

$$\sum_{i=1}^{k} c_i\varphi_i = \sum_{i=1}^{k} \langle x, \varphi_i\rangle\varphi_i.$$

The square error is

$$\|x - \sum_{i=1}^{k} c_i\varphi_i\|^2 = \|x\|^2 - \sum_{i=1}^{k} |c_i|^2$$
$$= \|x\|^2 - \sum_{i=1}^{k} |\langle x, \varphi_i\rangle|^2 \geq 0.$$

Hence

$$\|x\|^2 \geq \sum_{i=1}^{k} |\langle x, \varphi_i\rangle|^2.$$

Thus the square of the length of any vector is greater than or equal to the sum of the squares of the lengths of its projections on perpendicular axes. When can we, for every x, substitute an equality sign in the above inequality? The answer is that our orthonormal set must be extensive enough so that the sum of the projections is just x. This will happen for every x if and only if the set $\{\varphi_1, \ldots, \varphi_k\}$ is a *basis*. Since we are working in $E_n^{(c)}$, this means that the set should have *exactly n* elements. An orthonormal set is a basis for $E_n^{(c)}$ if and only if it has exactly n elements. We now develop alternative criteria for an orthonormal set to be a basis. Why should we bother to give such alternative criteria when counting up to n is so easy? The answer is found when we try to extend these criteria to $\mathcal{L}_2^{(c)}(a, b)$. It is not enough to say that the orthonormal set has an infinite number of elements (deleting a single element from an infinite orthonormal basis in $\mathcal{L}_2$ yields an infinite orthonormal set which is no longer a basis, since the deleted element has no expansion in the remaining elements). All the alternative criteria to be developed for E_n go over easily to $\mathcal{L}_2$; only the original criterion based on counting the elements fails for $\mathcal{L}_2$.

Given an orthonormal set $\{\varphi_1, \ldots, \varphi_k, \ldots\}$ consisting of a finite or infinite number of elements, we associate with any x in $\mathcal{L}_2^{(c)}(a, b)$ the expansion

$$\sum_{i} c_i\varphi_i = \sum_{i} \langle x, \varphi_i\rangle\varphi_i.$$

We show that this series must converge. Indeed for any finite index k,

$$\|x - \sum_{i=1}^{k} c_i\varphi_i\|^2 = \|x\|^2 - \sum_{i=1}^{k} |\langle x, \varphi_i\rangle|^2 \geq 0,$$

which implies $\sum_{i=1}^{k} |c_i|^2 \leq \|x\|^2$. The series $\sum_{i=1}^{\infty} |c_i|^2$ has a sequence of partial sums which increases monotonically and is bounded above by the number $\|x\|^2$. The series $\sum_{i=1}^{\infty} |c_i|^2$ must therefore *converge* and

$$\|x\|^2 \geq \sum_{i=1}^{\infty} |c_i|^2.$$

Since $\sum_{i=1}^{\infty} |c_i|^2$ converges, it follows that $\lim_{i\to\infty} c_i = 0$ (this is known as the *Riemann-Lebesgue* lemma). By the Riesz-Fischer theorem we know that $\sum_{i=1}^{\infty} c_i\varphi_i$ converges to some element in $\mathcal{L}_2^{(c)}(a, b)$. Of course we have no guarantee that the series converges to x; indeed, it can be guaranteed to converge to x only if the set $\{\varphi_i\}$ is "extensive" enough, that is, if the set $\{\varphi_i\}$ is a basis. In any event, we have

$$\left\|x - \sum_{i=1}^{\infty} c_i\varphi_i\right\|^2 = \|x\|^2 - \sum_{i=1}^{\infty} |c_i|^2.$$

This leads directly to the characterizations of an orthonormal basis listed in (b) and (c) below.

Characterization of an Orthonormal Basis

We give below a number of necessary and sufficient conditions for an orthonormal set to be a basis (also known as a *complete orthonormal set*).

If *any* of the following criteria is met the orthonormal set $\{\varphi_1, \ldots, \varphi_k\}$ is complete.

(a) The set has exactly n elements.

(b) For every x in $E_n^{(c)}$, the Fourier sum of x in terms of the orthonormal set represents x exactly; that is, for every x,

$$x = \sum_i \langle x, \varphi_i \rangle \varphi_i.$$

(c) For every x in $E_n^{(c)}$,

$$\|x\|^2 = \sum_i |\langle x, \varphi_i \rangle|^2.$$

(d) The only vector x for which all the Fourier coefficients vanish is the 0 vector.

(e) There exists no vector φ in $E_n^{(c)}$ such that $\{\varphi, \varphi_1, \varphi_2, \ldots, \varphi_k\}$ is an orthonormal set.

If *any* of the following criteria is met, the orthonormal set $\{\varphi_1, \ldots, \varphi_k, \ldots\}$ is complete.

(b) For every x in $\mathscr{L}_2$,

$$x = \sum_i \langle x, \varphi_i \rangle \varphi_i.$$

(b$_1$) For every continuous $x(t)$ in $\mathscr{L}_2$,

$$x = \sum_i \langle x, \varphi_i \rangle \varphi_i.$$

(c) *Parseval's identity.* For every x in $\mathscr{L}_2$,

$$\|x\|^2 = \sum_i |\langle x, \varphi_i \rangle|^2.$$

(c$_1$) For every continuous $x(t)$ in $\mathscr{L}_2$,

$$\|x\|^2 = \sum_i |\langle x, \varphi_i \rangle|^2.$$

(d) The only x in $\mathscr{L}_2$ for which all the Fourier coefficients vanish is the 0 function.

(d$_1$) The only continuous $x(t)$ in $\mathscr{L}_2$ for which all the Fourier coefficients vanish is the 0 function.

(e) There exists no function $\varphi(t)$ in $\mathscr{L}_2$ such that $\{\varphi, \varphi_1, \ldots, \varphi_k, \ldots\}$ is an orthonormal set.

(e$_1$) There is no continuous function $\varphi(t)$ in $\mathscr{L}_2$, such that $\{\varphi, \varphi_1, \ldots, \varphi_k, \ldots\}$ is an orthonormal set.

We now prove the equivalence of (b), (c), (d), and (e) for $\mathscr{L}_2$[(b$_1$), (c$_1$), (d$_1$), (e$_1$) require a small additional effort; see Exercise 2.12]. We shall show that (e) implies (d), that (d) implies (b), that (b) implies (c), and that (c) in turn implies (e), thereby completing the equivalence of the four criteria.

1. (e) implies (d). If there exists a function x in $\mathscr{L}_2$ whose Fourier coefficients $\langle x, \varphi_i \rangle$ are all 0 but which does not vanish, then $y = x/\|x\|$ satisfies $\langle y, \varphi_i \rangle = 0$ for all i and $\|y\| = 1$. We could then adjoin y to the set $\{\varphi_i\}$ and enlarge the orthonormal set, thereby contradicting assumption (e).

2. (d) implies (b). The sum $\sum_i \langle x, \varphi_i \rangle \varphi_i$ converges to some element y of $\mathscr{L}_2$ (see discussion on preceding pages). We must show that $y = x$. We note that $\langle y, \varphi_i \rangle = \langle x, \varphi_i \rangle$; hence $\langle y - x, \varphi_i \rangle = 0$ for all i; therefore, by (d), $y = x$.

3. (b) implies (c). This is immediate since

$$\left\| x - \sum_i \langle x, \varphi_i \rangle \varphi_i \right\|^2 = \|x\|^2 - \sum_i |\langle x, \varphi_i \rangle|^2.$$

4. (c) implies (e). If there exists a function φ such that $\{\varphi, \varphi_1, \ldots, \varphi_k, \ldots\}$ is an orthonormal set, then $\|\varphi\| = 1$ and $\langle \varphi, \varphi_i \rangle = 0$ for all i. This in turn implies from (c) that $\|\varphi\|^2 = \sum_i |\langle \varphi, \varphi_i \rangle|^2 = 0$, which is a contradiction; hence no such function φ can exist.

Before proceeding to some examples, we prove two fundamental theorems.

Theorem 1. *A spanning set consisting of orthonormal elements is complete.*

Proof. If $\{\varphi_1, \ldots, \varphi_k, \ldots\}$ is a spanning set, then for each x and $\varepsilon > 0$ there exist an index N and numbers $a_1, \ldots, a_N$ such that $\left\| x - \sum_{k=1}^{N} a_k \varphi_k \right\|^2 < \varepsilon$; the coefficients $\{a_k\}$ may of course depend on ε. On the other hand, the set $\{\varphi_i\}$ is an orthonormal set; therefore, the best approximation to x in terms of $\varphi_1, \ldots, \varphi_N$ is furnished by $\sum_{k=1}^{N} c_k \varphi_k = \sum_{k=1}^{N} \langle x, \varphi_k \rangle \varphi_k$. Consequently, $\left\| x - \sum_{k=1}^{N} c_k \varphi_k \right\|^2 \leq \left\| x - \sum_{k=1}^{N} a_k \varphi_k \right\|^2 < \varepsilon$, where the coefficients $\{c_k\}$ are independent of ε. As we let $\varepsilon \to 0$, we have $x = \sum_{k=1}^{\infty} c_k \varphi_k$ and the set $\{\varphi_k\}$ is therefore an orthonormal basis (or complete orthonormal set).

The proof can be readily modified to show that a proper orthogonal spanning set is an orthogonal basis.

COROLLARY. *If the orthonormal set $\{\varphi_k\}$ is a spanning set for continuous functions, it is complete.*

Proof. Let y be an element of $\mathscr{L}_2^{(c)}(a, b)$; since continuous functions are dense in $\mathscr{L}_2$, then, for any $\varepsilon > 0$, there exists a continuous function $x(t)$ such that $\|y - x\| < \varepsilon$. By assumption there exists a linear combination $\sum_{k=1}^{N} c_k \varphi_k$ such that $\left\| x - \sum_{k=1}^{N} c_k \varphi_k \right\| < \varepsilon$; therefore,

$$\left\| y - \sum_{k=1}^{N} c_k \varphi_k \right\| \leq \|y - x\| + \left\| x - \sum_{k=1}^{N} c_k \varphi_k \right\| = 2\varepsilon;$$

hence $\{\varphi_k\}$ is an orthonormal spanning set for $\mathscr{L}_2^{(c)}(a, b)$ and, by Theorem 1, is complete.

Theorem 2 (*Projection Theorem*).   *Let M be a closed linear manifold in the Hilbert space $\mathscr{A}$ and let $M^\perp$ be the orthogonal complement of M; then each vector x in $\mathscr{A}$ has a unique representation as a sum $x_p + z$, where x_p lies in M and z is in $M^\perp$.*

Proof.   Although the theorem is true for any Hilbert space, we prove it only for a separable space $\mathscr{A}$. In this case M is itself a separable Hilbert space (of finite or infinite dimension) and we can find an orthonormal basis in M. Let this basis be $\{\psi_1, \ldots, \psi_k, \ldots\}$; the explicit expression for x_p is $\sum_k \langle x, \psi_k \rangle \psi_k$, and $z = x - \sum_k \langle x, \psi_k \rangle \psi_k$. We check that these vectors have the required properties. We first observe that the series $\sum_k \langle x, \psi_k \rangle \psi_k$ converges, since $\sum_k |\langle x, \psi_k \rangle|^2$ is finite by Bessel's inequality. Therefore, the vector x_p exists and is an element of M. Furthermore $\langle z, \psi_k \rangle = 0$ for all k; since any element f of M is of the form $\sum_k \alpha_k \psi_k$, $\langle z, f \rangle = \sum_k \alpha_k \langle z, \psi_k \rangle = 0$, and z is indeed a vector in $M^\perp$.

To show the uniqueness of the decomposition, suppose we had also $x = x_p' + z'$ with x_p' in M and z' in $M^\perp$. Then $\langle x_p', \psi_k \rangle = \langle x, \psi_k \rangle$, so that $x_p' = \sum_k \langle x_p', \psi_k \rangle \psi_k = \sum_k \langle x_p, \psi_k \rangle \psi_k = x_p$; hence $x_p' = x_p$ and $z' = z$.

Remarks on Orthonormal and Orthogonal Bases in $\mathscr{L}_2$

We revert to functional notation.

Example 1.   Let $\{\varphi_k(t)\}$ be an orthonormal basis in $\mathscr{L}_2^{(c)}(a, b)$; then, for any $x(t)$ in $\mathscr{L}_2^{(c)}(a, b)$, we have

$$x(t) = \sum_{k=1}^{\infty} c_k \varphi_k(t), \qquad \text{where } c_k = \int_a^b x(t) \bar{\varphi}_k(t) dt.$$

The equality sign in the above expansion means

$$\lim_{n \to \infty} \int_a^b \left| x(t) - \sum_{k=1}^{n} c_k \varphi_k(t) \right|^2 dt = 0.$$

It is clear that $\{\bar{\varphi}_k(t)\}$ is also an orthonormal basis for $\mathscr{L}_2^{(c)}(a, b)$ and

$$x(t) = \sum_{k=1}^{\infty} d_k \bar{\varphi}_k(t), \qquad \text{where } d_k = \int_a^b x(t) \varphi_k(t) dt.$$

Example 2.   If $\{\varphi_k(t)\}$ is an orthonormal basis and $\alpha_1, \ldots, \alpha_k, \ldots$ is a sequence of nonzero constants, the set $\{\psi_k(t) = \alpha_k \varphi_k(t)\}$ is an orthogonal basis. It is easily seen that

$$x(t) = \sum_{k=1}^{\infty} b_k \psi_k(t), \qquad \text{where } b_k = \frac{\int_a^b x(t) \bar{\psi}_k(t) dt}{|\alpha_k|^2}.$$

Example 3. Let $s(t)$ be a continuous, real, positive function in $a < t < b$. In applications to differential equations (see Chapter 4), one frequently encounters sets of functions which are orthogonal with weight $s(t)$, that is, such that

$$\int_a^b s(t)\varphi_k(t)\bar{\varphi}_j(t)dt = \begin{cases} 0, & k \neq j; \\ \neq 0, & k = j. \end{cases}$$

To treat expansions in terms of such functions, it is easiest to introduce a new inner product $\langle x, y \rangle_s = \int_a^b s(t)x(t)\bar{y}(t)dt$ and its corresponding norm $\|x\|_s = \left[\int_a^b s(t)x(t)\bar{x}(t)dt\right]^{1/2}$. With these definitions the space of functions $x(t)$ for which $\|x\|_s < \infty$ is a Hilbert space and our previous results hold. If $\{\varphi_k(t)\}$ is an orthonormal basis, then every $x(t)$ can be expanded in the form

$$x(t) = \sum_{k=1}^{\infty} c_k\varphi_k(t), \qquad c_k = \langle x, \varphi_k \rangle_s = \int_a^b s(t)x(t)\bar{\varphi}_k(t)dt.$$

The meaning of the equality sign is

$$\lim_{n \to \infty} \int_a^b s(t)\left| x(t) - \sum_{k=1}^{n} c_k\varphi_k(t) \right|^2 dt = 0.$$

Example 4. The Legendre polynomials are obtained by using the Gram-Schmidt procedure on the independent spanning set $1, t, t^2, \ldots$ over the interval $-1 \leq t \leq 1$. In lieu of the final normalization one requires instead that each polynomial should take on the value 1 at $t = 1$. Thus the Legendre polynomials form a proper orthogonal spanning set, hence a basis.

Example 5. The following sets are complete orthonormal sets of trigonometric functions.

(a) *In any interval of length 2π:*

$$\left(\frac{1}{2\pi}\right)^{1/2}, \quad \left(\frac{1}{2\pi}\right)^{1/2}e^{it}, \quad \left(\frac{1}{2\pi}\right)^{1/2}e^{-it}, \quad \left(\frac{1}{2\pi}\right)^{1/2}e^{2it}, \quad \left(\frac{1}{2\pi}\right)^{1/2}e^{-2it}, \ldots$$

$$(2.26)$$

(b) *In any interval of length 2π:*

$$\left(\frac{1}{2\pi}\right)^{1/2}, \quad \left(\frac{1}{\pi}\right)^{1/2}\cos t, \quad \left(\frac{1}{\pi}\right)^{1/2}\sin t, \quad \left(\frac{1}{\pi}\right)^{1/2}\cos 2t, \quad \left(\frac{1}{\pi}\right)^{1/2}\sin 2t, \ldots$$

$$(2.27)$$

(c) *In $0 \leq t \leq \pi$:*

$$\left(\frac{1}{\pi}\right)^{1/2}, \quad \left(\frac{2}{\pi}\right)^{1/2}\cos t, \quad \left(\frac{2}{\pi}\right)^{1/2}\cos 2t, \ldots \qquad (2.28)$$

(d) *In $0 \leq t \leq \pi$:*

$$\left(\frac{2}{\pi}\right)^{1/2}\sin t, \quad \left(\frac{2}{\pi}\right)^{1/2}\sin 2t, \ldots \qquad (2.29)$$

(a_1) *In any interval of length* $2L$:

$$\left\{ \left(\frac{1}{2L}\right)^{1/2} e^{ik\pi t/L} \right\}; \qquad k = \dots, -2, -1, 0, 1, 2, \dots. \qquad (2.30)$$

(b_1) *In any interval of length* $2L$:

$$\left(\frac{1}{2L}\right)^{1/2}, \quad \left\{ \left(\frac{1}{L}\right)^{1/2} \cos \frac{k\pi t}{L} \right\}, \quad \left\{ \left(\frac{1}{L}\right)^{1/2} \sin \frac{k\pi t}{L} \right\}; \qquad k = 1, 2, \dots.$$

$$(2.31)$$

(c_1) *In* $0 \leq t \leq L$:

$$\left(\frac{1}{L}\right)^{1/2}, \quad \left\{ \left(\frac{2}{L}\right)^{1/2} \cos \frac{k\pi t}{L} \right\}; \qquad k = 1, 2, \dots. \qquad (2.32)$$

(d_1) *In* $0 \leq t \leq L$:

$$\left\{ \left(\frac{2}{L}\right)^{1/2} \sin \frac{k\pi t}{L} \right\}; \qquad k = 1, 2, \dots. \qquad (2.33)$$

Expansions using the functions in (a_1) or (b_1) are known as *full-range* expansions; using (c_1) or (d_1), *half-range* expansions. To prove orthonormality is a simple exercise in integration. The proof of completeness is a more serious undertaking. Such a proof can be based either on an adaptation of the Weierstrass approximation theorem (see Exercises 2.14 to 2.18), or on the general theorem, 6, in Section 3.3.

EXERCISES

2.11 Introduce the orthonormal basis $\{\varphi_1, \dots, \varphi_n\}$ in E_n. If $x^{(k)} = \sum_{i=1}^{n} \xi_i^{(k)} \varphi_i$ is a Cauchy sequence of elements in E_n, show that $\xi_i^{(k)}$ is a Cauchy sequence of numbers. Setting $\lim_{k \to \infty} \xi_i^{(k)} = \xi_i$, we see that $\lim_{k \to \infty} x^{(k)} = \sum_{i=1}^{n} \xi_i \varphi_i$. This proves that E_n is complete.

2.12 Let $\{\varphi_1, \dots, \varphi_k, \dots\}$ be an orthonormal set over $a \leq t \leq b$. Show that the criteria (b_1), (c_1), (d_1), (e_1) (under characterization of complete orthonormal sets) are correct. (HINT: Use the corollary following Theorem 1.)

2.13 Consider a finite interval $a \leq t \leq b$; show that uniform convergence implies convergence in the mean. For an infinite interval, uniform convergence does *not* imply convergence in the mean [in $0 \leq t \leq \infty$, consider the sequence

$$x_n(t) = \begin{cases} \dfrac{1}{\sqrt{n}}, & 0 \leq t \leq n; \\[2mm] 0, & t > n. \end{cases}$$

This sequence converges uniformly to 0 but does not converge in the mean],

2.14 (a) Show that $\cos^k u$ is a linear combination of $1, \cos u, \ldots, \cos ku$. [HINT: Write $\cos u = (e^{iu} + e^{-iu})/2$ and use the binomial expansion.]

(b) Let $f(u)$ be a complex-valued continuous function on $0 \le u \le \pi$. The change of variables $t = \cos u$ is a one-to-one continuous transformation which maps the interval $0 \le u \le \pi$ onto the interval $-1 \le t \le 1$. The function $g(t) = f(\arccos t)$ is continuous on $-1 \le t \le 1$ and can therefore be uniformly approximated by polynomials in t (Weierstrass theorem). Hence $f(u)$ can be uniformly approximated by polynomials in $\cos u$ over the interval $0 \le u \le \pi$. Using the result in **(a)**, there exist N and $c_0, c_1, \ldots, c_N$ such that

$$|f(u) - (c_0 + c_1 \cos u + \cdots + c_N \cos Nu)| < \varepsilon, \qquad 0 \le u \le \pi.$$

Therefore,

$$\left\| f(u) - \sum_{k=0}^{N} c_k \cos ku \right\| = \left[\int_0^\pi \left| f(u) - \sum_{k=0}^{N} c_k \cos ku \right|^2 du \right]^{1/2} \le \varepsilon \pi^{1/2};$$

thus, the set $(1/\pi)^{1/2}, (2/\pi)^{1/2} \cos u, (2/\pi)^{1/2} \cos 2u, \ldots$ is an orthonormal spanning set for continuous functions on $0 \le u \le \pi$. By the corollary following Theorem 1, the set is complete over $(0, \pi)$.

2.15 (a) As in Exercise 2.14(a), show that $\sin^k u$ is a linear combination of 1, $\sin u, \cos u, \ldots, \sin ku, \cos ku$. Observe that the cosine contributions drop out when k is odd, whereas the sine contributions drop out when k is even.

(b) Let $f(x, y)$ be a complex-valued continuous function defined on the circle $x^2 + y^2 \le 1$. By the extension of the Weierstrass theorem, $f(x, y)$ can be uniformly approximated by polynomials (that is, linear combinations of $x^k y^m$). Introducing polar coordinates $x = \rho \cos \theta$, $y = \rho \sin \theta$, we see that the arbitrary continuous function $f(1, \theta)$ can be uniformly approximated by linear combinations of $\cos^k \theta \sin^m \theta$ on $0 \le \theta \le 2\pi$. Using Exercises 2.14(a) and 2.15(a), and the standard formulas for the sine and cosine of sums of angles, it follows that $f(1, \theta)$ can be uniformly approximated over $0 \le \theta \le 2\pi$ by finite linear combinations of the orthonormal set in Example 5(b) (immediately preceding these exercises). By an argument similar to the one used at the end of Exercise 2.14(b), we show that the set

$$\left(\frac{1}{2\pi}\right)^{1/2}, \left(\frac{1}{\pi}\right)^{1/2} \cos \theta, \left(\frac{1}{\pi}\right)^{1/2} \sin \theta, \ldots$$

is a complete orthonormal set over $0 \le \theta \le 2\pi$. Since all the functions have period 2π, the set (2.27) is a complete orthonormal set over any 2π interval.

2.16 Show that the set (2.26) is complete. (This is quite easy using the result of Exercise 2.15.)

2.17 The set (2.27) has been shown to be complete over any 2π interval, for instance, over $-\pi \le t \le \pi$. Therefore, if $f(t)$ is in $\mathscr{L}_2^{(c)}(-\pi, \pi)$, we have in the sense of convergence in the mean

$$f(t) = a_0 \left(\frac{1}{2\pi}\right)^{1/2} + \left(\frac{1}{\pi}\right)^{1/2} \sum_{k=1}^{\infty} (a_k \cos kt + b_k \sin kt),$$

where

$$a_0 = \left(\frac{1}{2\pi}\right)^{1/2} \int_{-\pi}^{\pi} f(t)dt; \ a_k = \left(\frac{1}{\pi}\right)^{1/2} \int_{-\pi}^{\pi} f(t) \cos kt \, dt;$$

$$b_k = \left(\frac{1}{\pi}\right)^{1/2} \int_{-\pi}^{\pi} f(t) \sin kt \, dt.$$

(a) Let $f(t)$ be an odd function; that is, $f(-t) = -f(t)$. Show that $a_0, a_1, \dots$ all vanish. Since $f(t)$ is arbitrary in $(0, \pi)$ we have shown that the set (2.29) is a complete orthonormal set over $(0, \pi)$.

(b) Let $f(t)$ be an even function; that is, $f(-t) = f(t)$. The coefficients $b_1, b_2, \dots$ all vanish. Since $f(t)$ is arbitrary in $(0, \pi)$ we have shown that the set (2.28) is a complete orthonormal set over $(0, \pi)$. This was proved in a different manner in Exercise 2.14.

(c) Show that (2.26) is complete on the indicated interval.

2.18 (a) Let $\{\varphi_n(t)\}$ be an orthonormal set on $-1 \le t \le 1$. Show that

$$\left(\frac{2}{b-a}\right)^{1/2} \varphi_n \left[\frac{2}{b-a}\left(t - \frac{b+a}{2}\right)\right]$$

is an orthonormal set on $a \le t \le b$.

(b) Using (a) and Exercise 2.17, show that the sets (2.30), (2.31), (2.32), and (2.33) are complete over the indicated intervals.

2.19 Suppose $\{\varphi_k\}$ is an orthonormal spanning set for some set of functions dense in $\mathscr{L}_2$. Show that $\{\varphi_k\}$ is a complete orthonormal set.

2.20 Let $\{\varphi_k\}$ be a complete orthonormal set over $a \le t \le b$. Let $f(t)$ and $g(t)$ belong to $\mathscr{L}_2^{(c)}(a, b)$ and let their Fourier coefficients be denoted by $\{c_k\}$ and $\{d_k\}$, respectively. Show that $\int_a^b f\bar{g} \, dt = \sum_{k=1}^{\infty} c_k \bar{d}_k$.

2.21 Let $\mathscr{A}$ be a Hilbert space. The sequence $\{x_n\}$ is said to *converge weakly* to x if, for every h, $\langle x_n, h \rangle \to \langle x, h \rangle$. If $x_n \to x$, it was shown that x_n must converge weakly to x. The converse is true for E_n but not for $\mathscr{L}_2$.

Consider $\mathscr{L}_2^{(c)}(0, \pi)$ and let $x_n(t) = (2/\pi)^{1/2} \sin nt$; then, by the Riemann-Lebesgue lemma, $\langle x_n, h \rangle \to 0$ for every h; hence x_n converges weakly to 0, yet x_n does not converge.

Show that if x_n converges weakly to x, and $\|x_n\| \to \|x\|$, then x_n converges to x.

2.22 Consider the space $\mathscr{L}_2^{(c)}(0, \infty)$, which consists of functions $x(t)$ for which $\int_0^\infty |x|^2 \, dt$ exists and is finite. Consequently, $\lim_{b \to \infty} \int_b^\infty |x|^2 \, dt = 0$; surprisingly enough this does not imply that $\lim_{t \to \infty} x(t) = 0$, as is illustrated by the function, belonging to $\mathscr{L}_2^{(c)}(0, \infty)$,

$$x(t) = \begin{cases} 1, & k \le t \le k + \left(\dfrac{1}{k+1}\right)^2 \\ & \\ 0, & \text{otherwise.} \end{cases} \qquad k = 0, 1, 2, \ldots;$$

To show that this space is separable we must exhibit a countable spanning set. Consider the subset S of $\mathscr{L}_2^{(c)}(0, \infty)$ consisting of functions which vanish identically for sufficiently large t. This set is dense in $\mathscr{L}_2^{(c)}(0, \infty)$; indeed if $x(t)$ is in $\mathscr{L}_2^{(c)}(0, \infty)$, define

$$x_k(t) = \begin{cases} x(t), & 0 \le t \le k; \\ 0, & t > k. \end{cases}$$

It is clear that x_k is in S and that $\lim_{k \to \infty} \|x_k - x\| = 0$. Hence the set S is dense in $\mathscr{L}_2^{(c)}(0, \infty)$. The reader can now prove that the countable set

$$t_k^m = \begin{cases} t^m, & 0 \le t \le k; \\ 0, & t > k, \end{cases}$$

with $m = 0, 1, 2, \ldots, k = 1, 2, \ldots$, is a spanning set for $\mathscr{L}_2^{(c)}(0, \infty)$.

2.23 Expand $|t|$ in a series of Legendre polynomials in $-1 \le t \le 1$. Why is it impossible to rearrange this series in a power series?

2.24 Show that in $\mathscr{L}_2$ there exist bounded sets which are not compact (a set S is bounded if there exists a constant C such that $\|x\| < C$ for all x in S).

2.25. In $0 \le t \le 1$, consider the sequence $x_n(t) = n^\alpha t e^{-nt}$, where α is a fixed positive number.

    (a) Show that, in the sense of pointwise convergence, $x_n(t) \to 0$.

    (b) Show that, if $\alpha < 1$, the convergence to 0 is uniform in $0 \le t \le 1$. If $\alpha \ge 1$, the convergence is not uniform.

(c) By performing the required integration show that, for $\alpha < 2$,

$$\lim_{n \to \infty} \int_0^1 x_n(t) dt = 0.$$

(d) For what values of α does $x_n(t)$ converge to 0 in the mean (over $0 \le t \le 1$)?

(e) Show that if $0 < \alpha < 2$, $n^\alpha t e^{-nt} < 1/t^{\alpha-1}$ for $t > 0$ and all positive integers n. [HINT: Take the log of both sides and use the inequality $\alpha(\log u) - u < 0$.] Prove that the results in (c) can then be obtained from the Lebesgue convergence theorem.

2.5   FUNCTIONALS

We consider complex-valued functionals defined on a subset S of a Hilbert space $\mathscr{A}$.

DEFINITION.   If to each x in S there is defined a complex number $T[x]$, T is said to be a *functional* on S.

The numbers $T[x]$ may, of course, be different for different x, but to each x there corresponds only one complex number $T[x]$. For emphasis we sometimes say that T is single-valued, although this is an integral part of the definition.

A functional is *bounded* on S if there exists a constant c such that, *for all x in S, $|T[x]| \le c\|x\|$*. The smallest constant c, for which this inequality holds for all x in S, is known as the *norm* of T and is written $\|T\|$.

What is meant by continuity of T at the point x in S? Whenever y is in S and near x, Ty should be close to Tx. Precisely: To each $\varepsilon > 0$ there must exist $\delta > 0$ such that $|Tx - Ty| < \varepsilon$ whenever $\|x - y\| < \delta$. The definition of continuity given below is based on sequences but can be shown to be equivalent to the one above. A functional is *continuous* at the point x (in S) if, whenever $\{x_n\}$ is a sequence in S with limit x, then $T[x_n] \to T[x]$. If a functional is continuous at every point of S, it is said to be continuous on S. If the set S is fixed in a particular discussion, reference to it may be omitted.

A functional is *linear* if

$$T[x_1 + x_2] = T[x_1] + T[x_2];$$

$$T[\alpha x] = \alpha T[x].$$

It follows that $T\left[\sum_{i=1}^{k} \alpha_i x_i\right] = \sum_{i=1}^{k} \alpha_i T[x_i]$ for any *finite* k, and $T[0] = 0$.

To exploit these properties, the domain of definition of a linear functional is chosen to be a linear manifold. This linear manifold will be labeled D_T, to remind us that it is the domain of T. *We shall deal only with linear functionals defined on linear manifolds.*

EXAMPLE $T(x+y) = \|x+y\| \le \|x\| + \|y\|$

The functional $T[x] = \|x\|$ is *not* linear; the functional $T[x] = \langle x, f \rangle + \alpha$, where α is a nonzero complex number and f is a fixed vector, is *not* linear; the functional $T[x] = \langle x, f \rangle$ is linear; the functional $T[x] = \langle f, x \rangle$ is *not* linear, since $T[\alpha x] = \bar{\alpha} T[x]$ (this last functional is known as an *antilinear functional*).

Theorem. *If a linear functional is continuous at $x = 0$ it is continuous on its entire domain of definition D_T.*

Proof. Let $\{x_n\}$ be a sequence of elements of D_T, with $\lim_{n \to \infty} x_n = x$, x in D_T. We are to show $T[x_n] \to [Tx]$ or $T[x] - T[x_n] \to 0$. By the linearity of T, we have $T[x] - T[x_n] = T[x - x_n]$; the sequence $y_n = x - x_n$ is in D_T and approaches 0, and since T is continuous at the origin, $T[y_n] \to 0$ and $T[x_n] \to T[x]$, as desired.

Theorem. *Boundedness and continuity are equivalent for linear functionals.*

Proof. Suppose first that T is bounded; then $|T[x_n] - T[x]| = |T[x_n - x]| \le \|T\| \, \|x_n - x\|$; hence as $x_n \to x$, $T[x_n] \to T[x]$, and T is therefore continuous. Suppose next that T is continuous; we must show it is bounded. If T is not bounded, a sequence x_n must exist such that $|T[x_n]| \ge n\|x_n\|$; hence the sequence $y_n = x_n/n\|x_n\|$ (which approaches 0) has the property $|T[y_n]| = (1/n\|x_n\|)|T[x_n]| \ge 1$, which violates the continuity assumption.

The simplest example of a continuous linear functional is the inner product with respect to a fixed element. If f is an element of $\mathscr{A}$, then $\langle x, f \rangle$ is a continuous linear functional on $\mathscr{A}$. The following theorem due to F. Riesz shows that every continuous linear functional is of the form $\langle x, f \rangle$.

Theorem (*Riesz Representation Theorem*). *Each continuous linear functional $T[x]$ on the Hilbert space $\mathscr{A}$ can be expressed in the form $\langle x, f \rangle$, where f is an element of $\mathscr{A}$ unambiguously determined from T.*

Proof. Consider the set N of vectors x for which $T[x] = 0$. It can be verified that N is a closed linear manifold. If N coincides with $\mathscr{A}$, we can choose $f = 0$. If N is a proper subset of $\mathscr{A}$, there exists a nonzero element in $N^{\perp}$; by normalization we can choose an element f_0 in $N^{\perp}$ such that $\|f_0\| = 1$. We claim that the required vector f is $\bar{T}[f_0]f_0$. Consider $y = T[x]f_0 - xT[f_0]$ as x runs through $\mathscr{A}$. Clearly $T[y] = 0$; therefore y is in N and

$$\langle T[x]f_0 - xT[f_0], f_0 \rangle = 0;$$

hence

$$T[x] - T[f_0]\langle x, f_0 \rangle = 0$$

and

$$T[x] = T[f_0]\langle x, f_0 \rangle = \langle x, \bar{T}[f_0]f_0 \rangle,$$

as predicted. To prove uniqueness of the vector f, suppose that $\langle x, f \rangle = \langle x, g \rangle$ for all x; then $\langle x, f - g \rangle = 0$ for all x; hence choosing $x = f - g$, $\|f - g\|^2 = 0$ and $f = g$.

Extension of Bounded Linear Functionals

Let T be a bounded linear functional defined on the linear manifold D_T in the Hilbert space $\mathscr{A}$. We want to define the functional on all elements of $\mathscr{A}$ (without changing its values on D_T) so that the functional remains linear and bounded. If D_T is closed, the extension is easily achieved; since D_T is itself a Hilbert space, the Riesz theorem guarantees the existence of a unique element f in D_T such that $T[x] = \langle x, f \rangle$. We merely use this last formula to define $T[x]$ for all x in $\mathscr{A}$; this procedure is equivalent to defining $T[x] = 0$ for x in $(D_T)^\perp$ and using linearity to define $T[x]$ for all x in $\mathscr{A}$. If D_T is not closed (a possibility which cannot arise in $E_n^{(c)}$) we first extend T to $\bar{D}_T$ by "continuity." Let $\{x_n\}$ be a sequence of vectors in D_T whose limit x is in $\bar{D}_T$ but not in D_T. The sequence of numbers $T[x_n]$ is a Cauchy sequence, since $|T[x_m] - T[x_n]| \le \|T\| \, \|x_m - x_n\|$; $T[x_n]$ must therefore converge to some complex number α. If $\{y_n\}$ is another sequence of vectors in D_T with the same limit x, then $x_n - y_n \to 0$ and $T[x_n] - T[y_n] \to 0$; hence $T[y_n] \to \alpha$. It is therefore natural to define $T[x]$ to be α; one observes without difficulty that $T[x]$ is a linear bounded functional defined on $\bar{D}_T$. By the method previously described, T can be extended to the whole of $\mathscr{A}$. It should be noted that $\|T\|$ is unchanged in this extension procedure.

The point of the above discussion is that, when dealing with bounded linear functionals, we may as well assume that they are defined on the whole of the Hilbert space $\mathscr{A}$. We now prove the following important theorem:

Theorem. *Every linear functional on E_n is bounded.*

Proof. It suffices to show that $\lim_{k \to 0} T[x^{(k)}] = 0$ for every sequence $x^{(k)}$ such that $\lim_{k \to \infty} x^{(k)} = 0$. Introduce the orthonormal basis $\{\varphi_1, \ldots, \varphi_n\}$; then $x^{(k)} = \sum_{i=1}^{n} \xi_i^{(k)} \varphi_i$, where $\xi_i^{(k)} = \langle x^{(k)}, \varphi_i \rangle$. Appealing to the continuity of the inner product, we infer from $x^{(k)} \to 0$ that $\xi_i^{(k)} \to 0$. Hence

$$\lim_{k \to \infty} T[x^{(k)}] = \lim_{k \to \infty} \sum_{i=1}^{n} \xi_i^{(k)} T[\varphi_i] = 0,$$

which completes the proof.

The argument in this proof fails for an infinite-dimensional space. If $\{\varphi_1, \ldots, \varphi_n, \ldots\}$ is an orthonormal basis for $\mathscr{L}_2$, we still have $x = \sum_{i=1}^{\infty} \xi_i \varphi_i$

with $\xi_i = \langle x, \varphi_i \rangle$ and $T[x] = T\left[\sum\limits_{i=1}^{\infty} \xi_i \varphi_i\right]$, but a linearity argument is not

sufficient to enable us to write this last quantity as $\sum\limits_{i=1}^{\infty} \xi_i T[\varphi_i]$.

There exist unbounded linear functionals in $\mathscr{L}_2$. Although it is possible to give examples of such functionals defined on all of $\mathscr{L}_2$, the ones that occur in applications are usually defined only on a dense subset of $\mathscr{L}_2$. Consider, for instance, the linear functional $T[x] = x(0)$, which is well defined for all functions continuous at $t = 0$ and belonging to $\mathscr{L}_2^{(c)}(-\infty, \infty)$. This functional played an important role in the study of distributions in Chapter 1. According to the definition of continuity used in $\mathscr{L}_2$, this functional is discontinuous. Indeed, let

$$x_n(t) = \begin{cases} n, & -\dfrac{1}{n} \leq t \leq \dfrac{1}{n}; \\[2mm] 0, & \text{otherwise.} \end{cases}$$

Then $\|x_n\| = \sqrt{2n}$, and $x_n(0) = n$, but there exists no constant c such that $|x_n(0)| \leq c\|x_n\|$ for every n. The functional is therefore unbounded, that is, discontinuous.

Representation of Linear Functionals on $E_n^{(c)}$. Dual Bases

Let $\{e_1, \ldots, e_n\}$ be a fixed, arbitrary basis in $E_n^{(c)}$. We claim that the effect of T on any vector x is completely described by the n complex numbers $T[e_1], \ldots, T[e_n]$; indeed $x = \sum\limits_{i=1}^{n} \xi_i e_i$ and $T[x] = T\left[\sum\limits_{i=1}^{n} \xi_i e_i\right] = \sum\limits_{i=1}^{n} \xi_i T[e_i]$. Conversely, if n complex numbers $\alpha_1, \ldots, \alpha_n$ are given, there exists exactly one linear functional T satisfying $T[e_i] = \alpha_i$, $i = 1, \ldots, n$.

Many computations with linear functionals and linear transformations will be facilitated by introducing the so-called *dual or reciprocal* basis $\{e_1^*, \ldots, e_n^*\}$, which has the property

$$\langle e_i, e_j^* \rangle = \begin{cases} 0, & i \neq j; \\ 1, & i = j. \end{cases}$$

We now prove that the dual basis exists and is unambiguously determined from $\{e_1, \ldots, e_n\}$. From the preceding discussion we know there exists exactly one linear functional $T_1[x]$ satisfying $T_1[e_1] = 1, T_1[e_2] = 0, \ldots, T_1[e_n] = 0$. By the Riesz theorem there is therefore a unique vector e_1^* such that $T_1[x] = \langle x, e_1^* \rangle$, and consequently $\langle e_1, e_1^* \rangle = 1, \langle e_2, e_1^* \rangle = 0, \ldots, \langle e_n, e_1^* \rangle = 0$, as desired. Similarly, the vectors $e_2^*, \ldots, e_n^*$ exist, and each is uniquely determined and has the required properties.

Resume of Properties of Linear Functionals

$E_n^{(c)}$	$\mathscr{L}_2^{(c)}(a, b)$
Boundedness = continuity. Every functional is bounded.	Boundedness = continuity. There are unbounded functionals [example, $T[x] = x(0)$].
If $e_1, \ldots, e_n$ is a basis and $x = \sum_{i=1}^{n} \xi_i e_i$ then $T[x] = \sum_{i=1}^{n} \xi_i T[e_i]$.	If $e_1, \ldots, e_n, \ldots$ is a basis, $x = \sum_{i=1}^{\infty} \xi_i e_i$ and if T is *bounded*, then $$T[x] = \sum_{i=1}^{\infty} \xi_i T[e_i].$$
Every functional $T[x]$ is of the form $\langle x, f \rangle$, where f is unambiguously determined from T.	Every bounded functional $T[x]$ is of the form $\langle x, f \rangle$, where f is unambiguously determined from T; that is, every bounded functional is of the form $\int_a^b x(t) \bar{f}(t) dt$.

2.6 TRANSFORMATIONS

A transformation or operator A from the Hilbert space $\mathscr{A}$ into itself is a correspondence which assigns to each element x in $\mathscr{A}$ a well-defined element y (written Ax) also belonging to $\mathscr{A}$. A slightly more general definition is obtained if we allow A to be defined only on a subset S of $\mathscr{A}$. To emphasize that this subset is the domain of the operator A, we use the symbol D_A instead of S. The set of all images (that is, the set of all vectors of the form Ax for some x in D_A) is labeled R_A and is known as the *range* of A. The set N_A of all vectors x in D_A for which $Ax = 0$ is called the *null space* of A. Two operators A and B are *equal*, $A = B$, if $D_A = D_B$ and $Ax = Bx$ for all x in the common domain.

If A and B are operators with domains D_A and D_B, respectively, we define new operators as follows:

1. $C = \alpha A$: $Cx = \alpha(Ax)$, where α is a given complex number. The domain of C is the same as that of A.

2. $D = A + B$: $Dx = Ax + Bx$. The operator D is defined on a domain which is the intersection of the domains of A and B. We observe that $A + B = B + A$.

3. $E = AB$: $Ex = A(Bx)$. The operator E is defined only for those elements x for which Bx is in D_A. In general, AB and BA are different; if $AB = BA$, the operators are said to *commute*.

If A and B are defined on the whole of $\mathscr{A}$, so are C, D, and E.

The transformation A is *one-to-one* if the image vector unambiguously determines the original vector; thus A is one-to-one if and only if $Af = Ag$ implies $f = g$.

If A is one-to-one with domain D_A and range R_A, we define the inverse operator A^{-1} as follows:

$$A^{-1}f = g \text{ if and only if } Ag = f.$$

Since this last equation has one and only one solution for f in R_A, our definition makes sense and $D_{A^{-1}} = R_A$, $R_{A^{-1}} = D_A$. A one-to-one transformation is therefore invertible.

A transformation is *linear* if

$$A(x_1 + x_2) = Ax_1 + Ax_2;$$

$$A(\alpha x) = \alpha Ax.$$

The domain of definition of a linear transformation will be chosen to be a linear manifold, so as to take advantage of the linearity properties of the transformation. *We shall deal solely with linear transformations defined on linear manifolds.* For any such transformation, $A(0) = 0$ and R_A and N_A are linear manifolds.

A transformation A is bounded on its domain if, for all x in D_A, there exists a constant c such that $\|Ax\| \le c\|x\|$. The smallest number c which satisfies this inequality simultaneously for all x in D_A is known as the norm of A and is written $\|A\|$. We see with no difficulty that

$$\|A\| = \text{l.u.b.}_{x \ne 0} \frac{\|Ax\|}{\|x\|}.$$

Even if A is bounded there may not exist an element $x \ne 0$ for which $\|Ax\| = \|A\|\,\|x\|$, but there exist nonzero elements for which $\|Ax\|$ is as close to $\|A\|\,\|x\|$ as we please (see Example 2 in this section).

A transformation A is *continuous at* x in D_A if, whenever $\{x_n\}$ is a sequence in D_A with limit x, then $Ax_n \to Ax$. A transformation is continuous on D_A if it is continuous at every point of D_A. If D_A is fixed in a particular discussion, we may omit reference to the domain and speak of a continuous transformation.

Theorem. *If a linear transformation is continuous at the single point $x = 0$, it is continuous on all of D_A.*

Theorem. *A linear transformation is continuous if and only if it is bounded.*

The proofs of these theorems are omitted because they follow almost word for word the lines of the similar theorems for linear functionals.

In E_n all linear transformations are bounded! Indeed, let A be a linear transformation on E_n with range in E_n. It is enough to show that, if $\lim_{k \to \infty} x^{(k)} = 0$, then $\lim_{k \to \infty} Ax^{(k)} = 0$. Let $\{\varphi_1, \ldots, \varphi_n\}$ be an orthonormal basis in E_n. In terms of this basis we can write $x^{(k)} = \sum_{i=1}^{n} \xi_i^{(k)}\varphi_i$, with $\xi_i^{(k)} = \langle x^{(k)}, \varphi_i \rangle$; from the continuity of the inner product, we obtain $\lim_{k \to \infty} \xi_i^{(k)} = 0$. Now $Ax^{(k)} = A\left(\sum_{i=1}^{n} \xi_i^{(k)} \varphi_i\right) = \sum_{i=1}^{n} \xi_i^{(k)} A\varphi_i$; hence $\lim_{k \to \infty} Ax^{(k)} = 0$, as was to be shown.

We now return to linear operators on a general Hilbert space $\mathscr{A}$.

DEFINITION. A linear operator B is called an *extension* of the linear operator A if

(a) The domain of B is at least as large as the domain of A (that is, $D_B \supset D_A$).

(b) $Bx = Ax$ for all x in D_A.

If B is an extension of A, we write $A \subset B$ or $B \supset A$. If B is an extension of A, A is called a *restriction* of B.

Construction of Extensions

1. If A is defined on a closed linear manifold D_A, we can extend A to the whole of $\mathscr{A}$ by merely defining the new operator to be 0 on $(D_A)^\perp$. If x is a vector in $\mathscr{A}$, it can be decomposed in a unique manner as the sum $x_p + z$, where x_p is in D_A and z is in $(D_A)^\perp$. We then have $Bx = Bx_p + Bz = Bx_p = Ax_p$. The operator B is clearly linear on $\mathscr{A}$, and $Bx = Ax$ whenever x is in D_A; moreover, $\|B\| = \|A\|$.

2. If A is a *bounded* linear transformation defined on a linear manifold D_A which is not closed, we can extend to $\bar{D}_A$ by "continuity." We now elaborate on this procedure. Let $\{x_n\}$ be a sequence of points in D_A converging to x in $\bar{D}_A$; since $\|A(x_n - x_m)\| \leq \|A\| \|x_n - x_m\|$, Ax_m is a Cauchy sequence and must therefore have a limit, say f, in $\mathscr{A}$. If $\{y_n\}$ is any other sequence in D_A converging to x, $\{y_n - x_n\}$ is in D_A and $(y_n - x_n) \to 0$; since A is continuous at 0, $A(y_n - x_n) \to 0$, and $\lim_{n \to \infty} Ay_n = \lim_{n \to \infty} Ax_n = f$. Thus every sequence $\{x_n\}$ in D_A which approaches x yields the same limiting value f for Ax_n. We therefore include x in the domain of A and define Ax to be f. In this way the domain of definition of A is easily extended to $\bar{D}_A$; the new operator is still linear and its norm is unchanged. By the construction in (1) the operator can be extended from the closed linear manifold $\bar{D}_A$ to the whole of $\mathscr{A}$ (again without altering the norm of the operator). *In the light of the above discussion, bounded linear operators can always be regarded as defined on the whole space $\mathscr{A}$.*

The situation is more difficult for unbounded linear operators, as can be gauged by a study of their behavior near $x = 0$. Let $\{x_n\}$ be a sequence of points in D_A for which $\lim_{n \to \infty} x_n = 0$; such a sequence will be called a *null sequence in D_A*. Three possibilities arise: $Ax_n \to 0$, or $Ax_n \to f$ $(f \neq 0)$, or Ax_n has no limit as $n \to \infty$. If the first case occurs for *all* null sequences in D_A, then A is continuous at $x = 0$, hence on all of D_A. If there exists a null sequence in D_A for which $Ax_n \to f \neq 0$, we have an extremely unpleasant operator on our hands; indeed the sequence αx_n is a null sequence in D_A for any complex α and $A(\alpha x_n) \to \alpha f$; hence there exist null sequences $\{y_n\}$ in D_A which yield *any* preassigned multiple of f as a limiting value for Ay_n! Fortunately, such "highly discontinuous" operators do not occur in the study of differential or integral equations. We shall encounter only "mildly discontinuous" operators. Such an operator has the property that for some null sequences $\{x_n\}$ in D_A, $Ax_n \to 0$, whereas for other null sequences in D_A, Ax_n has no limit; but there will *not* exist a null sequence in D_A for which $Ax_n \to f \neq 0$.

DEFINITION. A linear operator is *closable* if for every null sequence $\{x_n\}$ in D_A either $Ax_n \to 0$ or else Ax_n has no limit.†

Suppose now that A is closable and $\{x_n\}$ is a sequence in D_A which approaches x (which may or may not be in D_A), and suppose further that $Ax_n \to f$. Consider any other sequence $\{y_n\}$ in D_A whose limit is x; then $\{x_n - y_n\}$ is a null sequence in D_A; since A is closable, either $A(x_n - y_n)$ approaches 0 or has no limit, therefore Ay_n either approaches f or has no limit. This last property is true for any sequence which is in D_A and approaches x; only sheer obstinacy can refrain us from including x in D_A and defining $Ax = f$. If we do this for all convergent sequences $\{x_n\}$ in D_A for which $\{Ax_n\}$ has a limit, we obtain an extension of A called the *closure* of A and denoted by $\bar{A}$. We observe that $\bar{A}$ is a linear operator.

DEFINITION. Let A be a linear operator defined on a linear manifold D_A. We say that A is *closed* if it has the following property: Whenever $\{x_n\}$ is in D_A and $x_n \to x$ and $Ax_n \to f$, then x is in D_A and $Ax = f$.

REMARKS. 1. If A is closable, $\bar{A}$ is a closed operator.
2. The distinction between closed and continuous transformations is the following: If A is continuous, $x_n \to x$ implies $Ax_n \to Ax$, whereas if A is merely closed all we know is that different sequences approaching x cannot yield different limiting values for the transformation. It is easily seen that a continuous operator on a closed domain is necessarily a closed operator. In particular, a continuous operator defined on the whole of $\mathcal{A}$ is closed. On the other hand, closed operators are not necessarily continuous; in Example 7 below, we introduce the differentiation operator which is the prototype of closed, unbounded operators. We quote a famous theorem which plays a central role in the development of the theory of operators: *A closed operator on a closed domain is continuous.* Therefore closed, unbounded, operators cannot be defined on the whole space $\mathcal{A}$; instead we encounter closed, unbounded,

---

† If A is an arbitrary linear operator defined on a linear manifold D_A, there surely exist some null sequences $\{x_n\}$ for which $Ax_n \to 0$. In fact, if $x \neq 0$ is in D_A and $\{\alpha_n\}$ is a sequence of complex numbers such that $\lim_{n \to \infty} \alpha_n = 0$, the sequence $\{\alpha_n x\}$ is a null sequence in D_A for which $\lim_{n \to \infty} A(\alpha_n x) = 0$.

operators which are defined over domains D_A which are dense in $\mathscr{A}$ (that is, such that $\bar{D}_A = \mathscr{A}$).

3. In view of the fact discussed above, that neither the range nor the domain of a closed operator is necessarily closed, the use of the word closed in "closed operator" requires explanation. Consider the space of ordered pairs (x,y), where x and y are in $\mathscr{A}$. We can define a norm on this new space in many ways; probably the simplest is to set $\|(x, y)\| = \|x\| + \|y\|$, where $\|x\|$ and $\|y\|$ are the ordinary norms in $\mathscr{A}$. The set of ordered pairs of the form (x, Ax), where x is in D_A, is known as the *graph* of A. (See Section 2.1 for the analogous definition for a real function of a real variable.) Now it can be shown that A is a closed operator if and only if the set of ordered pairs (x, Ax) is closed (in the space of ordered pairs). In other words, A is a closed operator if and only if its graph is closed.

4. *The null space of a closed operator is a closed set.* If $\{x_n\}$ is in N_A and $x_n \to x$, $Ax_n = 0$; hence $Ax_n \to 0$. Since A is closed, x must be in D_A and $Ax = 0$. Therefore x is in N_A.

EXAMPLES OF LINEAR TRANSFORMATIONS ON $\mathscr{L}_2$

Example 1. (a) The zero transformation $0: 0x = 0$ for every x. This transformation is clearly bounded and $\|0\| = 0$.

(b) The identity transformation: $Ix = x$ for every x. The transformation is bounded and $\|I\| = 1$.

Example 2. On $\mathscr{L}_2^{(c)}(0, 1)$, consider the transformation corresponding to multiplication by the independent variable t. Thus $y(t) = Ax = tx(t)$. The transformation is defined for all elements of $\mathscr{L}_2^{(c)}(0, 1)$ and is linear. We now show that it is bounded. We have

$$\|Ax\|^2 = \int_0^1 t^2 |x|^2 \, dt \le \int_0^1 |x|^2 \, dt = \|x\|^2;$$

therefore, $\|A\| \le 1$. Let $x(t)$ be 0 except on a small interval $1 - \varepsilon \le t \le 1$, where $x(t) = 1$. Then $\|x\|^2 = \int_{1-\varepsilon}^1 1 \, dt = \varepsilon$, and $\|Ax\|^2 = \int_{1-\varepsilon}^1 t^2 \, dt = \varepsilon[1 - \varepsilon + (\varepsilon^2/3)]$. Therefore for this particular $x(t)$, $\|Ax\|/\|x\| = \sqrt{1 - \varepsilon + (\varepsilon^2/3)}$. By choosing ε sufficiently small, this ratio of norms can be made arbitrarily close to 1; therefore, $\|A\|$ cannot be smaller than 1. Taken in conjunction with the previous inequality, this yields $\|A\| = 1$. We observe that although $\|A\| = 1$, there is no vector $x \neq 0$ for which $\|Ax\| = \|x\|$.

Example 3. On $\mathscr{L}_2^{(c)}(0, 1)$ consider the transformation defined by $y(t) = Ax = f_0(t)x(t)$, where $f_0(t)$ is a fixed function (not necessarily in $\mathscr{L}_2$).

(a) If $f_0(t)$ is continuous in $0 \le t \le 1$, then A is defined as a linear bounded operator over the whole of $\mathscr{L}_2$. One can show that

$$\|A\| = \max_{0 \le t \le 1} |f_0(t)|.$$

$$\|x\| = \langle x, x \rangle^{\frac{1}{2}} = \left[\int_a^b |x(t)|^2 \, dt \right]^{\frac{1}{2}}$$

(b) If $f_0(t)$ becomes infinite at some point $0 \le t \le 1$, A will be a linear, unbounded, operator, and the domain of definition will not be the whole of $\mathcal{L}_2$. For instance, if $f_0(t) = 1/t$, then $f_0(t)x(t)$ is in $\mathcal{L}_2$ only if $x(t)$ vanishes sufficiently fast at $t = 0$. To show that A is unbounded, consider the function in D_A:

$$x(t) = \begin{cases} 0, & 0 \le t \le \varepsilon; \\ 1, & \varepsilon < t \le 1. \end{cases}$$

For this particular x, we have

$$= \langle x, x \rangle = \int_\varepsilon^1 1^2 dt = (1-\varepsilon)$$

$$\|x\|^2 = 1 - \varepsilon, \qquad \|Ax\|^2 = \int_\varepsilon^1 \frac{1}{t^2}\, dt = -1 + \frac{1}{\varepsilon}.$$

For ε sufficiently small, the ratio $\|Ax\|/\|x\|$ becomes arbitrarily large, so that A is unbounded.

$$\varepsilon \to 0 \quad \sqrt{\frac{(1-\varepsilon)^2}{\varepsilon}}$$

Example 4. In $\mathcal{L}_2^{(c)}(-\infty, \infty)$, consider the translation operator defined by $Ax = x(t + h)$, where h is a fixed real number. The transformation is bounded and $\|A\| = 1$.

Example 5. In $\mathcal{L}_2^{(c)}(0, 1)$, consider the integration operator defined by $y(t) = Ax = \int_0^t x(s)ds$. This operator is defined for all x in $\mathcal{L}_2$ [since this implies that x is integrable over any subinterval of $(0, 1)$]. The operator is linear and we now show that it is bounded. We have

$$|y(t)|^2 = \left| \int_0^t x(s)ds \right|^2 \le \left| \int_0^t 1^2\, ds \right| \left| \int_0^t |x|^2\, ds \right| \le t\|x\|^2.$$

Therefore, $\|y\|^2 = \int_0^1 |y(t)|^2\, dt \le \frac{1}{2}\|x\|^2$ for all x; hence $\|A\| \le (\frac{1}{2})^{1/2}$. The exact expression for $\|A\|$ is $2/\pi$ (see Exercise 2.26).

Example 6. In $\mathcal{L}_2^{(c)}(a, b)$ consider the *integral operator* defined by

$$y(t) = Ax = \int_a^b k(t, \xi)x(\xi)d\xi.$$

Here $k(t, \xi)$ is a given function defined over the square $a \le t,\ \xi \le b$. [The case $a = 0, b = 1$,

$$k(t, \xi) = \begin{cases} 1, & \xi < t; \\ 0, & t < \xi, \end{cases}$$

yields Example 5.] The function $k(t, \xi)$ is known as the *kernel* of the operator. The transformation A is said to be generated by the kernel. We shall show in Chapter 3 that A is bounded whenever $\int_a^b \int_a^b |k^2(t, \xi)|\, dt\, d\xi < \infty$. It is obvious that A is linear.

Example 7. (a) On $\mathscr{L}_2^{(c)}(0, 1)$, consider the differentiation operator defined by $y(t) = Ax = dx/dt$. The operator cannot be defined sensibly for all functions in $\mathscr{L}_2$; we need two properties for $x(t)$ to belong to D_A: (1) $x(t)$ should be differentiable in some sense and, (2) the derivative of $x(t)$ should be in $\mathscr{L}_2^{(c)}(0, 1)$. Property (1) will be interpreted as follows: $x(t)$ should be an indefinite integral of its derivative. This class of functions is known as the class of *absolutely continuous functions*. The class includes continuous functions which are only piecewise differentiable. Consider the operator $A = d/dt$ defined on the domain D_A consisting of absolutely continuous functions whose derivatives are in $\mathscr{L}_2^{(c)}(0, 1)$. This operator is linear. Its range R_A is the whole of $\mathscr{L}_2^{(c)}(0, 1)$. Moreover the operator is closed. Of course, the operator is *not* continuous; every member of the sequence $x_n = \sqrt{2} \sin n\pi t$ has norm 1, yet $\|dx_n/dt\| = n\pi$, so that the differentiation operator is clearly *unbounded*.

(b) One can also arrive at the operator above by the following procedure. First define $A_1 = d/dt$ only for $x(t)$ differentiable everywhere in $(0, 1)$ with the derivative in $\mathscr{L}_2^{(c)}(0, 1)$. Next we observe that A_1 is closable. Let $\{x_n\}$ be a null sequence in D_{A_1} for which $dx_n/dt \to f$; we must show that $f = 0$. For such a sequence and any $u(t)$ we have $\lim_{n\to\infty} \langle u, dx_n/dt \rangle = \langle u, f \rangle$, so the equality must surely hold for any $u(t)$ with a continuous derivative and $u(0) = u(1) = 0$. But for such functions $u(t)$, $\langle u, dx_n/dt \rangle = \int_0^1 u(d\bar{x}_n/dt)dt = -\int_0^1 \bar{x}_n(du/dt)dt = -\langle du/dt, x_n \rangle$, and $\langle u, f \rangle = -\lim_{n\to\infty} \langle du/dt, x_n \rangle = 0$ (since $x_n \to 0$). Hence $\langle u, f \rangle = 0$ for a class of functions $u(t)$ which is easily seen to be dense in $\mathscr{L}_2^{(c)}(0, 1)$; consequently, $f = 0$. The operator A_1 is closable, but it is not closed as it stands. Our sin is one of omission; we have carelessly left out from the domain of the operator some elements which properly belong to it. Let $\{x_n\}$ be a sequence of differentiable functions in D_{A_1} which approaches a continuous function $x(t)$ which is only piecewise-differentiable (e.g., the sequence of partial sums of the Fourier trigonometric series associated with a piecewise differentiable function). We have $x_n(t) \to x(t)$, and $x_n'(t)$ will have a limit; the only reason this limit is not A_1x is that A_1x has not been defined! All we must do is to extend the domain of A_1 so that functions like $x(t)$ have a derivative. This extension is the closure of A_1 and leads to the operator A defined in part (a); $\bar{A}_1 = A$.

Before embarking on the difficult study of linear operators in $\mathscr{L}_2$, we consider the much simpler analysis of linear operators on E_n.

EXERCISES

2.26 Consider Example 5 above. Expand $x(s)$ in the complete orthonormal set $\{\sqrt{2} \cos[(2n - 1)/2]\pi s\}$. Show that $\|y\| \leq (2/\pi)\|x\|$. Exhibit a specific function x for which $\|y\| = (2/\pi)\|x\|$. This proves that $\|A\| = 2/\pi$.

2.27 Consider Example 6; assume that a and b are finite and that $k(t, \xi)$ is a continuous function on the square $a \leq t, \xi \leq b$. Prove that the operator A is bounded and

$$\|A\| \leq \left[\int_a^b \int_a^b |k^2(t, \xi)| \, dt \, d\xi \right]^{1/2}.$$

2.28 In $\mathscr{L}_2^{(c)}(0, 1)$ consider the operator d/dt defined for absolutely continuous functions $x(t)$ such that x and x' are in $\mathscr{L}_2^{(c)}(0, 1)$, and such that $x(0) = 0$. Show that this operator is closed.

2.29 Consider the operator in Exercise 2.28 with the additional restriction on the domain that $x'(0) = 0$. Show that this operator is closable but not closed.

2.30 Let $\mathscr{A}$ be a Hilbert space and M a closed linear manifold in $\mathscr{A}$. Each vector in x can be decomposed in a unique manner as $y + z$, where y is in M and z is in $M^\perp$. Since y is determined from x, we can write

$$y = P_M x,$$

where P_M is an operator known as the *projection operator* on M. The domain of this operator is $\mathscr{A}$ and its range is M. Show that P_M is a linear operator with $\|P_M\| = 1$, and that $P_M^2 = P_M$.

2.7 LINEAR TRANSFORMATIONS ON $E_n^{(c)}$

Introduction

Let A be a linear operator from $E_n^{(c)}$ to $E_n^{(c)}$. We wish to describe the effect of A by a set of numbers. To this end, introduce the fixed but arbitrary basis $B: (e_1, \ldots, e_n)$. Each vector in $E_n^{(c)}$ has a unique representation in this basis; thus $x = \sum_{i=1}^n \xi_i e_i$ and $y = Ax = \sum_{i=1}^n \eta_i e_i$. Our aim is to find the formula which relates the coordinates (η_i) of the image vector y to the coordinates (ξ_i) of the original vector x. It will come as no surprise to the reader that this relation is the linear one: $\eta_i = \sum_{j=1}^n a_{ij} \xi_j$, $i = 1, \ldots, n$. To obtain this traditional formula, where the summation is on the second index, we shall have to introduce the numbers (a_{ij}) in a somewhat peculiar manner in (2.33) below.

The Matrix of a Linear Transformation on $E_n^{(c)}$

Let A be the linear transformation and let $B: (e_1, \ldots, e_n)$ be the fixed basis. Then $Ax = \sum_{i=1}^n \xi_i A e_i$ and A is completely described by the n *vectors*

$Ae_1, \ldots, Ae_n$. Each of these vectors can in turn be written

$$Ae_j = \sum_{i=1}^{n} a_{ij} e_i, \qquad j = 1, \ldots, n. \tag{2.34}$$

The n^2 complex numbers appearing as coefficients in (2.34) completely describe the effect of A. The array of numbers

$$\begin{bmatrix} a_{11} & \cdots & a_{1n} \\ \vdots & & \\ a_{n1} & \cdots & a_{nn} \end{bmatrix}$$

is known as the matrix of A in the basis B. The shorter notation $[A]_B$ or $[a_{ij}]$ will often be used for the matrix. Observe that the first index in a_{ij} gives the row location, whereas the second index indicates the column location. According to (2.34), the matrix $[A]_B$ is obtained by writing the coordinates of the image of e_j in the jth column.

We have claimed that the coordinates of the image vector can be calculated from the coordinates of the original vector through the use of this matrix. We now substantiate this claim; we have

$$x = \sum_{i=1}^{n} \xi_i e_i,$$

$$y = \sum_{i=1}^{n} \eta_i e_i = Ax = A\left(\sum_{j=1}^{n} \xi_j e_j \right) = \sum_{j=1}^{n} \xi_j A e_j = \sum_{j=1}^{n} \xi_j \left(\sum_{i=1}^{n} a_{ij} e_i \right) = \sum_{i=1}^{n} \left(\sum_{j=1}^{n} a_{ij} \xi_j \right) e_i.$$

This leads to the desired relationship

$$\eta_i = \sum_{j=1}^{n} a_{ij} \xi_j.$$

We observe that the matrix $[a_{ij}]$ is used in different ways here and in (2.34). The vector Ae_j is calculated by "multiplying" the jth *column* of the matrix by $(e_1, \ldots, e_n)$ and adding, that is, $Ae_j = a_{1j} e_1 + \cdots + a_{nj} e_n$. To obtain η_i, we "multiply" the ith *row* of the matrix by $(\xi_1, \ldots, \xi_n)$ and add:

$$\eta_i = a_{i1} \xi_1 + \cdots + a_{in} \xi_n.$$

We can state the relationship between a transformation and its matrix as follows:

Relative to a given basis B, each linear transformation A determines a unique matrix $[a_{ij}]$ and, conversely, each matrix generates a unique linear transformation by means of (2.34). If we are dealing with transformations on a real Euclidean space $E_n^{(r)}$, the statements above are still valid but the matrix $[a_{ij}]$ now contains only real elements.

EXAMPLES OF LINEAR TRANSFORMATIONS

Example 1. (a) On $E_n^{(c)}$ consider the null transformation 0: $0x = 0$ for every x. Relative to any basis whatever, the matrix of 0 has all elements equal to zero.

(b) On $E_n^{(c)}$ consider the identity transformation I: $Ix = x$ for every x. Relative to any basis, the matrix of I has the form

$$\begin{bmatrix} 1 & 0 \cdots 0 \\ 0 & 1 \cdots 0 \\ \vdots & \\ & \\ 0 & 0 \cdots 1 \end{bmatrix}.$$

Example 2. (a) On the real plane $E_2^{(r)}$, consider the transformation A which rotates each vector counterclockwise through the angle θ. What is the matrix of A relative to a right-handed orthonormal basis (φ_1, φ_2)? By drawing a sketch, the reader will easily convince himself that $A\varphi_1 = (\cos \theta)\varphi_1 + (\sin \theta)\varphi_2$, $A\varphi_2 = (-\sin \theta)\varphi_1 + (\cos \theta)\varphi_2$. From the definition of the matrix of A, $A\varphi_1 = a_{11}\varphi_1 + a_{21}\varphi_1$ and $A\varphi_2 = a_{12}\varphi_1 + a_{22}\varphi_2$; hence

$$[A] = \begin{bmatrix} a_{11} & a_{12} \\ a_{21} & a_{22} \end{bmatrix} = \begin{bmatrix} \cos \theta & -\sin \theta \\ \sin \theta & \cos \theta \end{bmatrix}.$$

The coordinates (η_1, η_2) of the image (rotated) vector y are related to the coordinates (ξ_1, ξ_2) of the original vector x by $\eta_1 = \xi_1 \cos \theta - \xi_2 \sin \theta$, $\eta_2 = \xi_1 \sin \theta + \xi_2 \cos \theta$.

(b) On the complex space $E_2^{(c)}$, we can consider a linear transformation A whose matrix relative to some orthonormal basis is

$$\begin{bmatrix} \cos \theta & -\sin \theta \\ \sin \theta & \cos \theta \end{bmatrix}.$$

The formulas in **(a)** remain the same, but now $\xi_1, \xi_2, \eta_1, \eta_2$ may be complex numbers, and the geometric significance of the operator is lost (although we still call it a rotation operator).

Example 3. (a) On the real plane $E_2^{(r)}$, consider the linear transformation A whose matrix, relative to the right-handed orthonormal basis (φ_1, φ_2), is

$$\begin{bmatrix} 1 & 1 \\ 0 & 1 \end{bmatrix}.$$

The coordinates (η_1, η_2) of the image vector y are related to the coordinates (ξ_1, ξ_2) of the original vector x by $\eta_1 = \xi_1 + \xi_2$, $\eta_2 = \xi_2$. A glance at a diagram shows that the transformation A represents a *shearing* deformation.

(b) The matrix $\begin{bmatrix} 1 & 1 \\ 0 & 1 \end{bmatrix}$ may also be viewed as the matrix of a linear transformation on $E_2^{(c)}$; although the geometric significance is lost, the transformation is still known as a *shear transformation*.

Example 4. *Projection operator.* Let M be a linear manifold of dimension k in $E_n^{(c)}$. Each vector x in $E_n^{(c)}$ has a unique decomposition $x = y + z$, where y is in M and z is orthogonal to y; that is, z lies in $M^\perp$. The vector y is known as the *projection* of x on M and is unambiguously determined from x; we can therefore write $y = Px$, where P is a transformation on $E_n^{(c)}$. The transformation P is easily seen to be linear and has a simple matrix relative to a basis constructed as follows: Let $(e_1, \dots, e_k)$ be a basis for M and $(e_{k+1}, \dots, e_n)$ be a basis for $M^\perp$; then $(e_1, \dots, e_n)$ forms a basis B for $E_n^{(c)}$, and schematically,

$$[P]_B = \begin{bmatrix} I & 0 \\ \hline 0 & 0 \end{bmatrix}.$$

The upper-left-hand k by k matrix is an identity matrix (the elements are 1 along the principal diagonal; otherwise 0); the rest of the n by n matrix $[P]_B$ consists of zero elements.

The Two Roles of Matrices in Connection with Linear Transformations

1. A linear transformation A moves the vector x into $y = Ax$. The matrix $[A]_B = [a_{ij}]$ is a set of numbers, defined from (2.34), which enables us to compute the coordinates of the image vector y when the coordinates of the original vector x are known. (All coordinates are in the same fixed basis B.)

2. Given two bases B and B', each vector x in $E_n^{(c)}$ has unique representations in B and B': $x = \sum_{i=1}^{n} \xi_i e_i = \sum_{i=1}^{n} \xi_i' e_i'$. A matrix is again involved in determining the relation between the coordinates (ξ_i') and (ξ_i). Consider the linear transformation A, easily shown to be unique, which transforms e_j into e_j'; that is, $Ae_j = e_j'$. Let $[a_{ij}]$ be the matrix of A in the basis B; hence $e_j' = \sum_{i=1}^{n} a_{ij} e_i$.

Since $x = \sum_{j=1}^{n} \xi_j' e_j'$, we have

$$x = \sum_{j=1}^{n} \xi_j' \left(\sum_{i=1}^{n} a_{ij} e_i \right) = \sum_{i=1}^{n} \left(\sum_{j=1}^{n} a_{ij} \xi_j' \right) e_i;$$

but x is also given by $\sum_{i=1}^{n} \xi_i e_i$; therefore

$$\xi_i = \sum_{j=1}^{n} a_{ij} \xi_j'. \tag{2.35}$$

Thus matrices are also useful in describing linear changes of coordinates. In most of our applications, matrices will arise in connection with the point of view described in (1).

Simple Calculations with Matrices

Let $[A]_B = [a_{ij}]$ and $[B]_B = [b_{ij}]$; we wish to compute the matrices of $C = \alpha A$, $D = A + B$, and $E = AB$. It is easily shown that

$$[C]_B = [\alpha a_{ij}]; \tag{2.36}$$

$$[D]_B = [a_{ij} + b_{ij}]; \tag{2.37}$$

$$[E]_B = \left[\sum_{k=1}^{n} a_{ik} b_{kj} \right]. \tag{2.38}$$

To prove the last of these formulas, note that by definition

$$Ae_k = \sum_{i=1}^{n} a_{ik} e_i, \qquad Be_j = \sum_{k=1}^{n} b_{kj} e_k;$$

therefore,

$$Ee_j = A(Be_j) = A\left(\sum_{k=1}^{n} b_{kj} e_k \right) = \sum_{k=1}^{n} b_{kj} Ae_k = \sum_{k=1}^{n} b_{kj} \left(\sum_{i=1}^{n} a_{ik} e_i \right)$$

$$= \sum_{i=1}^{n} \left(\sum_{k=1}^{n} a_{ik} b_{kj} \right) e_i.$$

Comparing with (2.34), we observe that the element in the ith row and jth column of $[E]_B$ is $\sum_{k=1}^{n} a_{ik} b_{kj}$, which is just what we wished to prove. In the usual first treatment of matrices, formula (2.38) for multiplication is postulated without justification; we have seen that if matrices are to play a role in the theory of linear transformations, we *must* define multiplication of matrices as we did.

Given a transformation A and a basis B: $(e_1, \ldots, e_n)$, we wish to calculate the elements in the matrix $[A]_B$. This is easily done using inner products. Introducing the dual basis B^*: $(e_1^*, \ldots, e_n^*)$ with the property

$$\langle e_i, e_j^* \rangle = \delta_{ij} = \begin{cases} 0, & i \neq j; \\ 1, & i = j, \end{cases}$$

we have

$$\langle Ae_j, e_i^* \rangle = \left\langle \sum_{k=1}^{n} a_{kj} e_k, e_i^* \right\rangle = a_{ij}.$$

Therefore,

$$a_{ij} = \langle Ae_j, e_i^* \rangle = \overline{\langle e_i^*, Ae_j \rangle}. \tag{2.39}$$

If the basis B is orthonormal, the dual basis coincides with B, and we have the simpler formula

$$a_{ij} = \langle A\varphi_j, \varphi_i \rangle = \overline{\langle \varphi_i, A\varphi_j \rangle}. \tag{2.40}$$

The Inverse of a Linear Transformation on $E_n^{(c)}$

Let A be a linear operator such that the homogeneous equation $Ax = 0$ has only the trivial solution $x = 0$. The inhomogeneous equation $Ax = f$ can therefore have at most one solution; in particular, if f is in the range of A, there is exactly one solution. In a general Hilbert space $\mathscr{A}$ it is possible for R_A to be different from $\mathscr{A}$ even though $Ax = 0$ has only the 0 solution; but if this last condition is satisfied in $E_n^{(c)}$, R_A must coincide with $E_n^{(c)}$, and the inhomogeneous equation has exactly one solution for any f in $E_n^{(c)}$. This result is the content of the following theorem:

Theorem. *If $Ax = 0$ has only the trivial solution, then, for each f in $E_n^{(c)}$, $Ax = f$ has exactly one solution.*

Proof. Since the inhomogeneous equation has at most one solution, it remains only to show that the range of A is the whole of $E_n^{(c)}$. Let us introduce the basis $\{e_1, \ldots, e_n\}$; we first prove that the vectors $Ae_1, \ldots, Ae_n$ also form a basis. If this were not the case, there would exist constants $\alpha_1, \ldots, \alpha_n$, not all zero, such that $\sum_{k=1}^{n} \alpha_k Ae_k = 0$, or $A\left(\sum_{k=1}^{n} \alpha_k e_k\right) = 0$. Since $Ax = 0$ has only the 0 solution, $\sum_{k=1}^{n} \alpha_k e_k = 0$, and because $e_1, \ldots, e_n$ are independent, $\alpha_1, \ldots, \alpha_n$ must all be zero, which is a contradiction. The vectors $Ae_1, \ldots, Ae_n$ therefore form a basis; an arbitrary vector f in $E_n^{(c)}$ can be written $\sum_{i=i}^{n} \beta_i Ae_i$ and a solution of $Ax = f$ is therefore $\sum_{i=1}^{n} \beta_i e_i$. The solution is already known to be unique, and the theorem is proved.

DEFINITION If $Ax = 0$ has only the zero solution, A is a *regular* transformation; if $Ax = 0$ has a nonzero solution, A is a *singular* transformation.

The preceding theorem may be restated: The necessary and sufficient condition for $Ax = f$ to have exactly one solution for each f in $E_n^{(c)}$ is that A be regular. If we introduce the basis $B: (e_1, \ldots, e_n)$, with $x = \sum_{i=1}^{n} \xi_i e_i$, the equation $Ax = 0$ becomes the homogeneous system $\sum_{j=1}^{n} a_{ij} \xi_j = 0$, $i = 1, \ldots, n$. The matrix $[a_{ij}]$ is the matrix of A relative to the basis B. It is known from elementary algebra that this homogeneous system has a nontrivial solution if and only if the determinant of $[a_{ij}]$ is zero. We can therefore state:

If $\det[A]_B$ is 0 in some basis, it is 0 in all bases, and A is singular; if $\det[A]_B \neq 0$ in some basis, it is different from 0 in all bases and A is regular. (Actually it can be shown that the determinant of A has the same value in all bases, and we therefore omit the basis subscript for $\det A$.)

Assuming that A is regular we can construct $[A^{-1}]_B$. The equation $Ax = f$ becomes the inhomogeneous system $\sum_{j=1}^{n} a_{ij}\xi_j = f_i$, where $x = \sum_{i=1}^{n} \xi_i e_i$ and $f = \sum_{i=1}^{n} f_i e_i$. The solution of this system of equations is given from elementary algebra by $\xi_i = \sum_{j=1}^{n} b_{ij} f_j$, where $b_{ij} = (-1)^{i+j} A_{ji}/\det A$. (Here A_{ij} is the minor of the element a_{ij} in the matrix $[a_{ij}]$.) Thus

$$[A^{-1}]_B = [b_{ij}] = \frac{(-1)^{i+j} A_{ji}}{\det A}.$$

The Adjoint of a Linear Transformation on $E_n^{(c)}$

Let A be a linear transformation and f a fixed vector in $E_n^{(c)}$; then $\langle Ax, f \rangle$ is a linear functional which, like all linear functionals on $E_n^{(c)}$, must be continuous. The Riesz theorem tells us that $\langle Ax, f \rangle$ is the inner product of x with some vector g; that is,

$$\langle Ax, f \rangle = \langle x, g \rangle, \qquad \text{for all } x \text{ in } E_n^{(c)}.$$

It is clear that g is a function of f, and we can write $g = A^*f$. One observes without difficulty that A^* is a linear transformation (hence bounded); the transformation A^* is unambiguously determined from A; A^* is known as the *adjoint* of A. For each pair of vectors (x, y) in $E_n^{(c)}$, we have

$$\langle Ax, y \rangle = \langle x, A^*y \rangle. \tag{2.41}$$

We note that $(\alpha A)^* = \bar{\alpha}A^*$, $(A^*)^* = A$.

Let $[a_{ij}]$ and $[a_{ij}^*]$ be the matrices of A and A^*, respectively, relative to the orthonormal basis B. By (2.40) we have $a_{ij} = \langle A\varphi_j, \varphi_i \rangle$ and $a_{ij}^* = \langle A^*\varphi_j, \varphi_i \rangle$. Therefore, $a_{ij} = \langle A\varphi_j, \varphi_i \rangle = \langle \varphi_j, A^*\varphi_i \rangle = \langle A^*\varphi_i, \varphi_j \rangle$; hence $\bar{a}_{ji} = \langle A^*\varphi_j, \varphi_i \rangle = a^*_{ij}$.

Relative to an orthonormal basis, the matrix of the adjoint is obtained from the original matrix by

$$a_{ij}^* = \bar{a}_{ji}. \tag{2.42}$$

The operator A is *self-adjoint* if $A = A^*$. The matrix of a self-adjoint operator with respect to an orthonormal basis satisfies the relations

$$a_{ij} = \bar{a}_{ji}. \tag{2.43}$$

A matrix which satisfies (2.43) is said to be *symmetric* (or complex symmetric, or Hermitian). A self-adjoint operator is therefore also called *symmetric*. For unbounded operators in $\mathscr{L}_2$, an important distinction exists between symmetry and self-adjointness, but this distinction disappears for operators in $E_n^{(c)}$. The adjoint operator plays a special role in the solution of the equation $Ax = f$. This equation has exactly one solution if $Ax = 0$ has only the trivial solution; even if $Ax = 0$ has nontrivial solutions, it is possible for the inhomogeneous equation to have a solution (which cannot be unique, since we can add to it any solution of the homogeneous equation). We would like to determine when $Ax = f$ has solutions, that is, when a vector f is in the range of A.

Alternative Theorem. *The equation $Ax = f$ has solution(s) if and only if $\langle f, z \rangle = 0$ for every z which is a solution of $A^*z = 0$. Stated in other words, the necessary and sufficient condition for f to be in R_A is that f be orthogonal to the null space of A^*; that is, $R_A = (N_{A^*})^\perp$.†*

Proof. We prefer to show $N_{A^*} = (R_A)^\perp$, because this result is valid for arbitrary linear operators on any Hilbert space, whereas the alternative theorem might fail. Of course, if R_A is a closed set (which is certainly true when A is an operator on E_n), the statements $N_{A^*} = (R_A)^\perp$ and $R_A = (N_{A^*})^\perp$ are equivalent, because $(R_A)^{\perp\perp} = R_A$. We proceed to show $N_{A^*} = (R_A)^\perp$ by showing (a) that every element in N_{A^*} is also in $(R_A)^\perp$ and (b) that every element in $(R_A)^\perp$ is in N_{A^*}.

(a) Let z be in N_{A^*} and f in R_A; thus $A^*z = 0$ and there exists an element x for which $Ax = f$. Then $\langle f, z \rangle = \langle Ax, z \rangle = \langle x, A^*z \rangle = \langle x, 0 \rangle = 0$.

(b) Let z be in $(R_A)^\perp$; thus $\langle f, z \rangle = 0$ for every f in R_A. Since the domain of A is the whole space, we have, for every x, $\langle Ax, z \rangle = 0$. Hence $\langle x, A^*z \rangle = 0$ for every x, and $A^*z = 0$.

COROLLARY 1. $N_A = (R_{A^*})^\perp$.

Proof. Apply the alternative theorem to A^* and note that $(A^*)^* = A$.

COROLLARY 2. A and A^* are either both regular or singular; that is, if $Ax = 0$ has only the 0 solution, then $A^*z = 0$ has only the 0 solution, and vice versa.

Proof. If A is regular, $Ax = f$ has exactly one solution for each f in E_n; hence $R_A = E_n$ and therefore N_{A^*} is empty, so that A^* is regular. Applying the same argument to A^* and recalling that $(A^*)^* = A$, we find that if A^* is regular, so is A.

We now try to obtain information on the number of solutions of $Ax = f$ when A is singular and f is in R_A; to this end the following definitions will be useful. The *rank* of A, denoted by $\rho(A)$, is the dimension of the range of A. The *nullity* of A, denoted by $v(A)$, is the dimension of the null space of A.

Theorem. $\rho(A) = \rho(A^*), v(A) = v(A^*)$.

Proof. We have already shown that the range of A and the null space of A^* are orthogonal complements; therefore their dimensions must add up to the

---

† This was called the "consistency condition(s)" in Chapter 1.

dimension of E_n which is n; that is, $\rho(A) + \nu(A^*) = n$. Similarly, from Corollary 1, $\rho(A^*) + \nu(A) = n$. Now let $e_1, \ldots, e_\nu$ be a basis for the ν-dimensional space N_A and let $e_{\nu+1}, \ldots, e_n$ be a basis for the $(n - \nu)$-dimensional space R_{A^*}. The set $(e_1, \ldots, e_n)$ is obviously a basis for E_n. Let $x = \sum_{k=1}^{n} \xi_k e_k$ be an arbitrary vector in E_n; then $Ax = \sum_{k=1}^{n} \xi_k Ae_k$, but since $0 = Ae_1 = \cdots = Ae_\nu$,

$Ax = \sum_{k=\nu+1}^{n} \xi_k Ae_k$. Therefore the range of A is a linear combination of $n - \nu$ vectors and $\rho(A) \leq n - \nu(A)$. Substituting A^* for A, we obtain $\rho(A^*) \leq n - \nu(A^*)$. Since $n - \nu(A) = \rho(A^*)$ and $n - \nu(A^*) = \rho(A)$, we have $\rho(A) \leq \rho(A^*)$ and $\rho(A^*) \leq \rho(A)$; therefore, $\rho(A) = \rho(A^*)$ and $\nu(A) = \nu(A^*)$. The usual form of this theorem is in terms of matrices (see Exercise 2.33).

Collecting the results we have:

Theorem *Complete Form of Alternative Theorem on a Finite-dimensional Space.* (a) *If $Ax = 0$ has only the trivial solution, $A^*z = 0$ has only the trivial solution, and $Ay = f$ has exactly one solution.*

(b) *If $Ax = 0$ has ν independent solutions, say $x_1, \ldots, x_\nu$, then $A^*z = 0$ also has ν independent solutions, say $z_1, \ldots, z_\nu$; moreover, $Ay = f$ has solutions if and only if the consistency conditions $0 = \langle f, z_1 \rangle = \cdots = \langle f, z_\nu \rangle$ are satisfied. If these conditions are satisfied, the general solution of $Ay = f$ is $y = c_1 x_1 + \cdots + c_\nu x_\nu + y'$, where y' is some particular solution of $Ay = f$ and $c_1, \ldots, c_\nu$ are arbitrary constants.*

Eigenvalues and Eigenvectors

An important and illuminating method for solving the inhomogeneous equation $Ay = f$ (or even the equation $Ay - \lambda y = f$, where λ is a given complex number) is based on the accessory problem: Find all nonzero vectors which are left unchanged in "direction" by the transformation A, that is, all nonzero vectors x for which $Ax = \lambda x$ for some complex number λ. Any such "invariant" vector x is known as an eigenvector of A; the scale factor λ, by which x is multiplied, is the corresponding eigenvalue. Suppose that A is such that we can find n *independent* eigenvectors $x_1, \ldots, x_n$ corresponding, respectively, to the eigenvalues $\lambda_1, \ldots, \lambda_n$; thus $Ax_i = \lambda_i x_i$, $i = 1, \ldots, n$. Whether the eigenvalues are distinct or not is of no consequence to us, but the eigenvectors must be independent. The vectors $x_1, \ldots, x_n$ then form a basis in $E_n^{(c)}$, and this basis is especially suitable for solving $Ay - \lambda y = f$, where f and λ are given. We can write $f = \sum_{i=1}^{n} \gamma_i x_i$, where the coordinates $\{\gamma_i\}$ are regarded as known; moreover, if a solution y exists, then $y = \sum_{i=1}^{n} \xi_i x_i$, where the coordinates $\{\xi_i\}$ are unknown but are about to be calculated.

The equation $Ay - \lambda y = f$ implies

$$A\left(\sum_{i=1}^{n} \xi_i x_i\right) - \lambda \sum_{i=1}^{n} \xi_i x_i = \sum_{i=1}^{n} \gamma_i x_i.$$

Since A is linear and $Ax_i = \lambda_i x_i$, we obtain

$$\sum_{i=1}^{n} [\xi_i(\lambda_i - \lambda) - \gamma_i]x_i = 0.$$

From the independence of the vectors $x_1, \ldots, x_n$, we infer

$$\xi_i(\lambda_i - \lambda) - \gamma_i = 0, \qquad i = 1, \ldots, n. \tag{2.44}$$

If the given value λ differs from each of the numbers $\lambda_1, \ldots, \lambda_n$, we have

$$\xi_i = \frac{\gamma_i}{\lambda_i - \lambda}, \qquad i = 1, \ldots, n \tag{2.45}$$

and

$$y = \sum_{i=1}^{n} \frac{\gamma_i}{\lambda_i - \lambda} x_i, \tag{2.46}$$

One easily checks by substitution that $\sum_{i=1}^{n} [\gamma_i/(\lambda_i - \lambda)]x_i$ actually satisfies $Ay - \lambda y = f$. We have therefore shown that if A has n independent eigenvectors and if λ is not an eigenvalue of A, the one and only solution of $Ay - \lambda y = f$ is $y = \sum_{i=1}^{n} [\gamma_i/(\lambda_i - \lambda)]x_i$.

The success of the above method of solution (known as an eigenvector expansion) can be attributed to the fact that the eigenvectors of A form a basis. *In this basis* the matrix of A is diagonal:

$$\begin{bmatrix} \lambda_1 & 0 & \cdots & 0 \\ 0 & \lambda_2 & \cdots & 0 \\ \vdots & & & \\ 0 & 0 & \cdots & \lambda_n \end{bmatrix}.$$

The matrix of $A - \lambda I$ is also diagonal:

$$\begin{bmatrix} \lambda_1 - \lambda & 0 & \cdots & 0 \\ 0 & \lambda_2 - \lambda & \cdots & 0 \\ \vdots & & & \\ 0 & 0 & \cdots & \lambda_n - \lambda \end{bmatrix}.$$

The inhomogeneous equation $(A - \lambda I)y = f$ then reduces to the n *separate* equations (2.44) for the n coordinates of y. We now proceed to study the eigenvalues and eigenvectors of operators on $E_n^{(c)}$ with the particular aim of characterizing the class of operators whose eigenvectors form a basis.

Consider the equation

$$Ax = \lambda x \text{ (or, equivalently, } Ax - \lambda x = 0, \quad (A - \lambda I)x = 0). \qquad (2.47)$$

A *nonzero* vector x, for which the above equation holds for some complex number λ, is known as an *eigenvector* of A. A complex number λ, for which (2.47) has a nonzero solution x, is called an *eigenvalue* of A. Observe that although the vector 0 cannot be an eigenvector (by definition!), it is possible for $\lambda = 0$ to be an eigenvalue (if the null space of A contains nonzero vectors, that is, if $Ax = 0$ has a nontrivial solution). It is clear that eigenvectors and eigenvalues are associated with each other: An eigenvector x satisfies (2.47) for precisely one value of λ, but to some λ there may be more than one non-zero solution of (2.47). This last statement is borne out by the following observation. If x is an eigenvector associated with the particular value λ, then cx is also an eigenvector associated with the same eigenvalue; if x and y are eigenvectors associated with λ, then $x + y$ is an eigenvector associated with λ. Thus the set of eigenvectors, corresponding to a particular value of λ, is a linear manifold, the null space of the operator $A - \lambda I$; this manifold is known as the *eigenmanifold* corresponding to λ; the dimension of the eigenmanifold is called the *geometric multiplicity* of λ.

To compute the eigenvectors and eigenvalues of A, we introduce an arbitrary, fixed basis B: $(e_1, \ldots, e_n)$. A vector x has the representation $\sum\limits_{i=1}^{n} \xi_i e_i$ and (2.47) becomes the homogeneous system of linear equations

$$\begin{aligned} (a_{11} - \lambda)\xi_1 + a_{12}\xi_2 + \cdots + a_{1n}\xi_n &= 0, \\ &\vdots \\ a_{n1}\xi_1 + a_{n2}\xi_2 + \cdots + (a_{nn} - \lambda)\xi_n &= 0. \end{aligned} \qquad (2.48)$$

Here $[a_{ij}]$ is the matrix of A in the basis B; the matrix which appears in (2.48) is the matrix of $A - \lambda I$ relative to the basis B:

$$[A - \lambda I]_B = [a_{ij} - \lambda\delta_{ij}],$$

where

$$\delta_{ij} = \begin{cases} 0, & i \neq j; \\ 1, & i = j. \end{cases}$$

The system (2.48) has a nontrivial solution $(\xi_1, \ldots, \xi_n)$ if and only if the determinant of the coefficients vanishes, that is, if and only if†

$$\det(A - \lambda I) = \begin{vmatrix} a_{11} - \lambda & a_{12} & \cdots & a_{1n} \\ \vdots & & & \\ a_{n1} & a_{n2} & \cdots & a_{nn} - \lambda \end{vmatrix} = 0. \qquad (2.49)$$

Equation (2.49) is the *secular* equation. The determinant that appears in this equation is a polynomial of degree n in λ. This polynomial therefore

---

† As already pointed out, the determinant of an operator is independent of the basis used, and we therefore write $\det(A - \lambda I)$ without subscript.

has n roots (not necessarily distinct), which we label $\lambda_1, \ldots, \lambda_n$. Equation (2.49) may be written in the form

$$(\lambda - \lambda_1) \cdots (\lambda - \lambda_n) = 0. \tag{2.50}$$

If a root occurs k times in (2.50), we say it has *algebraic multiplicity k*. We now substitute in turn the distinct roots of (2.50) in (2.48). To each such root the system (2.48) must have a nontrivial solution which then yields an eigenvector corresponding to that root; for instance, if we substitute λ_1 in (2.48) we obtain at least one nontrivial solution $(\xi_1^{(1)}, \ldots, \xi_n^{(1)})$, and A has the eigenvector $x_1 = \xi_1^{(1)} e_1 + \cdots + \xi_n^{(1)} e_n$ associated with eigenvalue λ_1. *We have shown that every operator A on $E_n^{(c)}$ has at least one eigenvalue and eigenvector;* this result does not hold for operators on $E_n^{(r)}$, since it is possible for a polynomial with real coefficients to have no real root (see the example of the rotation operator). We now ask for the relation between algebraic multiplicity [the number of times a root occurs in (2.50)] and geometric multiplicity [the number of independent solutions of (2.49) corresponding to that root].

Let m be the *geometric multiplicity* of λ_1; we can choose a basis in $E_n^{(c)}$ whose first m elements are in the eigenmanifold corresponding to λ_1. In this basis the matrix of A has the form

$$
\begin{array}{c}
\text{row } 1 \\
\\
\\
\text{row } m
\end{array}
\left[
\begin{array}{cccc|c}
\lambda_1 & 0 & \cdots & 0 & \\
0 & \lambda_1 & \cdots & 0 & B \\
\vdots & & & & \\
0 & 0 & \cdots & \lambda_1 & \\
\hline
& & 0 & & C
\end{array}
\right]
$$

Therefore the matrix of $A - \lambda I$ has the form

$$
\begin{array}{c}
\text{row } 1 \\
\\
\\
\text{row } m
\end{array}
\left[
\begin{array}{cccc|c}
\lambda_1 - \lambda & 0 & \cdots & 0 & \\
0 & \lambda_1 - \lambda & \cdots & 0 & B \\
\vdots & & & & \\
0 & 0 & \cdots & \lambda_1 - \lambda & \\
\hline
& & 0 & & C - \lambda I
\end{array}
\right]
$$

The secular equation is $\det(A - \lambda I) = 0$, which becomes

$$(\lambda_1 - \lambda)^m \det(C - \lambda I) = 0;$$

hence λ_1 is at least an m-fold root of the secular equation. It follows that the algebraic multiplicity of an eigenvalue must be greater than or equal to its geometric multiplicity.

EXAMPLES

Example 1. $0x = \lambda x$; $\lambda = 0$ is the only eigenvalue; every vector is an eigenvector; the secular equation is $\lambda^n = 0$.

$Ix = \lambda x$; $\lambda = 1$ is the only eigenvalue; every vector is an eigenvector; the secular equation is $(1 - \lambda)^n = 0$.

Example 2. The rotation operator whose matrix is $\begin{bmatrix} \cos \theta & -\sin \theta \\ \sin \theta & \cos \theta \end{bmatrix}$ in the basis $B = (\varphi_1, \varphi_2)$.

The secular equation is $(\cos \theta - \lambda)^2 + \sin^2 \theta = 0$. Therefore,

$$\lambda^2 - 2\lambda \cos \theta + 1 = 0, \qquad \lambda = \cos \theta \pm i \sin \theta.$$

We set $\lambda_1 = e^{i\theta}$, $\lambda_2 = e^{-i\theta}$. Assuming $\theta \neq k\pi$, these eigenvalues are distinct (if $\theta = k\pi$ the transformation becomes either the identity or the reflection about the origin). The coordinates of the eigenvectors are determined from

$$\xi_1 \cos \theta - \xi_2 \sin \theta = \lambda \xi_1, \qquad \xi_1 \sin \theta + \xi_2 \cos \theta = \lambda \xi_2.$$

Substituting in turn $\lambda_1 = e^{i\theta}$, then $\lambda_2 = e^{-i\theta}$, we first obtain $\xi_1^{(1)} = i\xi_2^{(1)}$, then $i\xi_1^{(2)} = \xi_2^{(2)}$. Every eigenvector corresponding to λ_1 is therefore of the form $c(i\varphi_1 + \varphi_2)$, and every eigenvector corresponding to λ_2 is of the form $c(\varphi_1 + i\varphi_2)$.

If the rotation operator is considered on $E_2^{(r)}$ with $\theta \neq k\pi$, we find no eigenvalues (hence of course no eigenvectors).

Example 3. The shear operator, whose matrix is $\begin{bmatrix} 1 & 1 \\ 0 & 1 \end{bmatrix}$ in $B: (\varphi_1, \varphi_2)$, has the secular equation $(1 - \lambda)^2 = 0$; therefore $\lambda = 1$ is an eigenvalue of algebraic multiplicity 2, yet we see below that it has geometric multiplicity 1. If we substitute $\lambda = 1$ in the system

$$(1 - \lambda)\xi_1 + \xi_2 = 0;$$

$$0\xi_1 + (1 - \lambda)\xi_2 = 0,$$

we obtain $\xi_2 = 0$, ξ_1 arbitrary; hence every eigenvector is of the form $c\varphi_1$. This is in sharp contrast with the identity transformation $\begin{bmatrix} 1 & 0 \\ 0 & 1 \end{bmatrix}$, for which $\lambda = 1$ has algebraic multiplicity 2 but for which we can find two independent eigenvectors, for example, φ_1, φ_2.

Example 4. Let M be a linear manifold of dimension k in $E_n^{(c)}$; if x is in $E_n^{(c)}$, let $y = Px$ be the projection of x on M. Every vector in M is an eigenvector of P with eigenvalue 1; every vector in $M^\perp$ is an eigenvector of P with eigenvalue 0; there are no other eigenvalues or eigenvectors. The algebraic and geometric multiplicities of $\lambda = 1$ are both equal to k; the algebraic and geometric multiplicities of $\lambda = 0$ are both equal to $n - k$.

Operators with n Distinct Eigenvalues

In the event that all n roots of (2.50) are distinct, the eigenvectors form a basis. The desired result is essentially contained in the following theorem: If $x_1, \ldots, x_k$ are eigenvectors corresponding, respectively, to the *distinct* eigenvalues $\lambda_1, \ldots, \lambda_k$, then $x_1, \ldots, x_k$ are independent. The proof is by mathematical induction on the integer k. The assertion clearly holds for $k = 1$; it remains to show that if the statement is true for the first $k - 1$ eigenvectors. it must also hold for k eigenvectors. Let us apply the operator A to the equation $\alpha_1 x_1 + \cdots + \alpha_k x_k = 0$; this yields

$$\alpha_1 \lambda_1 x_1 + \cdots + \alpha_k \lambda_k x_k = 0$$

or

$$\alpha_1 (\lambda_1 - \lambda_k) x_1 + \cdots + \alpha_{k-1}(\lambda_{k-1} - \lambda_k) x_{k-1} = 0.$$

Since, by the induction hypothesis, $x_1, \ldots, x_{k-1}$ are independent and $(\lambda_j - \lambda_k) \neq 0$, $j = 1, \ldots, k - 1$, it follows that $\alpha_1 = 0, \ldots, \alpha_{k-1} = 0$. The vector x_k is not 0, since it is an eigenvector; consequently, the equation $\alpha_1 x_1 + \cdots + \alpha_k x_k = 0$ can be satisfied only if $\alpha_1 = \cdots = \alpha_k = 0$ and the vectors $x_1, \ldots, x_k$ are independent. This completes the proof by induction.

Now suppose A has n distinct eigenvalues $\lambda_1, \ldots, \lambda_n$; let the corresponding eigenvectors be $x_1, \ldots, x_n$. These eigenvectors must be independent by the theorem proved above; hence they form a basis. This implies that the geometric multiplicity of each eigenvalue is 1.

Although this state of affairs is very satisfactory, it is usually difficult to determine whether or not a given operator has n distinct eigenvalues so that, even if an operator satisfies the conditions on the theorem, we may not know it!

Symmetric Operators

We have just established that if A has n distinct eigenvalues, its eigenvectors form a basis. Another class of operators for which the eigenvectors can be selected so as to form a basis (even though the n eigenvalues may not all be distinct) is the class of symmetric operators.

Let A be symmetric; the following properties hold:

1. $\langle Ax, x \rangle$ *is real for every x in $E_n^{(c)}$.* Indeed from the properties of the inner product $\langle Ax, x \rangle = \langle x, Ax \rangle$; the symmetry of A means that $\langle Ax, x \rangle = \langle x, Ax \rangle$; therefore, $\langle \overline{Ax, x} \rangle = \langle Ax, x \rangle$ and $\langle Ax, x \rangle$ is real. (The converse also holds: If $\langle Ax, x \rangle$ is real for every x in $E_n^{(c)}$, then A is symmetric. When dealing with operators in $E_n^{(r)}$, this converse is *not* valid, since $\langle Ax, x \rangle$ is always real, regardless of whether or not A is symmetric.)

2. *The eigenvalues of A are real.* If $Ax = \lambda x$, then $\langle Ax, x \rangle = \lambda \langle x, x \rangle$; both $\langle Ax, x \rangle$ and $\langle x, x \rangle$ are real, and $\langle x, x \rangle \neq 0$; therefore λ is real.

3. *Eigenvectors associated with different eigenvalues are orthogonal.* Let $Ax = \lambda x$, $Ay = \mu y$. Then $\langle Ax, y \rangle = \langle \lambda x, y \rangle$, and $\langle x, Ay \rangle = \langle x, \mu y \rangle$. Since $\langle Ax, y \rangle = \langle x, Ay \rangle$, we have $\langle \lambda x, y \rangle = \langle x, \mu y \rangle$, or $\lambda \langle x, y \rangle = \bar{\mu} \langle x, y \rangle$. Because μ is real and $\mu \neq \lambda$, we have $\bar{\mu} \neq \lambda$ and $\langle x, y \rangle = 0$.

4. *The eigenvectors form a basis.* From previous analysis we know that any operator has at least one eigenvalue, say λ_1. Let the corresponding eigenmanifold be M_1 with dimension n_1. If x is in M_1, then $Ax = \lambda_1 x$ and the effect of A on any vector in M_1 is completely determined. Every vector in $E_n^{(c)}$ can be decomposed in the form $x + y$, where x is in M_1 and y is in $(M_1)^\perp$; we now investigate the effect of A on vectors in $(M_1)^\perp$. If x is in M_1 and y in $(M_1)^\perp$, the symmetry of A implies $\langle x, Ay \rangle = \langle Ax, y \rangle = \lambda_1 \langle x, y \rangle = 0$. Thus, for a symmetric operator, if y is in $(M_1)^\perp$ so is Ay. We can therefore consider A as an operator on the $(n - n_1)$-dimensional space $(M_1)^\perp$. This operator has therefore at least one eigenvalue, say λ_2, with eigenmanifold M_2 of dimension n_2 [note that M_2 is part of $(M_1)^\perp$ and therefore M_2 is orthogonal to M_1]. Now consider the set of vectors perpendicular to both M_1 and M_2. This set will be denoted by $(M_1 + M_2)^\perp$. If y is in $(M_1 + M_2)^\perp$, Ay is also in $(M_1 + M_2)^\perp$; therefore we can consider A as an operator on the $(n - n_1 - n_2)$-dimensional space $(M_1 + M_2)^\perp$. This operator has at least one eigenvalue, say λ_3, with eigenmanifold M_3 of dimension n_3 [the manifold M_3 is part of $(M_1 + M_2)^\perp$]. We can continue this process *until* $(M_1 + \cdots + M_k)^\perp$ is empty. We have thereby constructed k eigenvalues $\lambda_1, \ldots, \lambda_k$ of A with respective geometric multiplicities $n_1, \ldots, n_k$. Since $(M_1 + \cdots + M_k)^\perp$ must be empty for the process to stop, we have $n_1 + \cdots + n_k = n$.

We collect our results in the *spectral theorem for symmetric operators on* $E_n^{(c)}$: Let A be a symmetric operator; then there exist $k(1 \leq k \leq n)$ real, distinct numbers $\lambda_1, \ldots, \lambda_k$ and k linear manifolds $M_1, \ldots, M_k$ with the following properties:

(a) If x is in M_j then $Ax = \lambda_j x$; that is, each λ_j is an eigenvalue of A with corresponding eigenmanifold M_j.

(b) The eigenmanifolds are pairwise orthogonal; that is, if $i \neq j$ and x is in M_i and y is in M_j, $\langle x, y \rangle = 0$.

(c) Each vector x in $E_n^{(c)}$ can be decomposed in one and only one way as $x = x_1 + \cdots + x_k$, with x_i in M_i. If n_i is the dimension of M_i, $\sum_{i=1}^{k} n_i = n$.

(d) The numbers $\lambda_1, \ldots, \lambda_k$ and the manifolds $M_1, \ldots, M_k$ are uniquely determined (except for order) by A.

REMARKS. 1. We can reformulate the spectral theorem in operator notation. Let P_i be the projection on M_i, that is, $P_i x = x_i$; we can then write

$$x = x_1 + \cdots + x_k = \sum_{i=1}^{k} P_i x,$$

which implies the operator equation known as a *resolution of the identity*:

$$I = P_1 + \cdots + P_k. \tag{2.51}$$

Furthermore, $Ax = A(x_1 + \cdots + x_k) = \lambda_1 x_1 + \cdots + \lambda_k x_k = \lambda_1 P_1 x + \cdots + \lambda_k P_k x = \left(\sum_{i=1}^{k} \lambda_i P_i \right) x$. This leads to the operator equation known as the *spectral resolution of A*:

$$A = \sum_{i=1}^{k} \lambda_i P_i. \tag{2.52}$$

We observe that the operators P_i are pairwise orthogonal; that is, $P_i P_j$ is the null operator whenever $i \neq j$.

An alternative form which is better suited for extension to infinite-dimensional Hilbert spaces is obtained as follows: Let the eigenvalues be indexed in increasing order, $\lambda_1 < \lambda_2 < \cdots < \lambda_k$, and define $Q_{\lambda_j} = \sum_{i=1}^{j} P_i$; thus Q_{λ_j} is the projection on the manifold generated by linear combinations of vectors in $M_1, \ldots, M_j$. Then, with the additional definition $Q_{\lambda_0} = 0$, we have

$$I = \sum_{i=1}^{k} (Q_{\lambda_i} - Q_{\lambda_{i-1}}), \qquad A = \sum_{i=1}^{k} \lambda_i (Q_{\lambda_i} - Q_{\lambda_{i-1}}).$$

Denoting $Q_{\lambda_i} - Q_{\lambda_{i-1}}$ by ΔQ_{λ_i}, we obtain

$$I = \sum_{i=1}^{k} \Delta Q_{\lambda_i}, \qquad A = \sum_{i=1}^{k} \lambda_i \Delta Q_{\lambda_i}.$$

These formulas suggest the integral representations

$$I = \int dQ_\lambda, \qquad A = \int \lambda \, dQ_\lambda. \tag{2.53}$$

Considerable difficulties must be overcome to give meaning to such integrals and to prove the validity of these representations in an infinite-dimensional Hilbert space. The upshot is that such representations do exist for each self-adjoint operator (even if unbounded); excellent treatments of the problem are found in the books by Lorch and by Riesz and Sz-Nagy.† We shall approach the question from a somewhat different point of view in Chapters 3 and 4.

2. Let us choose a basis within each eigenmanifold M_i; the collection of all these vectors forms a basis for $E_n^{(c)}$. The matrix representation of

† E. R. Lorch, *Spectral Theory*, Oxford University Press, New York, 1962; F. Riesz and B. Sz-Nagy, *Functional Analysis*, Ungar, New York, 1955.

A in this basis takes on the simple diagonal form

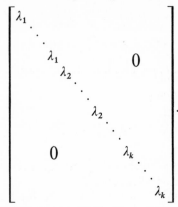

All elements outside the principal diagonal are 0. On the diagonal λ_1 occurs n_1 times, λ_2 occurs n_2 times, $\ldots$, λ_k occurs n_k times.

It is often convenient to choose the basis within M_i to be orthonormal; if this is done for each M_i, the collection of all these "little bases" forms an orthonormal basis $(\varphi_1, \ldots, \varphi_n)$ for $E_n^{(c)}$. We also introduce the new notation $\mu_1 = \cdots = \mu_{n_1} = \lambda_1; \mu_{n_1+1} = \cdots = \mu_{n_1+n_2} = \lambda_2; \ldots$. In this way each eigenvalue is now listed as often as its multiplicity (the algebraic multiplicity and geometric multiplicity are of course equal for a symmetric operator). We can then write

$$x = \sum_{i=1}^{n} \langle x, \varphi_i \rangle \varphi_i \tag{2.54}$$

and

$$Ax = \sum_{i=1}^{n} \mu_i \langle x, \varphi_i \rangle \varphi_i. \tag{2.55}$$

3. Every symmetric operator A which is not the 0 operator has at least one nonzero eigenvalue [this follows directly from (2.52) or (2.55)]. A nonsymmetric operator may have only the 0 eigenvalue, yet not be the 0 operator $\left(\text{consider } \begin{bmatrix} 0 & 1 \\ 0 & 0 \end{bmatrix}\right)$.

Extremal Principles for Symmetric Operators

Let us agree to write the eigenvalues in order of *decreasing* magnitude (each with the proper multiplicity); $|\mu_1| \geq |\mu_2| \geq \cdots \geq |\mu_n|$. The corresponding eigenvectors $\varphi_1, \ldots, \varphi_n$ have been chosen so as to form an orthonormal basis. We consider the following functionals, all of which are nonlinear:

$$I_1[x] = \|Ax\|, \qquad I_2[x] = \frac{\|Ax\|}{\|x\|}.$$

$$I_3[x] = |\langle Ax, x \rangle|, \qquad I_4[x] = \frac{|\langle Ax, x \rangle|}{\|x\|^2}.$$

We infer from the definition of $\|A\|$ that

$$\underset{x \neq 0}{\text{l.u.b.}} \, I_2[x] = \|A\|, \qquad \underset{\|x\|=1}{\text{l.u.b.}} \, I_1[x] = \|A\|.$$

We can substitute max for l.u.b. if we can exhibit a vector for which the least upper bound is attained. We show below that $x = \varphi_1$ has this property and, moreover, that $\|A\| = |\mu_1|$.

Theorem

$$\underset{\|x\|=1}{\max} I_1 = \underset{\|x\|\neq 0}{\max} I_2 = \underset{\|x\|=1}{\max} I_3 = \underset{\|x\|\neq 0}{\max} I_4 = |\mu_1| = \|A\|.$$

Proof.   We content ourselves with proofs for I_1 and I_4. We have

$$I_1[x] = \|Ax\| = \left\| \sum_{i=1}^{n} \mu_i \langle x, \varphi_i \rangle \varphi_i \right\|;$$

hence

$$I_1^2 = \sum_{i=1}^{n} |\mu_i|^2 |\langle x, \varphi_i \rangle|^2 \leq |\mu_1|^2 \sum_{i=1}^{n} |\langle x, \varphi_i \rangle|^2.$$

Since $\|x\|^2 = \sum_{i=1}^{n} |\langle x, \varphi_i \rangle|^2$, we have

$$I_1^2 \leq |\mu_1|^2, \qquad \text{for all } x \text{ such that } \|x\| = 1.$$

On the other hand, $I_1^2[\varphi_1] = |\mu_1|^2$; therefore

$$\underset{\|x\|=1}{\max} I_1 = |\mu_1|.$$

Now turning to $I_4[x]$,

$$I_4[x] = \frac{|\langle Ax, x \rangle|}{\|x\|^2} \leq \frac{\|Ax\| \, \|x\|}{\|x\|^2} \leq \|A\| = |\mu_1|.$$

But again $I_4[\varphi_1] = |\lambda_1|$, so that

$$\underset{\|x\|\neq 0}{\max} I_4 = |\mu_1|.$$

REMARK.   In the case of nonsymmetric operators, all that can be said is

$$|\mu_1| \leq \underset{\|x\|=1}{\max} I_1 = \underset{\|x\|\neq 0}{\max} I_2 = \|A\|;$$

$$|\mu_1| \leq \underset{\|x\|=1}{\max} I_3 = \underset{\|x\|\neq 0}{\max} I_4 \leq \|A\|.$$

As an example, consider the operator on $E_n^{(c)}$ whose matrix in the orthonormal basis (φ_1, φ_2) is $\begin{bmatrix} 0 & 1 \\ 0 & 0 \end{bmatrix}$; then $A(\xi_1 \varphi_1 + \xi_2 \varphi_2) = \xi_2 \varphi_1$;

hence $\|A\| = 1$. One sees easily that the only eigenvalue of A is $\mu_1 = 0$. We also have

$$|\langle Ax, x \rangle| = |\langle \xi_2 \varphi_1, \xi_1 \varphi_1 + \xi_2 \varphi_2 \rangle| = |\xi_2 \bar{\xi}_1| = |\xi_2| \, |\xi_1|$$

and

$$\max_{\|x\|=1} |\langle Ax, x \rangle| = \max_{|\xi_1|^2 + |\xi_2|^2 = 1} |\xi_2| \, |\xi_1| = \tfrac{1}{2}.$$

EXERCISES

2.31 *Every bounded set in $E_n^{(c)}$ is compact.* This is an extension of the Bolzano-Weierstrass theorem for the real line. This theorem states that every sequence chosen from a bounded set of real numbers must contain a convergent subsequence. (In other words, every bounded set on the real line is compact.) Assuming this theorem, prove that every bounded set in $E_n^{(c)}$ is compact.

2.32. Consider $P_n(0, 1)$, the n-dimensional linear space of all polynomials $x(t)$ of degree less than n defined on $0 \le t \le 1$. If we differentiate such a polynomial we again get a polynomial in $P_n(0, 1)$. Prove that this differentiation operator is linear, and find its matrix in the basis $\{1, t, \ldots, t^{n-1}\}$.

2.33 Let $[A]_B$ be the matrix of A in the basis B: $\{e_1, \ldots, e_n\}$. Show that the maximal number of linearly independent rows of $[A]_B$ is just the rank $\rho(A)$ of the transformation A. Show further that the maximal number of linearly independent columns of $[A]_B$ equals $\rho(A^*)$.

2.34 Show that $(AB)^* = B^*A^*$.

2.35 (a) Show that the necessary and sufficient condition for A to be the 0 transformation (written $A = 0$) is that $\langle Ax, y \rangle = 0$ for all x and y.

    (b) Let A be a transformation on $E_n^{(c)}$. The *polar identity*

$$\langle A(\alpha x + \beta y), \alpha x + \beta y \rangle$$
$$= \bar{\alpha}\alpha \langle Ax, x \rangle + \bar{\beta}\beta \langle Ay, y \rangle + \alpha\bar{\beta} \langle Ax, y \rangle + \beta\bar{\alpha} \langle Ay, x \rangle$$

is easily derived by expanding the left side. Set $\alpha = 1, \beta = \pm 1$, and subtract the resulting forms of the polar identity to obtain

$$\langle Ax, y \rangle + \langle Ay, x \rangle = \tfrac{1}{2}\{\langle A(x + y), x + y \rangle - \langle A(x - y), x - y \rangle\}.$$

Set $\alpha = 1, \beta = \pm i$, and subtract the resulting forms of the polar identity to obtain

$$\langle Ax, y \rangle - \langle Ay, x \rangle = \tfrac{1}{2}\{\langle A(x + iy), x + iy \rangle - \langle A(x - iy), x - iy \rangle\}.$$

By adding the last two equations, we have

$$\langle Ax, y \rangle = \tfrac{1}{4}\{\langle A(x + y), x + y \rangle - \langle A(x - y), x - y \rangle$$
$$+ \langle A(x + iy), x + iy \rangle - \langle A(x - iy), x - iy \rangle\}.$$

This last identity expresses $\langle Ax, y \rangle$ solely in terms of quadratic forms of the type $\langle Af, f \rangle$.

(c) Show that the necessary and sufficient condition for the transformation A on $E_n^{(c)}$ to be the 0 transformation is that $\langle Ax, x \rangle = 0$ for all x in $E_n^{(c)}$. Observe that this theorem is not true for transformations on $E_n^{(r)}$.

(d) Show that the necessary and sufficient condition for the transformation A on $E_n^{(c)}$ to be symmetric is that $\langle Ax, x \rangle$ is real for all x in $E_n^{(c)}$.

2.36 A transformation A on $E_n^{(c)}$ is *positive* if $\langle Ax, x \rangle > 0$ for every $x \neq 0$. From Exercise 2.35 it follows that a positive transformation must be symmetric. If A is positive, show that its eigenvalues are all positive. If A is symmetric and its eigenvalues are all positive, show that A is positive. If A is positive, show that there exists a unique positive transformation B such that $B^2 = A$ (of course we call B the square root of A and write $B = \sqrt{A}$).

2.37 A transformation A on $E_n^{(c)}$ is *nonnegative* if $\langle Ax, x \rangle \geq 0$ for every x in $E_n^{(c)}$. From Exercise 2.35 it follows that a nonnegative transformation is symmetric. If A is nonnegative, prove that its eigenvalues are all nonnegative. If A is symmetric and its eigenvalues are all nonnegative, show that A is nonnegative. If A is nonnegative, show that there exists a unique nonnegative transformation B such that $B^2 = A$. (We write $B = \sqrt{A}$.) Observe that positive transformations are particular cases of nonnegative transformations.

2.38 Define negative and nonpositive transformations, and derive properties similar to those in Exercises 2.36 and 2.37. Of course there exist symmetric transformations which do not fall in any of the four categories mentioned in Exercises 2.36 and 2.37. Such transformations are called *indefinite*. Give an example of an indefinite symmetric transformation.

2.39 If A is an arbitrary transformation on $E_n^{(c)}$, $(A - \lambda I)^* = A^* - \bar{\lambda}I$. From the alternative theorem it follows that the eigenvalues of A^* are the complex conjugates of the eigenvalues of A. Show that A^*A and AA^* are nonnegative transformations (hence symmetric). Show by an example that A^*A and AA^* may be different, but prove that A^*A and AA^* always have the same eigenvalues. Let v_1 be the eigenvalue of largest magnitude of A^*A; show that $\|A\|^2 = |v_1|$.

2.8   THE INVERSE OF A LINEAR TRANSFORMATION IN HILBERT SPACE

We recall that a transformation A is one-to-one if the equality $Af = Ag$ implies $f = g$. A one-to-one transformation has an inverse A^{-1} whose domain is the range of A and whose range is the domain of A.

As usual, we restrict ourselves to linear transformations. Let A be a linear transformation on the linear manifold D_A. The following simple criterion can be used to decide whether or not A is one-to-one.

Theorem.   *The linear operator A is one-to-one (that is, has an inverse A^{-1}) if and only if $Ax = 0$ implies $x = 0$.*

Proof.   (a) Suppose A is one-to-one. For any linear operator $A0 = 0$; hence 0 is a solution of $Ax = 0$. Since A is one-to-one, this is the only solution.

(b) If $Ax = 0$ has only the 0 solution, let $Ax = f$ have solutions x_1 and x_2. The element $y = x_1 - x_2$ is in the domain of A (since this domain is a linear manifold); the linearity of A implies $Ay = Ax_1 - Ax_2 = f - f = 0$, so that $y = 0$ and $x_1 = x_2$. The operator A^{-1} is easily seen to be a linear operator whose domain is R_A and whose range is D_A.

The principal problem of operator theory is the solution of the inhomogeneous equation $Ax = f$. Here A is a known transformation, f is a given element of the Hilbert space $\mathscr{A}$, and we wish to find all solutions x. Four questions immediately come to mind:

1. For what elements f is a solution possible? (That is, how can we characterize R_A?)

2. Is the solution unique? This has already been answered. The solution is unique if and only if the homogeneous equation $Ax = 0$ has only the trivial solution.

3. Does the solution depend continuously on f? This is particularly important in applications; if the source function f is changed by a "small" amount, we would like the solution to be changed by a "small" amount. Mathematically we want A^{-1} to be continuous (that is, bounded).

4. How do we construct the solution(s)? This is of course the most difficult of these questions, and much of the remainder of this book is devoted to this problem in one form or another.

DEFINITION.   The transformation A is *regular* if all the following conditions are satisfied:
(a) $Ax = 0$ has only the 0 solution.
(b) $R_A = \mathscr{A}$.
(c) A^{-1} is bounded.

The first condition guarantees that $Ax = f$ has at most one solution, hence that A^{-1} exists. The second condition tells us that for each f in $\mathscr{A}$ there is at least one solution of $Ax = f$; hence by appealing to the first condition, $Ax = f$ has one and only one solution for each f in $\mathscr{A}$. The third condition guarantees that if f_1 and f_2 are close, say $\|f_1 - f_2\| < \varepsilon$, the respective solutions x_1 and x_2 are close; that is, $\|x_1 - x_2\| < \|A^{-1}\|\varepsilon$.

DEFINITION.   A transformation A is *essentially regular* if conditions (1) and (3) for a regular transformation are satisfied but $R_A \neq \mathscr{A}$, yet $\bar{R}_A = \mathscr{A}$.

see p9/4/ (2)

If A is essentially regular, it can be extended in a simple manner to a regular transformation. Since A^{-1} is bounded and defined on a dense set (R_A), it can be extended to the whole of $\mathscr{A}$ by continuity. Let us call this extension of A^{-1} by the letter B. The operator B is invertible and its inverse B^{-1} is clearly an extension of A. Furthermore B^{-1} is regular.

DEFINITION.   If A is neither regular nor essentially regular, it is said to be *singular*.

Classification of Singular Operators

If an operator A is singular, it can happen only in the following mutually exclusive ways:

1. $Ax = 0$ has a nontrivial solution (that is, A^{-1} does not exist).
2. $Ax = 0$ has only the trivial solution, but A^{-1} is unbounded and $\bar{R}_A = \mathscr{A}$. (That is, A^{-1} is unbounded and either $R_A = \mathscr{A}$ or $R_A \neq \mathscr{A}$, but R_A is dense in $\mathscr{A}$.)
3. $Ax = 0$ has only the trivial solution, but $\bar{R}_A \neq \mathscr{A}$. (Here A^{-1} may be bounded or unbounded.)

Although this classification is exhaustive, it is rather coarse-grained. Considerable simplifications and refinements ensue for special categories of operators.

In our work we encounter only closable operators; by the method outlined in Section 2.6, a closable operator can be extended in a natural way (through closure) to a closed operator. We attain certain simplifications in the case of a closed operator because of the following properties:

(a) If A is closed and A^{-1} exists, then A^{-1} is closed.
(b) If A is closed and its inverse is bounded, then R_A is a closed set.
(c) A closed operator on a closed domain is bounded.

To prove (a), let $f_n \to f$ and let $x_n = A^{-1}f_n \to x$. We must show that $A^{-1}f = x$. Since $Ax_n = f_n$ and $f_n \to f$ and $x_n \to x$, it follows from the fact that A is closed that x must be in the domain of A and that $Ax = f$. Therefore, $A^{-1}f = x$. To prove (b), let f_n be a sequence in R_A for which $f_n \to f$; we wish to show that f is in R_A. Let $Ax_n = f_n$; since f_n is a Cauchy sequence and A^{-1} is bounded, x_n is also a Cauchy sequence; therefore, x_n has a limit, say x. Thus $x_n \to x$ and $Ax_n = f_n \to f$; since A is closed we know that x is in D_A and $Ax = f$. Therefore, f is in R_A and R_A is closed. The proof of (c) is somewhat more difficult and is omitted. In the light of property (b), we note that a closed operator cannot be essentially regular (it must be either regular or singular). Moreover if a closed operator is singular in category 2, it must be so because A^{-1} is unbounded and $R_A \neq \mathscr{A}$, yet $\bar{R}_A = \mathscr{A}$. Indeed from property (a), A^{-1} is closed; since the domain of A^{-1} is R_A, it follows from property (c) that $R_A \neq \mathscr{A}$.

Classification of Closed Operators

A closed operator *must* fall in one of the following mutually exclusive classes:

1. A is regular.
2. $Ax = 0$ has a nontrivial solution (A^{-1} does not exist).
3. $Ax = 0$ has only the trivial solution, and A^{-1} is unbounded, and $R_A \neq \mathscr{A}$, and $\bar{R}_A = \mathscr{A}$.
4. $Ax = 0$ has only the trivial solution and $\bar{R}_A \neq \mathscr{A}$ (A^{-1} either bounded or unbounded).

We should observe an important distinction between cases 3 and 4; in case 4 there exist nonzero elements in $\mathscr{A}$ which are orthogonal to R_A, whereas in case 3 only the zero element in $\mathscr{A}$ is orthogonal to R_A.

The examples below show that any of the possibilities listed above can actually take place, even when the operator A is continuous.

EXAMPLES OF OPERATORS ON $\mathscr{L}_2$

Example 1. (a) The zero transformation is bounded, therefore closed. It is not one-to-one and therefore not invertible. The transformation is singular in category 2.

(b) The identity transformation is bounded and hence closed. It is one-to-one and $Ix = 0$ has only the 0 solution. The range of I is the whole of $\mathscr{A}$. Furthermore, $I^{-1} = I$, and the inverse is bounded. This operator is magnificently regular.

Example 2. $Ax = tx(t)$; $\mathscr{A} = \mathscr{L}_2^{(c)}(0, 1)$. The transformation is bounded and therefore closed. Since $Ax = 0$ has only the trivial solution, A^{-1} exists. The range of A contains only those elements f for which f/t is in $\mathscr{A}$. The element $f = 1$ is therefore not in R_A, but R_A includes all elements in $\mathscr{A}$ which vanish in a neighborhood of $t = 0$; such elements are dense in $\mathscr{A}$; hence $\bar{R}_A = \mathscr{A}$. The transformation is therefore in category 3, and A^{-1} must be unbounded [this has already been shown directly in Example 3(b) of Section 2.6].

Example 3. $Ax = x(t + h)$, h is a fixed real number; $\mathscr{A} = \mathscr{L}_2^{(c)}(-\infty, \infty)$. The transformation is bounded, invertible, and $A^{-1}f = f(t - h)$. We have $\|A^{-1}\| = 1$, $R_A = \mathscr{A}$, and A is regular.

Example 4. $Ax = \int_0^t x(s)ds$; $\mathscr{A} = \mathscr{L}_2^{(c)}(0, 1)$. This transformation is bounded, hence closed. Since $Ax = 0$ implies $x = 0$, the transformation is one-to-one and invertible. The range of A consists only of absolutely continuous functions which vanish at $t = 0$. Thus $R_A \neq \mathscr{A}$, but R_A is dense in $\mathscr{A}$. The transformation is therefore in category 3, and A^{-1} must be unbounded (indeed $A^{-1} = d/dt$ on R_A). As in Example 2 we observe that the inverse of a bounded operator may be unbounded.

Example 5. *The shift operator.* Let $\mathscr{A} = \mathscr{L}_2^{(c)}(0, 1)$, and consider a complete orthonormal set $\varphi_1(t), \ldots, \varphi_n(t), \ldots$ on $\mathscr{A}$. If $x(t)$ is an arbitrary element of $\mathscr{A}$, we have

$$x = a_1\varphi_1 + a_2\varphi_2 + \cdots = \sum_{k=1}^{\infty} a_k\varphi_k; \qquad a_k = \langle x, \varphi_k \rangle.$$

Define the linear transformation A by

$$y = Ax = a_1\varphi_2 + a_2\varphi_3 + \cdots = \sum_{k=1}^{\infty} a_k\varphi_{k+1}.$$

Thus the Fourier coefficients of x have been shifted to the right to obtain y. The necessary and sufficient condition for x to be in $\mathscr{A}$ is that $\sum_{k=1}^{\infty} |a_k|^2$ converges. Whenever x is in $\mathscr{A}$, it follows that y is in $\mathscr{A}$; moreover, $\|y\| = \|x\|$; hence A is bounded and $\|A\| = 1$. The range of A is the *closed* set consisting of all vectors in $\mathscr{A}$ having 0 component along φ_1; hence $R_A \neq \mathscr{A}$. This operator is in category 4. The inverse is easily calculated; let f be in R_A; that is, $f = \sum_{k=2}^{\infty} b_k\varphi_k$, where $\sum_{k=2}^{\infty} |b_k|^2$ converges. Then $Ax = f$ has the one and only solution $x = \sum_{k=1}^{\infty} b_{k+1}\varphi_k$. Note that A^{-1} is bounded and that $\|A^{-1}\| = 1$.

Example 6. *A modified shift operator.* The notation is the same as in Example 5, but we now define the linear operator B by

$$Bx = \sum_{k=1}^{\infty} \frac{a_k}{k^2} \varphi_{k+1}.$$

This operator is defined for all x in $\mathscr{A}$, and is bounded (in fact, $\|B\| = 1$), and therefore closed. Every vector f in R_B has the property $\langle f, \varphi_1 \rangle = 0$; the homogeneous equation $Bx = 0$ has only the trivial solution, hence B is in category 4. In contrast with Example 5, the range is not closed, and the inverse is unbounded (for a closed operator, the fact that the range is not closed implies that the inverse is unbounded). It is easy to see that R_B is not closed. Let S stand for the set of all vectors f such that $\langle f, \varphi_1 \rangle = 0$. By double inclusion, we prove that $S = \bar{R}_B$. If f is in $\bar{R}_B$, there exists a sequence f_n of vectors in R_B such that $f_n \to f$; since $\langle f_n, \varphi_1 \rangle = 0$, the continuity of the inner product implies $\langle f, \varphi_1 \rangle = 0$; hence $\bar{R}_B \subset S$. If f is in S, $f = \sum_{k=2}^{\infty} a_k\varphi_k$ and $f = \lim_{p \to \infty} f_p$, where $f_p = \sum_{k=2}^{p} a_k\varphi_k$; the element f_p is in R_B because $f_p = Bx_p$, where $x_p = \sum_{k=1}^{p-1} k^2 a_{k+1}\varphi_k$; therefore, f is in $\bar{R}_B$ and $\bar{R}_B \supset S$. Since $\bar{R}_B \subset S$ and $\bar{R}_B \supset S$, we must have $\bar{R}_B = S$; since the element $f = \sum_{k=2}^{\infty} \frac{1}{k} \varphi_k$ is in S but not in R_B, we have $R_B \neq S$, or $R_B \neq \bar{R}_B$.

The Adjoint Operator

We begin with the case of a bounded linear operator A defined over the whole Hilbert space $\mathscr{A}$. Consider $\langle Ax, y \rangle$, where y is a fixed element of $\mathscr{A}$ and x runs through all values in $\mathscr{A}$. It is clear that $\langle Ax, y \rangle$ is a bounded linear functional in x; by the Riesz representation theorem, there exists an unambiguous element g such that

$$\langle Ax, y \rangle = \langle x, g \rangle, \qquad \text{for all } x \text{ in } \mathscr{A}. \tag{2.56}$$

The element g depends on the choice of y. We write $g = A^*y$, and it is easily seen that A^* is a linear operator defined over the whole space $\mathscr{A}$. The operator A^* is known as the *adjoint* of A; A^* is bounded and $\|A^*\| = \|A\|$. If x and y are any two elements of $\mathscr{A}$, we have

$$\langle Ax, y \rangle = \langle x, A^*y \rangle. \tag{2.57}$$

Now let A be an unbounded linear operator defined on a linear manifold D_A which, for reasons that will soon become apparent, is taken to be dense in $\mathscr{A}$. Let y be a fixed element of $\mathscr{A}$ and consider $\langle Ax, y \rangle$ as x runs through D_A. Again $\langle Ax, y \rangle$ is a linear functional (possibly unbounded) for x in D_A. It may happen that for some elements y we can write

$$\langle Ax, y \rangle = \langle x, g \rangle, \qquad \text{for all } x \text{ in } D_A. \tag{2.58}$$

Any pair of elements (y, g) for which (2.58) holds for all x in D_A will be called an *admissible pair*. Clearly g will depend on y; in order to state that g is an operator acting on y, we must first establish that g is unambiguously determined from y. This is where the assumption that D_A is dense in $\mathscr{A}$ plays a crucial role. If (2.58) were valid for two different elements g_1 and g_2, it would follow that $\langle x, g_1 - g_2 \rangle = 0$ for all x in D_A. Since D_A is dense in $\mathscr{A}$, we conclude that $g_1 - g_2 = 0$; hence, for a given y, there is at most one g for which (2.58) holds. Now consider the set of *all* vectors y for which (2.58) holds; then g depends on y and we write $g = A^*y$. The operator A^* is the *adjoint* of A; A^* has a well-defined domain D_{A^*} which includes at least the 0 vector. Indeed,

$$\langle Ax, 0 \rangle = 0 = \langle x, 0 \rangle, \qquad \text{for all } x \text{ in } D_A;$$

comparing with (2.58) we see that $(0, 0)$ is an admissible pair; hence 0 is in D_{A^*} and $A^*0 = 0$. If x is any element in D_A and y is any element in D_{A^*}, we have

$$\langle Ax, y \rangle = \langle x, A^*y \rangle. \tag{2.59}$$

The operator A^* is easily seen to be linear. We now show that A^* is closed (whether or not A is closed). Let $y_1, \ldots, y_n, \ldots$ be a sequence in D_{A^*} which converges to y, and let $A^*y_1, \ldots, A^*y_n, \ldots$ converge to g. By the continuity of the inner product, $\lim_{n \to \infty} \langle Ax, y_n \rangle = \langle Ax, y \rangle$ and $\lim_{n \to \infty} \langle x, A^*y_n \rangle = \langle x, g \rangle$;

since $\langle Ax, y_n \rangle = \langle x, A^*y_n \rangle$ for all x in D_A, it follows that $\langle Ax, y \rangle = \langle x, g \rangle$ for all x in D_A. Hence (y, g) is an admissible pair; that is, y is in D_{A^*} and $g = A^*y$, so that A^* is a closed operator. The following proposition will be of some use to us. If B is an extension of A, then A^* is an extension of B^* (that is, if $B \supset A$, then $A^* \supset B^*$). We must show that if (y, g) is an admissible pair for the operator B, it is also admissible for the operator A (this guarantees that $D_{A^*} \supset D_{B^*}$ and that $A^*y = B^*y$ when y is in D_{B^*}; hence $A^* \supset B^*$). Let (y, g) be an admissible pair for B; then

$$\langle Bx, y \rangle = \langle x, g \rangle, \qquad \text{for all } x \text{ in } D_B.$$

Since by assumption $D_B \supset D_A$ and $Bx = Ax$ for x in D_A, we have

$$\langle Ax, y \rangle = \langle x, g \rangle, \qquad \text{for all } x \text{ in } D_A.$$

Hence (y, g) is admissible for A and $A^* \supset B^*$. We collect some useful properties of adjoint operators:

1. If D_A is dense in $\mathscr{A}$, A^* exists (and its domain D_{A^*} is unambiguously defined; without further information on A we can guarantee only that D_{A^*} includes the 0 element).

2. A^* is a linear operator.

3. A^* is closed (whether or not A is closed).

4. $B \supset A$ implies $A^* \supset B^*$.

5. If A is bounded and defined on the whole of $\mathscr{A}$, A^* is bounded and is defined on the whole of $\mathscr{A}$.

6. If A^{**} exists (that is, if D_{A^*} is dense in $\mathscr{A}$), then $A \subset A^{**}$ (see exercise 2.41).

7. If A is closable, A and $\bar{A}$ have the same adjoint; thus $A^* = (\bar{A})^*$ (see Exercise 2.40).

8. If A is closed and D_A is dense in $\mathscr{A}$, D_{A^*} is dense in $\mathscr{A}$. Hence A^{**} exists and moreover $A = A^{**}$ (proof omitted).

The adjoint operator plays a central role in determining the existence of solutions to the inhomogeneous equation $Ax = f$.

Theorem. $(R_A)^\perp = N_{A^*}$. *The null space of the adjoint is the orthogonal complement of the range of the original operator.*

Proof. (a) To show $N_A \supset (R_A)^\perp$. Let z be in $(R_A)^\perp$; then $\langle Ax, z \rangle = 0 = \langle x, 0 \rangle$ for every x in D_A. Thus $(z, 0)$ is an admissible pair, which means that z is in D_{A^*} and $A^*z = 0$; therefore, z is in N_{A^*}.

(b) To show $N_{A^*} \subset (R_A)^\perp$. Let z be in N_{A^*}; that is, $A^*z = 0$. Then $\langle x, A^*z \rangle = 0$ for every x (and a fortiori for every x in D_A); hence $\langle Ax, z \rangle = 0$ for every x in D_A. Therefore z is in $(R_A)^\perp$.

Combining the two inclusions, we have $N_A = (R_A)^\perp$.

COROLLARY 1. *Since* $\bar{R}_A = (R_A)^{\perp\perp}$, *we also have* $\bar{R}_A = (N_{A^*})^\perp$.

COROLLARY 2.   *If R_A is a closed set, $R_A = (N_{A*})^{\perp}$.*

We restate Corollary 2 as a theorem.

Alternative Theorem. *If R_A is closed, the necessary and sufficient condition for $Ax = f$ to have a solution is that $\langle f, z \rangle = 0$ for every z which is a solution of $A*z = 0$. (Of course, if f satisfies the " consistency" conditions $\langle f, z \rangle = 0$, the solution of $Ax = f$ may not be unique. We have $x = x_H + x_P$, where x_P is a particular solution of the inhomogeneous equation and x_H is the general solution of the homogeneous equation $Ax_H = 0$.)*

DEFINITION.   An operator is said to be *self-adjoint* if $A = A*$. Thus A is self-adjoint if and only if
(a) $D_A = D_{A*}$.
(b) $Ax = A*x$, for every x in D_A.

Alternative Theorem for Self-Adjoint Operators.   *Let A be self-adjoint and R_A be closed. The necessary and sufficient condition for $Ax = f$ to have a solution is that $\langle f, z \rangle = 0$ for every z which is a solution of $Az = 0$.*

DEFINITION.   An operator A is called *symmetric* if, for any pair of elements x and y both in D_A,

$$\langle Ax, y \rangle = \langle x, Ay \rangle. \tag{2.60}$$

If A is symmetric, then (y, Ay) is an admissible pair and therefore y is in D_{A*} and for such elements $A*y = Ay$. (Of course, this may not exhaust all elements in D_{A*}.) Thus, if A is symmetric, $A* \supset A$. On the other hand, if $A* \supset A$, then, whenever x and y are in D_A, we have $\langle Ax, y \rangle = \langle x, A*y \rangle = \langle x, Ay \rangle$; hence A is symmetric. Thus the necessary and sufficient condition for A to be symmetric is $A* \supset A$. The necessary and sufficient condition for a symmetric operator to be self-adjoint is $D_{A*} = D_A$. It may happen for an unbounded symmetric operator that D_{A*} is a larger domain than D_A; hence the operator would not be self-adjoint. If the symmetric operator is defined for the whole of $\mathscr{A}$ (as is the case for bounded symmetric operators), then $D_{A*} = D_A = \mathscr{A}$, and the operator is self-adjoint.
The examples below should help to clarify the preceding discussion.

EXAMPLES

Example 1. $Ax = tx(t)$; $\mathscr{A} = \mathscr{L}_2^{(c)}(0, 1)$. The domain of A is the whole of $\mathscr{A}$. Consider $\langle Ax, y \rangle$ for any two elements in $\mathscr{A}$; then

$$\langle Ax, y \rangle = \int_0^1 tx(t)\bar{y}(t)dt = \int_0^1 x(t)t\bar{y}(t)dt = \int_0^1 x\overline{A*y}\, dt,$$

where $A*y = ty$. Thus $A = A*$ and A is self-adjoint. The homogeneous equation $tx = 0$ has only the 0 solution, but the alternative theorem does not apply, because R_A is not closed. Thus the equation $Ax = f$ must be investigated directly; as we have already seen in previous investigation, a solution exists if and only if $\int_0^1 (|f|^2/t^2)dt < \infty$. The unique solution is then $x = f/t$.

Example 2. The identity operator is self-adjoint; λI has the adjoint $\bar{\lambda}I$. If A^* is the adjoint of A, $A^* - \bar{\lambda}I$ is the adjoint of $A - \lambda I$.

Example 3. $Ax = \int_0^t x(s)ds$; $\mathscr{A} = \mathscr{L}_2^{(c)}(0, 1)$. This operator is bounded and is defined over the whole of $\mathscr{A}$. Let x and y be two elements of $\mathscr{A}$; then

$$\langle Ax, y \rangle = \int_0^1 dt \left[\bar{y}(t) \int_0^t x(s)ds \right].$$

Interchanging the order of integration (the reader should visualize the triangular region over which the double integral is being performed), one obtains

$$\langle Ax, y \rangle = \int_0^1 x(s)ds \left[\int_s^1 \bar{y}(t)dt \right] = \int_0^1 x(s)\overline{A^*y}\, ds,$$

where $A^*y = \int_s^1 y(\alpha)d\alpha$. It is clear that A is not a symmetric operator.

The homogeneous equations $Ax = 0$ and $A^*x = 0$ have only the trivial solution. The range of A consists of all elements in $\mathscr{A}$ which are absolutely continuous and which vanish at $t = 0$. Thus R_A is not closed but is dense in $\mathscr{A}$. Since the alternative theorem is not applicable, we proceed from basic considerations to solve the inhomogeneous equation $\int_0^t x(s)ds = f(t)$.

If $f(t)$ is absolutely continuous, and $f(0) = 0$, the one and only solution of the inhomogeneous equation is given by $x(t) = f'(t)$. Therefore, A^{-1} is unbounded, and A is in category 3 (see the classification of closed operators).

Example 4. Let A be defined as in Example 3 and consider the bounded linear operator $A - \lambda I$, where λ is an arbitrary given complex number different from 0. The range of this operator will be denoted by $R(\lambda)$. Remarkably enough, the range is now the whole of $\mathscr{A}$. We first show that the homogeneous equations $Ax - \lambda x = 0$ and $A^*z - \bar{\lambda}z = 0$ have only the trivial solution. The first equation is $(1/\lambda)\int_0^t x(s)ds = x(t)$; this requires that $x(t)$ be differentiable and that $x(0) = 0$; differentiating, we obtain

$$\frac{1}{\lambda}x(t) = x'(t), \; x(0) = 0.$$

The solution of the differential equation is $Ce^{t/\lambda}$; the boundary condition yields $C = 0$. In a similar way we can show that the adjoint equation $\int^1 x(s)ds = \bar{\lambda}x(t)$ has only the trivial solution.

Consider now the inhomogeneous equation

$$Ax - \lambda x = \int_0^t x(s)ds - \lambda x(t) = f(t). \tag{2.61}$$

We can solve this equation by elementary methods; let $u(t) = f(t) + \lambda x(t)$; then

$$\int_0^t x(s)ds = u(t).$$

Hence $u(t)$ is differentiable and $u(0) = 0$; differentiation of the above equation yields

$$x(t) = u'(t) \qquad \text{or} \qquad u'(t) - \frac{u(t)}{\lambda} = -\frac{f(t)}{\lambda}.$$

The one and only solution of this equation satisfying $u(0) = 0$ is

$$u(t) = -\frac{e^{t/\lambda}}{\lambda} \int_0^t f(\tau)e^{-\tau/\lambda}\,d\tau.$$

Therefore,

$$x(t) = -\frac{f(t)}{\lambda} - \frac{e^{t/\lambda}}{\lambda^2} \int_0^t f(\tau)e^{-\tau/\lambda}\,d\tau. \tag{2.62}$$

One easily verifies that this last expression satisfies the inhomogeneous equation (2.61). Thus, for each f in $\mathscr{A}$ and each $\lambda \neq 0$, there exists one and only one solution of (2.61), namely (2.62). The statement that $R(\lambda)$ is the whole of $\mathscr{A}$ has been proved; it can be shown from (2.62) that the inverse of $A - \lambda I$ is bounded. Hence for each $\lambda \neq 0$, $A - \lambda I$ is *regular*. For $\lambda = 0$, we have seen in Example 3 that the operator is singular in category 3.

Example 5. We are interested in investigating the differentiation operator d/dt. The notion of an operator requires a specification of the domain of definition; since we are about to consider d/dt over many different domains we shall really be studying many different operators. We always require that an element $x(t)$ in the domain of any of these operators shall satisfy:

$$x(t) \text{ absolutely continuous}; \qquad x \text{ and } x' \text{ in } \mathscr{L}_2^{(c)}(0, 1). \tag{I}$$

Further restrictions on the domain will be in the nature of boundary conditions. These will be different in the various parts below.

(a) We impose no further restrictions on the domain; thus $A_1 = d/dt$ and the domain of A_1 (denoted by D_1) consists of all functions satisfying (I).

Let us first show that A_1 is closed. Let x_n be a sequence in D_1 such that $x_n \to x$ and $A_1 x_n = x_n' \to h$. Then

$$x_n(t) = \int_0^t x_n'(s)ds + x_n(0);$$

hence

$$\lim_{n \to \infty} x_n(t) = x(t) = \lim_{n \to \infty}\left[\int_0^t x_n'(s)ds + x_n(0) \right] = \int_0^t h(s)ds + \lim_{n \to \infty} x_n(0).$$

We infer from the above that $\lim_{n \to \infty} x_n(0)$ exists and that $x'(t) = h(t)$, so that A_1 is closed. To find A_1^* we must determine *all admissible pairs* of elements (y, g) such that

$$\langle A_1 x, y \rangle = \langle x, g \rangle, \qquad \text{for all } x \text{ in } D_1. \qquad (2.63)$$

Some admissible pairs (y, g) can be found in a simple manner (it will turn out that the procedure yields all such pairs). Assume that y satisfies condition (I); we can then integrate by parts to obtain

$$\langle A_1 x, y \rangle = \int_0^1 \bar{y} \frac{dx}{dt} \, dt = -\int_0^1 x \frac{d\bar{y}}{dt} \, dt + [\bar{y} x]_0^1. \qquad (2.64)$$

It is clear that if $y(0) = 0$, $y(1) = 0$, and $g = -dy/dt$, then

$$\langle A_1 x, y \rangle = \langle x, g \rangle, \qquad \text{for all } x \text{ in } D_1.$$

We have shown that if y satisfies condition (I) and

$$y(0) = 0, \qquad y(1) = 0, \qquad \text{(II)}$$

and if $g = -dy/dt$, then (y, g) is an admissible pair. Therefore, y is in the domain of A_1^*, and

$$g = A_1^* y = -\frac{dy}{dt}.$$

We now want to prove that if (y, g) is a pair for which (2.63) holds, then y *must* satisfy conditions (I) and (II) and g *must* be $-dy/dt$. The function $\int_0^t g(s) \, ds$ has $g(t)$ for a derivative; starting from the right side of (2.63) and integrating by parts,

$$\int_0^1 x \bar{g} \, dt = -\int_0^1 x' \left[\int_0^t \bar{g}(s) \, ds \right] dt + \left[x \int_0^t \bar{g}(s) \, ds \right]_0^1$$

$$= -\int_0^1 x' \left[\int_0^t \bar{g}(s) \, ds \right] dt + x(1) \int_0^1 \bar{g}(s) \, ds.$$

Since the constant function $x_1(t) = 1$ is in D_1 and $\langle A_1 x, y \rangle = 0$, we immediately conclude that $\int_0^1 \bar{g}(s) \, ds = 0$, or

$$\int_0^1 g(s) \, ds = 0. \qquad (2.65)$$

Thus

$$\langle x, g \rangle = -\int_0^1 x'(t) \left[\int_0^t \bar{g}(s) \, ds \right] dt.$$

Since $\langle A_1 x, y \rangle = \int_0^1 (dx/dt) \bar{y} \, dt$ and since we require $\langle A_1 x, y \rangle = \langle x, g \rangle$, we must have

$$\int_0^1 x'(t) \left[\bar{y} + \int_0^t \bar{g}(s) \, ds \right] dt = 0, \qquad \text{for all } x \text{ in } D_1. \qquad (2.66)$$

The function $x_0(t) = \int_0^t dt \left[y(u) + \int_0^u g(s)ds \right]$ is in D_1, and $x_0'(t) = y(t) + \int_0^t g(s)ds$. Substituting $x_0(t)$ for x in (2.66), we obtain

$$\int_0^1 \left| y(t) + \int_0^t g(s)ds \right|^2 dt = 0.$$

Hence $y(t) = -\int_0^t g(s)ds$. From this and (2.65) it follows that

$$g(t) = -\frac{dy}{dt}; \qquad y(0) = 0, \quad y(1) = 0.$$

Thus $A_1^* = -d/dt$ and the domain of A_1^* consists precisely of those elements satisfying conditions (I) and (II). [In the cumbersome terminology of Chapter 1, we say that $-d/dt$ is the formal adjoint of d/dt, and that the adjoint boundary conditions are given by (II).]

The homogeneous equation $A_1 x = 0$ has the nontrivial solution $x = C$; the adjoint equation $A_1^* y = 0$ has only the trivial solution $[-dy/dt = 0$ with $y(0) = 0$, $y(1) = 0$ has only the 0 solution]. The range of A_1 is the whole of $\mathscr{L}_2^{(c)}(0, 1)$ and hence is a closed set; the alternative theorem applies and $A_1 x = f$ (that is, $dx/dt = f$) always has solutions. The solution is not unique, the general solution being $x(t) = C + \int_0^t f(s)ds$.

(b) We impose the further restriction:

$$x(0) = 0. \tag{III}$$

Thus $A_2 = d/dt$ and the domain D_2 consists of all functions satisfying (I) and (III). It can be established that D_2 is dense in $\mathscr{L}_2^{(c)}(0, 1)$ and that A_2 is closed.

Proceeding heuristically, we can calculate A_2^*. Consider

$$\langle A_2 x, y \rangle = \int_0^1 \frac{dx}{dt} \bar{y} \, dt.$$

Integration by parts (assuming y to be differentiable) yields

$$\langle A_2 x, y \rangle = -\int_0^1 x \frac{d\bar{y}}{dt} \, dt + x(1)\bar{y}(1).$$

In order for the right side to be of the form $\langle x, g \rangle$ for all x in D_2, we need $y(1) = 0$ and $g = -dy/dt$. Thus A_2^* is the operator $-d/dt$ with domain consisting of all functions satisfying (I) and

$$x(1) = 0. \tag{IV}$$

A rigorous proof would follow the lines of **(a)**. One can show again that A_2 is closed and that it has a closed range [the whole of $\mathscr{L}_2^{(c)}(0, 1)$]. Since the homogeneous equations $A_2 x = 0$ and $A_2^* y = 0$ have only the trivial solution, $A_2 x = f$ always has a unique solution, $x(t) = \int_0^t f(s)ds$.

(c) In addition to (I), we impose the further restriction

$$x(0) = x(1). \tag{V}$$

Thus $A_3 = d/dt$ and D_3 consists of all elements satisfying (I) and (V). The operator A_3 is closed and D_3 is dense in $\mathscr{L}_2^{(c)}(0, 1)$. We have

$$\langle A_3 x, y \rangle = - \int_0^1 x \frac{d\bar{y}}{dt} dt + x(1)[\bar{y}(1) - \bar{y}(0)].$$

It is clear that $A_3^* = - d/dt$ and that the domain of A_3^* consists of all functions satisfying (I) and $y(0) = y(1)$. This last boundary condition is the same as (V), so the domain of A_3^* is the same as that of A_3.

The homogeneous equation $A_3 x = 0$ has the nontrivial solution $x = C$; similarly, $A_3^* x = 0$ has the nontrivial solution $x = C$. The range of A_3 is closed, so the necessary and sufficient condition for $A_3 x = f$ to have a solution is that $\int_0^1 f(t)dt = 0$. Although this result followed from the alternative theorem, it can easily be derived by elementary considerations. Note that if $\int_0^1 f(t)dt = 0$, the solution of $A_3 x = f$ is not unique $\left[x = C + \int_0^t f(s)ds \right]$.

(d) In addition to (I), we impose the conditions

$$x(0) = 0, \qquad x(1) = 0. \tag{VI}$$

Thus $A_4 = d/dt$ and D_4 consists of all elements satisfying (I) and (VI). A_4 is closed and D_4 is dense in $\mathscr{L}_2^{(c)}(0, 1)$. We have

$$\langle A_4 x, y \rangle = - \int_0^1 x \frac{d\bar{y}}{dt} dt.$$

Therefore $A_4^* = - d/dt$ and the domain of A_4^* consists of all functions satisfying condition (I) alone. The homogeneous equation $A_4 x = 0$ has only the 0 solution, but $A_4^* x = 0$ has the nontrivial solution $x = C$. Therefore $A_4 x = f$ has a solution if and only if $\int_0^1 f \, dt = 0$. Although this is the same consistency condition as in (c), the situation with respect to $A_4 x = f$ is quite different. If the consistency condition is satisfied, the solution is now *unique*, namely $x = \int_0^t f(s)ds$.

(e) Referring to examples (a), (b), and (d) above, we observe that $A_4 \subset A_2 \subset A_1$. By explicit calculation we found that $A_4^* \supset A_2^* \supset A_1^*$, as predicted by property 4 of adjoint operators. Generally one expects that, as more boundary conditions are imposed on an operator (that is, as its domain is restricted), there will be fewer boundary conditions on the adjoint (that is, its domain is extended). We now exhibit a case in which adding a boundary condition on an operator does not change the boundary conditions on the adjoint.

Let $A_5 = d/dt$ and let D_5 consist of all elements satisfying (I) and the further conditions

$$x(0) = 0, \qquad x'(0) = 0. \qquad\qquad (VII)$$

Again we can verify that D_5 is dense in $\mathscr{A}$.

Clearly $A_2 \supset A_5$, yet we will show that $A_5^* = A_2^*$. (One could show directly that $\bar{A}_5 = A_2$, and then use property 7 of adjoint operators; we prefer to calculate A_5^* explicitly from basic principles.) Since $A_5 \subset A_2$, we know that $A_5^* \supset A_2^*$. To prove that $A_5^* = A_2^*$, it suffices therefore to show that $A_2^* \supset A_5^*$. Let (y, g) be an admissible pair for A_5; then

$$\left\langle \frac{dx}{dt}, y \right\rangle = \langle x, g \rangle, \qquad \text{for all } x \text{ in } D_5. \qquad (2.67)$$

Now let $Z(t)$ be in D_2; hence Z' exists, is in $\mathscr{L}_2$, and $Z(0) = 0$. Consider the sequence

$$x_n(t) = \begin{cases} 0, & 0 \le t < \dfrac{1}{n}; \\[2ex] Z(t) - Z\left(\dfrac{1}{n}\right), & \dfrac{1}{n} < t \le 1. \end{cases}$$

Clearly $x_n(t)$ satisfies $x_n(0) = x_n'(0) = 0$; moreover, x_n is in $\mathscr{L}_2$, x_n is absolutely continuous, and x_n' is in $\mathscr{L}_2$. The last two properties follow from the explicit formula

$$x_n' = \begin{cases} 0, & 0 \le t < \dfrac{1}{n}; \\[2ex] Z', & \dfrac{1}{n} < t \le 1. \end{cases}$$

The sequence x_n is in D_5 and clearly

$$\lim_{n \to \infty} x_n(t) = Z(t), \qquad \lim_{n \to \infty} x_n'(t) = Z'(t).$$

Substituting x_n in (2.67), we have

$$\left\langle \frac{dx_n}{dt}, y \right\rangle = \langle x_n, g \rangle.$$

Taking the limit as $n \to \infty$, and appealing to the continuity of the inner product, we obtain

$$\left\langle \frac{dZ}{dt}, y \right\rangle = \langle Z, g \rangle.$$

Since Z is an arbitrary element of D_2, we have shown that (y, g) is an admissible pair for A_2. Therefore, $A_2^* \supset A_5^*$; taken in connection with the previous observation that $A_2^* \subset A_5^*$, this shows that $A_5^* = A_2^*$. [Using Exercise 2.44(b), it also shows that $\bar{A}_5 = A_2$.] Consider now the homogeneous equations $A_5 x = 0$ and $A_5^* x = 0$; clearly they have only the trivial solution, yet $A_5 x = f$ does not always have a solution! Indeed the system

$$\frac{dx}{dt} = f; \qquad x(0) = 0, \quad x'(0) = 0, \qquad (2.68)$$

has a solution only if f is continuous at $x = 0$ and $f(0) = 0$. If these conditions are fulfilled, (2.68) has the one and only solution

$$x(t) = \int_0^t f(s)ds.$$

We note that the alternative theorem is not applicable, because the range of A_5 is not closed.

EXERCISES

2.40 Prove that $(\bar{A})^* = A^*$. [HINT: Since $\bar{A} \supset A$, $A^* \supset (\bar{A})^*$, and it suffices to show that $A^* \subset (\bar{A})^*$.]

2.41 Prove that if D_{A^*} is dense in $\mathscr{A}$, then A^{**} exists and $A \subset A^{**}$.

2.42 Refer to Example 5 and consider the operator $A_6 = d/dt$ with domain consisting of elements $x(t)$ satisfying (I) and

$$x(0) = x(\tfrac{1}{2}) = x(1) = 0.$$

Show that A_6 is closed; find A_6^*. [HINT: The admissible pairs will now include functions $g(t)$ which are discontinuous at $t = \tfrac{1}{2}$.]

2.43 Consider successively the differential operator $i(d/dt)$ on the various domains defined in Example 5. Show that in (c) the operator is self-adjoint, that in (d) the operator is symmetric but not self-adjoint, and that in the other cases the operator is not symmetric (hence surely not self-adjoint).

2.44 (a) Let A and B be closed operators with respective domains dense in $\mathscr{A}$. If $A^* = B^*$, then $A = B$ (this follows directly from property 8 of adjoint operators).

(b) Let A be a closable operator and B a closed operator, each with domain dense in $\mathscr{A}$. Prove that if $A^* = B^*$, then $\bar{A} = B$.

2.45 All functions $x(t)$ in the domains of the operators $B_1, \ldots, B_5$ (to be defined below) will be required to satisfy the condition

$$x \text{ and } x' \text{ absolutely continuous}; \qquad x, x', x'' \text{ in } \mathscr{L}_2^{(c)}(0, 1), \qquad (2.69)$$

and further boundary conditions explicitly stated below.

(a) $B_1 x = \dfrac{d^2 x}{dt^2}$;   no further restriction on the domain.

(b) $B_2 x = \dfrac{d^2 x}{dt^2}$; $x(0) = 0, \quad x(1) = 0.$

(c) $B_3 x = \dfrac{d^2 x}{dt^2}$; $x'(0) = 0, \quad x'(1) = 0.$

(d) $B_4 x = \dfrac{d^2 x}{dt^2}$; $x(0) = 0, \quad x(1) = 0, \quad x'(0) = 0, \quad x'(1) = 0.$

(e) $B_5 x = \dfrac{d^2 x}{dt^2}$; $x(0) = 0, \quad x'(0) = 0.$

(f) $B_6 x = \dfrac{d^2 x}{dt^2}$; $x(0) = 0, \quad x'(0) = 0, \quad x''(0) = 0.$

The operators B_1, B_2, B_3, B_4, B_5 are closed, whereas B_6 is closable with $\bar{B}_6 = B_5$. Calculate the adjoint operators and show that the operators B_2, B_3, B_4 are symmetric and that B_2, B_3 are self-adjoint. In all cases discuss the inhomogeneous equation and the applicability of the alternative theorem.

2.9 THE SPECTRUM OF AN OPERATOR

The importance of the method of eigenvector expansion for solving inhomogeneous equations was indicated in the discussion of n-dimensional spaces. The principal difficulty encountered in extending these ideas to infinite dimensional spaces is attributable to the variety of ways in which an operator on such a space can be singular. (See the classification of operators in Section 2.8; by contrast, an operator on $E_n^{(c)}$ is singular if and only if the homogeneous equation has a nontrivial solution.) We begin by giving some general definitions for closed operators, and specialize later to symmetric closed operators and to self-adjoint operators (a self-adjoint operator is closed since $A = A^*$ and A^* is always closed). In Chapters 3 and 4 the theory is considerably refined for completely continuous operators and self-adjoint differential operators.

Let A be a closed linear operator defined on the linear manifold D_A which is assumed dense in the Hilbert space $\mathcal{A}$. The operator $A - \lambda I$, where λ is an arbitrary complex number and I is the identity operator, is also closed and is defined on the same domain D_A. The range of $A - \lambda I$ may depend on λ and will be denoted by $R_A(\lambda)$. We now classify all the points λ in the complex plane according to whether $A - \lambda I$ is regular or singular.

DEFINITION 1.   A value of λ in the complex plane, for which $A - \lambda I$ is regular, is called a *regular value* (or regular point) of A. The set of all regular points is known as the *resolvent set* of A. All values of λ which are not in the resolvent set comprise the *spectrum* of A. (Thus λ is in the spectrum of A if and only if $A - \lambda I$ is singular.)

The points in the spectrum of A are further subdivided according to the way in which the closed operator $A - \lambda I$ is singular (see Section 2.8).

DEFINITION 2.   If $(A - \lambda I)x = 0$ has a nontrivial solution (that is, if $Ax = \lambda x$ has a nontrivial solution), λ is called an *eigenvalue* of A. Any corresponding nontrivial solution x is an *eigenvector* of A belonging to λ. The set of all eigenvalues make up the *point spectrum* of A. The set of all eigenvectors belonging to the same eigenvalue λ is easily seen to be a linear manifold, called the *eigenmanifold* belonging to λ. The dimension of this eigenmanifold is the *multiplicity* of λ [this corresponds to the concept of geometric multiplicity in (2.7)].

DEFINITION 3.   If $(A - \lambda I)x = 0$ has only the trivial solution, but $(A - \lambda I)^{-1}$ is unbounded and $R_A(\lambda) \neq \mathscr{A}$, and $\bar{R}_A(\lambda) = \mathscr{A}$, λ belongs to the *continuous spectrum* of A.

DEFINITION 4.   If $(A - \lambda I)x = 0$ has only the trivial solution, but $\bar{R}_A(\lambda) \neq \mathscr{A}$, λ belongs to the *residual spectrum* of A. Since $\bar{R}_A(\lambda) \neq \mathscr{A}$, the closed linear manifold $[R_A(\lambda)]^{\perp}$ has positive dimension. This dimension is called the *deficiency* of λ.

Definitions 1, 2, 3, 4 correspond respectively to categories 1, 2, 3, and 4 for closed operators given in Section 2.8.

Theorem 1.   *Let λ be a point of deficiency m in the residual spectrum of A; then λ is an eigenvalue of multiplicity m of A^*.*

Proof.   Let x be in D_A and y in $[R_A(\lambda)]^{\perp}$; then

$$\langle (A - \lambda I)x, y \rangle = 0 = \langle x, 0 \rangle.$$

Therefore $(y, 0)$ is an admissible pair for $A - \lambda I$ from which we conclude that y is in the domain of $(A - \lambda I)^*$ and $(A - \lambda I)^* y = 0$. Since $(A - \lambda I)^* = A^* - \bar{\lambda} I$, the proof is complete.

Theorem 2.   *If A is symmetric, $\langle Ax, x \rangle$ is real for all x in D_A, and all eigenvalues of A are real.*

Proof.   Since A is symmetric, $\langle Ax, x \rangle = \langle x, Ax \rangle$; from the properties of the inner product we also have $\langle Ax, x \rangle = \overline{\langle x, Ax \rangle}$; hence $\langle x, Ax \rangle = \overline{\langle x, Ax \rangle}$ and $\langle Ax, x \rangle$ is real. If λ is an eigenvalue of A there exists a nonzero vector x such that $Ax = \lambda x$; hence $\langle Ax, x \rangle = \lambda \langle x, x \rangle$. But $\langle Ax, x \rangle$ is real and $\langle x, x \rangle$ is positive so that λ must be real.

The reader should have no difficulty in proving the following lemmas.

LEMMA 1.   *If B^{-1} is unbounded, there exists a sequence $\{x_n\}$ in D_B with $\|x_n\| = 1$ and $\|Bx_n\| < 1/n$.*

LEMMA 2.   *If A is symmetric, and $\lambda = \xi + i\eta$, where ξ and η are real, then*

$$\|(A - \lambda I)x\|^2 \geq \eta^2 \|x\|^2.$$

Theorem 3.   *The continuous spectrum of a symmetric operator A is limited to the real axis.*

Proof. Let $\lambda = \xi + i\eta$ with $\eta \neq 0$. Let $\{x_n\}$ be any sequence in D_A with $\|x_n\| = 1$; according to Lemma 2, $\|(A - \lambda I)x_n\| \geq |\eta|$. Since this inequality holds for all such sequences $\{x_n\}$, Lemma 1 tells us that $(A - \lambda I)^{-1}$ must be bounded, so that λ cannot be in the continuous spectrum.

REMARK.   If A is symmetric there may be nonreal points in the residual spectrum, but both the point spectrum and the continuous spectrum are confined to the real axis.

Theorem 4.   *The spectrum of a self-adjoint operator is entirely on the real axis, and its residual spectrum is empty.*

Proof. A self-adjoint operator is of course symmetric. By the remark above it will suffice to show that the residual spectrum is empty. Since $A = A^*$ and all eigenvalues are real, Theorem 1 guarantees that the residual spectrum is limited to the real axis. If a real value of λ is in the residual spectrum of A, it must also be an eigenvalue of A (again by Theorem 1), but by definition a point in the residual spectrum cannot be an eigenvalue.

EXAMPLES

Example 1. Let $Ax = \int_0^t x(s)\,ds$. The operator A is defined for each element $x(t)$ in the Hilbert space $\mathscr{L}_2^{(c)}(0, 1)$. If $\lambda \neq 0$, Example 4 of the preceding section shows that the range of $A - \lambda I$ is the whole space and $(A - \lambda I)^{-1}$ is bounded. Therefore only $\lambda = 0$ can be in the spectrum. This point is not an eigenvalue but is in the continuous spectrum ($R_A \neq \mathscr{A}$, $\overline{R}_A = \mathscr{A}$, A^{-1} unbounded).

Example 2. As in Example 5 of the preceding section, consider the differential operator d/dt on a linear manifold in $\mathscr{L}_2^{(c)}(0, 1)$ consisting of functions $x(t)$ satisfying the conditions

$$x(t) \text{ absolutely continuous;} \qquad x \text{ and } x' \text{ in } \mathscr{L}_2^{(c)}(0, 1). \tag{I}$$

(a) Let A_1 be the operator d/dt defined on D_1 which consists of all functions satisfying condition (I). The equation $A_1 x - \lambda x = 0$ has the nontrivial solution $Ce^{\lambda t}$, so every value of λ is an eigenvalue of A_1.

(b) Let A_2 be the operator d/dt defined on D_2 which consists of all functions $x(t)$ satisfying (I) and the further boundary condition $x(0) = 0$. The equation $A_2 x - \lambda x = 0$ becomes the system

$$\frac{dx}{dt} = \lambda x, \qquad 0 \le t \le 1; \qquad x(0) = 0.$$

The only solution of this system is $x(t) = 0$, so that the point spectrum of A_2 is empty. The inhomogeneous equation $A_2 x - \lambda x = f$ has a unique solution for each f. Indeed we can construct the Green's function which satisfies

$$\frac{dg}{dt} - \lambda g = \delta(t - \xi), \qquad 0 \le t, \xi \le 1; \qquad g|_{t=0} = 0.$$

By the usual procedure we find

$$g(t \mid \xi) = \begin{cases} e^{\lambda(t - \xi)}, & t > \xi; \\ 0, & t < \xi. \end{cases}$$

Therefore the equation $A_2 x - \lambda x = f$ has the unique solution

$$x(t) = \int_0^1 g(t \mid \xi) f(\xi) d\xi = e^{\lambda t} \int_0^t e^{-\lambda \xi} f(\xi) d\xi.$$

The operator $(A_2 - \lambda I)^{-1}$ is easily seen to be bounded. Thus the spectrum of A_2 is *empty*.

(c) Let A_3 be the operator d/dt defined on D_3 which consists of all functions $x(t)$ satisfying (I) and the additional boundary condition $x(0) = x(1)$. The equation $A_3 x - \lambda x = 0$ becomes the system

$$\frac{dx}{dt} = \lambda x, \qquad 0 \le t \le 1; \qquad x(0) = x(1).$$

A nontrivial solution of this system is possible only if $\lambda = 2n\pi i$, where n is an arbitrary integer. The corresponding eigenfunction is $Ce^{2n\pi i t}$. If $\lambda \ne 2n\pi i$, we can solve $A_3 x - \lambda x = f$ by a Green's function procedure. The Green's function $g(t \mid \xi)$ satisfies

$$\frac{dg}{dt} - \lambda g = \delta(t - \xi), \qquad 0 \le t, \xi \le 1; \qquad g|_{t=0} = g|_{t=1}.$$

A simple calculation shows that

$$g(t \mid \xi) = \begin{cases} \dfrac{e^{-\lambda \xi} e^{\lambda(t-1)}}{e^{-\lambda} - 1}, & t > \xi; \\[3mm] \dfrac{e^{-\lambda \xi}}{e^{-\lambda} - 1} e^{\lambda t}, & t < \xi. \end{cases}$$

Thus the solution of $A_3 x - \lambda x = f$ is

$$x(t) = \int_0^1 g(t \mid \xi) f(\xi) d\xi.$$

One can easily verify that $(A_3 - \lambda I)^{-1}$ is bounded. The spectrum of A_3 is therefore a pure point spectrum; the eigenvalues being $\lambda_n = 2n\pi i$, $n = \ldots, -2, -1, 0, 1, 2, \ldots$.

   (d) Let A_4 be the operator d/dt defined on the domain D_4 consisting of all functions satisfying (I) and the additional boundary conditions $x(0) = 0$, $x(1) = 0$. It is clear that $A_4 x - \lambda x = 0$ has no nontrivial solutions for any λ, so that the point spectrum of A_4 is empty. The inhomogeneous equation $A_4 x - \lambda x = f$ becomes the system

$$\frac{dx}{dt} - \lambda x = f, \qquad 0 \le t \le 1; \qquad x(0) = 0, \quad x(1) = 0.$$

The differential equation and the first boundary condition determine the solution uniquely [see (b)]:

$$x(t) = e^{\lambda t} \int_0^t e^{-\lambda \xi} f(\xi) d\xi.$$

The second boundary condition can be satisfied if and only if $0 = \int_0^t e^{-\lambda \xi} f(\xi) d\xi$. Thus the range of $A_4 - \lambda I$ contains only those functions $f(\xi)$ which are orthogonal to $e^{-\bar{\lambda} \xi}$ (of course, $e^{-\bar{\lambda} \xi}$ is the solution of the adjoint equation). If $f(\xi)$ satisfies this consistency condition, the solution of $A_4 x - \lambda x = f$ is the same as the solution of $A_2 x - \lambda x = f$, so that $(A_4 - \lambda I)^{-1}$ is bounded. It follows therefore that every value of λ is in the residual spectrum of A_4.

EXERCISES

2.46 Classify the spectra of the operators introduced in Exercise 2.43.

2.47 Classify the spectra of the operators of Exercise 2.45.

2.48 Show that the spectrum of a self-adjoint operator can be characterized as follows:
   (a) A point is regular if and only if $R_A(\lambda) = \mathscr{A}$.
   (b) A point is an eigenvalue if and only if $\bar{R}_A(\lambda) \ne \mathscr{A}$.
   (c) A point is in the continuous spectrum if and only if $R_A(\lambda) \ne \mathscr{A}$ but $\bar{R}_A(\lambda) = \mathscr{A}$.

2.10 COMPLETELY CONTINUOUS OPERATORS

   A set S of elements in the Hilbert space $\mathscr{A}$ is said to be *bounded* if there exists a constant c such that for all x in S, $\|x\| \le c$. A set S is *compact* if each sequence $\{x_n\}$ of elements chosen from S contains a convergent subsequence.

A set containing a finite number of elements is compact, since any sequence constructed from the set must include some element infinitely many times and therefore contains a convergent subsequence. It is clear that every compact set is bounded, but the converse is true only for finite-dimensional spaces (in $E_n^{(c)}$ the Bolzano-Weierstrass theorem guarantees that every bounded set is also compact). We now give an example of a bounded set in $\mathcal{L}_2^{(c)}(a, b)$ which is *not compact*. Consider the infinite orthonormal set $\{\varphi_1(t), \ldots, \varphi_n(t), \ldots\}$; since $\|\varphi_n\| = 1$, the set is bounded, but we claim that the sequence $\varphi_1(t), \ldots, \varphi_n(t), \ldots$ does not contain a converging subsequence. In fact, if such a subsequence, say $\psi_1, \psi_2, \ldots$, could be found, it would be an orthonormal sequence converging to an element ψ of norm 1; for each element h in $\mathcal{A}$ the Riemann-Lebesgue lemma implies that $\lim_{n \to \infty} \langle \psi_n, h \rangle = 0$; hence $\langle \psi, h \rangle = 0$ for all h and $\psi = 0$, which contradicts $\|\psi\| = 1$.

It is clear that an operator A is bounded if and only if it transforms bounded sets into bounded sets. An operator A is called *completely continuous* if it transforms bounded sets into compact sets. Obviously a completely continuous operator is continuous, but the converse is not necessarily true; even the identity operator on an infinite-dimensional space is *not* completely continuous! (The infinite orthonormal set $\{\varphi_n\}$ is bounded and is transformed into itself by the identity operator, yet the set is not compact.) Any bounded operator P whose range is finite-dimensional is completely continuous; indeed P transforms a bounded set in $\mathcal{A}$ into a bounded finite-dimensional set which is necessarily compact. In particular, any operator on $E_n^{(c)}$ is completely continuous. The most important completely continuous operators on $\mathcal{L}_2^{(c)}(a, b)$ are the Hilbert-Schmidt integral operators, which will be studied in Chapter 3. We now prove three theorems on completely continuous operators on an infinite-dimensional space.

Thm.

Theorem 1.   *If A is completely continuous and $\{\varphi_n\}$ is an infinite orthonormal sequence in $\mathcal{A}$, then $\lim_{n \to \infty} A\varphi_n = 0$.*

Proof.   If the contrary were true, there would exist a subsequence $\{\psi_n\}$ of $\{\varphi_n\}$ such that $\|A\psi_n\| > \varepsilon$ for all sufficiently large n. Since A is completely continuous, a subsequence $\{X_n\}$ can be extracted from $\{\psi_n\}$ such that AX_n converges, say to f. This element f is not the 0 element, because $\|AX_n\| > \varepsilon$ for sufficiently large n. By the continuity of the inner product we find $\langle AX_n, f \rangle \to \langle f, f \rangle$ $\|f\|^2 \neq 0$. On the other hand, $\langle AX_n, f \rangle = \langle X_n, A^*f \rangle$, which, by the Riemann-Lebesgue lemma, approaches 0. We have arrived at a contradiction and therefore $A\varphi_n \to 0$.

A generalization of this theorem can be found in Exercise 2.50.

A completely continuous operator not only maps convergent sequences into convergent sequences (this is true for any continuous operator) but also maps some nonconvergent sequences, as in Theorem 1, into convergent

sequences. Although this is a powerful property, it has a built-in drawback—
the inverse operator must transform some convergent sequences into nonconvergent sequences.

Theorem 2. *If A is a completely continuous, invertible operator on an infinite-dimensional space, its inverse is* unbounded.

Proof. Let $\{\varphi_n\}$ be an infinite orthonormal sequence in $\mathscr{A}$, and let $x_n = A\varphi_n$. Since A is invertible, $\varphi_n = A^{-1}x_n$. Now $\|\varphi_n\| = 1$ and $\|x_n\| \to 0$ by Theorem 1, so that A^{-1} is obviously unbounded.

Theorem 3. *If A can be approximated in norm by completely continuous operators (that is, if there exists a sequence A_n of completely continuous operators with the property $\|A - A_n\| \leq 1/n$), then A is completely continuous.*

Proof. It suffices to show that each bounded sequence $\{x_k\}$ contains a subsequence $\{y_k\}$ for which Ay_k converges. Since A_1 is completely continuous, there exists a subsequence $\{x_k^{(1)}\}$ of $\{x_k\}$ for which $A_1 x_k^{(1)}$ converges. There exists a subsequence $\{x_k^{(2)}\}$ of $\{x_k^{(1)}\}$ for which $A_2 x_k^{(2)}$ converges; proceeding in this manner we find a subsequence $\{x_k^{(n)}\}$ of $\{x_k^{(n-1)}\}$ such that $A_n x_k^{(n)}$ converges. Consider now the diagonal sequence

$$x_1^{(1)}, x_2^{(2)}, x_3^{(3)}, \ldots,$$

which is a subsequence of $\{x_n\}$ transformed into a convergent sequence by each of the operators $A_1, \ldots, A_n, \ldots$. We claim that A also transforms this diagonal sequence into a convergent sequence. Indeed, we have

$$\|Ax_n^{(n)} - Ax_m^{(m)}\| \leq \|Ax_n^{(n)} - A_k x_n^{(n)}\| + \|A_k x_n^{(n)} - A_k x_m^{(m)}\| + \|A_k x_m^{(m)} - Ax_m^{(m)}\|$$

$$\leq \|A - A_k\|\{\|x_n^{(n)}\| + \|x_m^{(m)}\|\} + \|A_k x_n^{(n)} - A_k x_m^{(m)}\|.$$

Since the sequence $\{x_k\}$ is bounded, so is its subsequence $\{x_n^{(n)}\}$ therefore, there exists a constant c such that $\|x_n^{(n)}\| + \|x_m^{(m)}\| \leq c$ for all m and n. Choose k so large that $\|A - A_k\| \leq \varepsilon/2c$. Since A_k transforms $x_n^{(n)}$ into a convergent sequence, we can choose m and n so large that $\|A_k x_n^{(n)} - A_k x_m^{(m)}\| \leq \varepsilon/2$. Therefore, for m and n sufficiently large, we have

$$\|Ax_n^{(n)} - Ax_m^{(m)}\| \leq \varepsilon.$$

Thus the sequence $Ax_n^{(n)}$ is a Cauchy sequence, hence converges. This completes the proof of the theorem.

EXERCISES

2.49 *Let A be a completely continuous operator.*

　　(a) Show that, if $\lambda \neq 0$ and λ is not an eigenvalue of A, the operator $(A - \lambda I)^{-1}$ is bounded and therefore the range of $A - \lambda I$ is closed. Moreover, it can be shown that the range of $A - \lambda I$ is the whole space $\mathscr{A}$.

(b) It can be shown that if $\lambda \neq 0$ is an eigenvalue of A, then $A - \lambda I$ has a closed range which is not the whole space $\mathscr{A}$. Moreover, the multiplicity of λ is finite.

(c) If $\lambda \neq 0$ is an eigenvalue of A, show that $\bar{\lambda}$ is an eigenvalue of A^*.

(d) *The alternative theorem for completely continuous operators.* Let λ be fixed, $\lambda \neq 0$, and consider the three related equations

$$Ax - \lambda x = 0; \tag{2.70}$$

$$A^*z - \bar{\lambda}z = 0; \tag{2.71}$$

$$Ay - \lambda y = f. \tag{2.72}$$

These equations are known as the direct homogeneous equation, adjoint homogeneous equation, and direct inhomogeneous equation, respectively.

(1) Either (2.70) and (2.71) both have only the trivial solution, or both have nontrivial solutions (of course these solutions may be different).

(2) The necessary and sufficient condition for (2.72) to have a nontrivial solution is that f be orthogonal to every solution of (2.71). In particular, if λ is not an eigenvalue of (2.70), then $\bar{\lambda}$ is not an eigenvalue of (2.71), and (2.72) has one and only one solution for each f in $\mathscr{A}$.

2.50 Prove that if A is completely continuous it maps every weakly convergent sequence into a strongly convergent sequence (for definition of weak convergence, see Exercise 2.21).

2.11 EXTREMAL PROPERTIES OF BOUNDED OPERATORS

Let A be a bounded operator defined on the whole of the Hilbert space $\mathscr{A}$.

Theorem 1. $\|A\| = \|A^*\|$.

Proof. For each pair of elements x, y in $\mathscr{A}$, we have

$$\langle Ax, y \rangle = \langle x, A^*y \rangle. \tag{2.73}$$

Substituting $y = Ax$ and observing that $\langle Ax, Ax \rangle$ is a nonnegative real number, we have, by the Schwarz inequality,

$$\langle Ax, Ax \rangle = \langle x, A^*Ax \rangle \leq \|x\| \, \|A^*Ax\|.$$

Thus

$$\|Ax\|^2 \leq \|A^*\| \, \|x\| \, \|Ax\| \qquad \text{and} \qquad \|Ax\| \leq \|A^*\| \, \|x\|.$$

This last inequality implies $\|A\| \leq \|A^*\|$. The opposite inequality can be obtained by setting $x = A^*y$ in (2.73).

see problem

$$\|A\| = \sup_{\|x\| \neq 0} \frac{\|Ax\|}{\|x\|} \quad \leq \quad \frac{\|Ax\|}{\|x\|} \leq \|A^*\|$$

$$\text{so} \quad \|A\| \leq \|A^*\|$$

Theorem 2. *For each $x \neq 0$,*

$$\frac{|\langle Ax, x \rangle|}{\|x\|^2} \le \|A\|, \tag{2.74}$$

and for each x such that $\|x\| = 1$,

$$|\langle Ax, x \rangle| \le \|A\|. \tag{2.74a}$$

Proof. By the Schwarz inequality,

$$|\langle Ax, x \rangle| \le \|Ax\| \, \|x\| \le \|A\| \, \|x\|^2.$$

COROLLARY 1. *Let M_A be the least upper bound for all $x \neq 0$ of $|\langle Ax, x \rangle|/\|x\|^2$. Then $M_A \le \|A\|$.*

The following theorem relates the spectrum of A to the norm of A and is a preliminary result in the important problem of the estimation of eigenvalues.

Theorem 3. *If λ is in the spectrum of A, then $|\lambda| \le \|A\|$.*

Proof. (a) Suppose first that λ is in the point spectrum of A; that is, there exists an element x with $\|x\| \neq 0$ such that $Ax - \lambda x = 0$. Then

$$\lambda \langle x, x \rangle = \langle Ax, x \rangle \quad \text{and} \quad \lambda = \frac{\langle Ax, x \rangle}{\langle x, x \rangle}.$$

By Theorem 2 it follows that $|\lambda| \le \|A\|$.

(b) If λ is in the residual spectrum of A, $\bar{\lambda}$ is an eigenvalue of A^*; hence $|\bar{\lambda}| \le \|A^*\|$. Since $\|A^*\| = \|A\|$ and $|\bar{\lambda}| = |\lambda|$, we again have $|\bar{\lambda}| \le \|A\|$.

(c) If λ is in the continuous spectrum of A, then $(A - \lambda I)^{-1}$ exists and is unbounded. Therefore, there is a sequence $\{x_n\}$ with $\|x_n\| = 1$ such that $Ax_n - \lambda x_n \to 0$. Hence $\lambda = \lim_{n \to \infty} \langle Ax_n, x_n \rangle$, and by Theorem 2, $|\lambda| \le \|A\|$.

Theorem 4. *If A is symmetric, $M_A = \|A\|$.*

Proof. From corollary 1, $M_A \le \|A\|$, so that it suffices to show that $M_A \ge \|A\|$. We start from the simple identity

$$\langle A(x + y), x + y \rangle - \langle A(x - y), x - y \rangle = 2 \langle Ax, y \rangle + 2 \langle Ay, x \rangle.$$

The symmetry of A implies that the two terms on the left side of the above identity are real. Using this fact and the definition of M_A, we obtain

$$\langle A(x + y), x + y \rangle \le M_A \|x + y\|^2$$

and

$$\langle A(x - y), x - y \rangle \ge -M_A \|x - y\|^2.$$

Subtracting these inequalities, we have

$$2\langle Ax, y\rangle + 2\langle Ay, x\rangle \leq M_A(\|x + y\|^2 + \|x - y\|^2),$$

or, using the parallelogram law,

$$\langle Ax, y\rangle + \langle Ay, x\rangle \leq M_A(\|x\|^2 + \|y\|^2).$$

If $Ax \neq 0$ we may substitute $y = (Ax/\|Ax\|)\|x\|$ to obtain

$$\langle Ax, Ax\rangle + \langle AAx, x\rangle \leq 2\|Ax\|\,\|x\|M_A.$$

Since $\langle AAx, x\rangle = \langle Ax, Ax\rangle$, we infer

$$2\|Ax\|^2 \leq 2\|Ax\|\,\|x\|M_A \qquad \text{or} \qquad \|Ax\| \leq M_A\|x\|.$$

This last inequality is obviously valid even if $Ax = 0$; it follows therefore that $\|A\| \leq M_A$.

Theorem 5. *If A is symmetric, there exists a sequence $\{x_k\}$ with $\|x_k\| = 1$, for which*

$$\lim_{k \to \infty} (Ax_k - \lambda_1 x_k) = 0,$$

where λ_1 is one of the numbers $\|A\|$ or $-\|A\|$.

Proof. By Theorem 4 we know that

$$\underset{x \neq 0}{\text{l.u.b.}} \frac{|\langle Ax, x\rangle|}{\|x\|^2} = \|A\|,$$

which implies

$$\underset{\|x\| = 1}{\text{l.u.b.}} |\langle Ax, x\rangle| = \|A\|.$$

Therefore there exists a sequence $\{z_k\}$, with $\|z_k\| = 1$, such that $\lim_{k \to \infty} |\langle Az_k, z_k\rangle| = \|A\|$. Since $\langle Az_k, z_k\rangle$ is real, the sequence $\{z_k\}$ must contain a subsequence $\{x_k\}$ such that either $\langle Ax_k, x_k\rangle \to \|A\|$ or $\langle Ax_k, x_k\rangle \to -\|A\|$. Thus the sequence $\{x_k\}$ has the property $\langle Ax_k, x_k\rangle \to \lambda_1$, where λ_1 is either $\|A\|$ or $-\|A\|$. We also have

$$\|Ax_k - \lambda_1 x_k\|^2 = \|Ax_k\|^2 + \lambda_1^2\|x_k\|^2 - 2\lambda_1\langle Ax_k, x_k\rangle$$
$$\leq \|A\|^2 + \lambda_1^2 - 2\lambda_1\langle Ax_k, x_k\rangle$$
$$= 2\lambda_1^2 - 2\lambda_1\langle Ax_k, x_k\rangle.$$

Since $\langle Ax_k, x_k\rangle \to \lambda_1$, $\|Ax_k - \lambda_1 x_k\|^2 \to 0$ and $Ax_k - \lambda_1 x_k \to 0$.

REMARK. Theorem 5 does not state that λ_1 is an eigenvalue of A. Such a conclusion can be reached only if $\{x_k\}$ or some subsequence of $\{x_k\}$ converges to an element x; this would imply that $Ax - \lambda_1 x = 0$.

Theorem 6. *If A is symmetric and completely continuous, at least one of the numbers $\|A\|$, $-\|A\|$ is an eigenvalue of A. Moreover, by Theorem 3, no eigenvalue of A has larger absolute value.*

Proof. By the definition of complete continuity, the sequence $\{x_k\}$ in Theorem 5 contains a subsequence, say $\{u_k\}$, for which Au_k converges. Since $Au_k - \lambda_1 u_k \to 0$, it follows that $\{u_k\}$ converges and there exists an element u of unit norm for which $Au - \lambda_1 u = 0$.

SUGGESTED READINGS FOR CHAPTER 2

The letters E, I, and A indicate elementary, intermediate, and advanced books, respectively.

Matrices and Linear Algebra
(I)   Gelfand, I. M., *Lectures on Linear Algebra*, Interscience, New York, 1961.
(I)   Halmos, P. R., *Finite-Dimensional Vector Spaces*, Van Nostrand, Princeton, 1958.

Metric Spaces, Hilbert Spaces, Banach Spaces
(A)   Akhiezer, N. I., and I. M. Glazman, *Theory of Linear Operators in Hilbert Space*, Vols. I and II, Ungar, New York, 1961, 1963.
(A)   Dunford, N., and J. T. Schwartz, *Linear Operators*, Vol. I, Interscience, New York, 1964.
(I)   Kolmogorov, A. N., and S. V. Fomin, *Functional Analysis*, Vols. I and II, Graylock, Albany, 1957, 1961.
(A)   Lorch, E. R., *Spectral Theory*, Oxford University Press, New York, 1962.
(I)   Riesz, F., and B. Sz-Nagy, *Functional Analysis*, Ungar, New York, 1955.

Chapter 3

LINEAR INTEGRAL EQUATIONS

3.1 INTRODUCTION

In mathematical physics, integral equations may occur in their own right, but more often they are merely alternative formulations of problems in differential equations. In the first instance we have no choice, but why do we bother to study the integral equation in the second case? The reason is three-fold: (1) the integral equation involves an operator which is usually bounded, and often completely continuous, whereas the differential operator is unbounded. General theorems about eigenfunction expansions, solutions of inhomogeneous equations, etc., are more easily derived within the framework of bounded operators; (2) the integral equation serves as a basis for numerical and variational approximations which complement similar approximations appropriate for the differential equation formulation; and (3) the integral equation incorporates the boundary conditions on the differential equation; thus, each solution of the integral equation automatically satisfies these boundary conditions.

We begin with the notion of an integral operator or integral transformation. Let $k(x, \xi)$ be a complex-valued function of two real variables; $k(x, \xi)$ is defined over the square $a \leq x, \xi \leq b$, where we allow the possibilities $a - -\infty$ and $b = +\infty$. This function generates an integral transformation through

$$z(x) = Ku = \int_a^b k(x, \xi)u(\xi)d\xi. \tag{3.1}$$

A complex-valued function $u(x)$ defined on $a \leq x \leq b$ is transformed by (3.1) into a complex-valued function $z(x)$ also defined over the interval $a \leq x \leq b$.

REMARK. The function $k(x, \xi)$ is frequently defined for values of x outside (a, b), so that the function $z(x)$ may also be considered outside this interval. There is usually little advantage in this point of view.

In fact, our main interest centers on the solution $u(x)$ of the integral equation (3.1), where $z(x)$ is given; it turns out that if $z(x)$ is given over an interval larger than (a, b), the problem is usually inconsistent, whereas if $z(x)$ is specified over a smaller interval the problem is usually underdetermined.

The function $k(x, \xi)$ is known as the *kernel* of the transformation (3.1). The transformation K is linear, since $K(u_1 + u_2) = Ku_1 + Ku_2$ and $K(\alpha u) = \alpha Ku$. We are particularly interested in the case of bounded transformations from $\mathscr{L}_2^{(c)}(a, b)$ into $\mathscr{L}_2^{(c)}(a, b)$. We recall that a transformation K is *bounded* if there exists a constant M (independent of u) such that $\|z\| = \|Ku\| \leq M\|u\|$, for all u. The symbol $\|u\|$ stands, of course, for the $\mathscr{L}_2^{(c)}(a, b)$ norm, $\|u\| = \left[\int_a^b |u(x)|^2 dx\right]^{1/2}$. The smallest constant M for which $\|z\| \leq M\|u\|$ for all u is the *norm of the transformation* and is denoted by $\|K\|$. We have the two equivalent characterizations of $\|K\|$:

$$\|K\| = \underset{\|u\|=1}{\text{l.u.b.}} \|Ku\| \qquad \text{or} \qquad \|K\| = \underset{\|u\|\neq0}{\text{l.u.b.}} \frac{\|Ku\|}{\|u\|}. \qquad (3.2)$$

We also recall that if K is bounded, it is continuous, and vice versa. [We are referring to the continuity and boundedness of K as an integral operator, and not to the continuity and boundedness of $k(x, \xi)$ as a function of two variables.]

Criterion for Complete Continuity of K; Hilbert-Schmidt Kernels

It is fortunate that many of the integral operators that arise in applications are not only bounded but have the stronger property of *complete continuity* (see Section 2.10). We begin with separable kernels and then move on to Hilbert-Schmidt kernels.

DEFINITION.   The kernel $s(x, \xi) = \sum_{i=1}^{n} p_i(x)q_i(\xi)$, where $\int_a^b |p_i|^2 \, dx < \infty$ and $\int_a^b |q_i|^2 \, dx < \infty$, is called a *separable* kernel.

Theorem. *A separable kernel $s(x, \xi)$ generates a completely continuous integral transformation S.*

Proof. For each f in $\mathscr{L}_2^{(c)}(a, b)$, we have

$$Sf = \int_a^b \sum_{i=1}^n p_i(x)q_i(\xi)f(\xi)d\xi = \sum_{i=1}^n c_i p_i(x),$$

so that the range of S is a finite-dimensional subspace of $\mathscr{L}_2^{(c)}(a, b)$. We obtain an estimate of $\|Sf\|$ as follows:

$$\|Sf\| = \left\| \sum_{i=1}^n c_i p_i \right\| \leq \sum_{i=1}^n |c_i| \, \|p_i\| \leq \sum_{i=1}^n \|p_i\| \int_a^b |q_i| \, |f| d\xi.$$

By Schwarz's inequality we find that the last expression is dominated by $M\|f\|$, where $M = \sum_{i=1}^{n} \|p_i\| \|q_i\|$. Thus S is a bounded operator with finite-dimensional range, so it is completely continuous (Section 2.10). *see pg 185*

DEFINITION. A kernel $k(x, \xi)$ for which $\int_a^b \int_a^b |k^2(x, \xi)| dx \, d\xi < \infty$ is called a *Hilbert-Schmidt (or H.-S.) kernel* and the transformation K it generates is known as a *Hilbert-Schmidt integral operator.*

We show next that a H.-S. operator is bounded and we obtain an estimate for $\|K\|$. We have

$$|z(x)|^2 = \left| \int_a^b k(x, \xi)u(\xi)d\xi \right|^2 \leq \int_a^b |k(x, \xi)|^2 \, d\xi \int_a^b |u(\xi)|^2 \, d\xi \qquad \text{by Schwarz}$$

or

$$|z(x)|^2 \leq \|u\|^2 \int_a^b |k(x, \xi)|^2 \, d\xi.$$

Therefore,   *by def of norm in $L_2(a,b)$*

$$\|z\|^2 = \int_a^b |z(x)|^2 \, dx \leq \left[\int_a^b \int_a^b |k(x, \xi)|^2 \, dx \, d\xi \right] \|u\|^2.$$

Thus, for all u,

$$\|z\| \leq M\|u\|, \qquad \text{with } M = \left[\int_a^b \int_a^b |k(x, \xi)|^2 \, dx \, d\xi \right]^{1/2}.$$

It follows that

$$\|K\| \leq \left[\int_a^b \int_a^b |k(x, \xi)|^2 \, dx \, d\xi \right]^{1/2}. \tag{3.3}$$

Since we have used some rather crude inequalities in obtaining this estimate, we shall not be astounded to find an appreciable difference in the two sides of (3.3). There are kernels with $\|K\| = 1$ for which the right side is infinite (see Example 6). We interrupt the presentation to prove the following useful lemma.

LEMMA 1. *Let $\{\varphi_i(x)\}_{i=1}^{i=\infty}$ be a complete orthonormal set over $a \leq x \leq b$ and let $\{\psi_i(\xi)\}_{i=1}^{i=\infty}$ be a complete orthonormal set over $c \leq \xi \leq d$. Then the set $\varphi_1(x)\psi_1(\xi)$, $\varphi_1(x)\psi_2(\xi)$, $\varphi_2(x)\psi_1(\xi)$, $\varphi_2(x)\psi_2(\xi), \ldots$ is a complete two-dimensional orthonormal set over the rectangle $a \leq x \leq b$, $c \leq \xi \leq d$.*

REMARKS. 1. Although a single index could be introduced to label the product set $\{\varphi_i(x)\psi_j(\xi)\}$, it is more convenient to retain the natural double indexing.

2. The diagonal set $\{\varphi_i(x)\psi_i(\xi)\}$ is an orthonormal set over the desired rectangle, but it is *not* complete.

Proof of lemma. It is easy to verify by integration that $\{\varphi_i(x)\psi_j(\xi)\}$ is in fact an orthonormal set over the rectangle. To prove completeness, it suffices to show that every continuous function $f(x, \xi)$ of finite two-dimensional norm (that is, $\int_a^b \int_c^d |f|^2 \, dx \, d\xi < \infty$), whose Fourier coefficients with respect to the set are all zero, vanishes identically over the rectangle. Suppose then that

$$\eta_{ij} = \int_a^b \int_c^d f(x, \xi) \bar{\varphi}_i(x) \bar{\psi}_j(\xi) dx \, d\xi = 0; \qquad i, j = 1, 2, \ldots .$$

This implies that for $i = 1, 2, \ldots,$

$$\int_c^d \left\{ \int_a^b f(x, \xi) \bar{\varphi}_i(x) dx \right\} \bar{\psi}_j(\xi) d\xi = 0, \qquad \text{for all } j.$$

Since the set $\{\psi_j\}$ is complete over $c \leq \xi \leq d$, we can conclude that

$$\eta_i(\xi) = \int_a^b f(x, \xi) \bar{\varphi}_i(x) dx$$

is the zero function on $c \leq \xi \leq d$; that is, $\int_c^d |\eta_i|^2 \, d\xi = 0$. It can easily be established that $\eta_i(\xi)$ is a continuous function of ξ, so that $\eta_i(\xi) \equiv 0, c \leq \xi \leq d$. Now $\{\eta_i(\xi)\}$ are the Fourier coefficients of the continuous function $f(x, \xi)$ with respect to the complete set $\{\varphi_i(x)\}$. It follows that for each ξ, $f(x, \xi)$ vanishes as a function of x; hence $f(x, \xi)$ is identically 0 over the rectangle and our theorem is proved.

We show that every H.-S. operator can be approximated in norm by a separable operator. Let K be the H.-S. operator, and let $\psi_1(x), \ldots, \psi_n(x), \ldots$ be an arbitrary, complete, orthonormal set over $a \leq x \leq b$. By the preceding lemma, the set $\{\psi_i(x)\bar{\psi}_j(\xi)\}$ is therefore a complete orthonormal set over the square $a \leq x, \xi \leq b$. We expand $k(x, \xi)$ in this set:

$$k(x, \xi) = \sum_{i,j=1}^{\infty} a_{ij}\psi_i(x)\bar{\psi}_j(\xi),$$

where

$$a_{ij} = \int_a^b \int_a^b k(x, \xi) \bar{\psi}_i(x) \psi_j(\xi) dx \, d\xi. \; = \; \left\langle k(x,\xi), \psi_i \, \bar{\psi}_j \right\rangle$$

By Parseval's identity, we have

$$\int_a^b \int_a^b |k(x, \xi)|^2 \, dx \, d\xi = \sum_{i,j=1}^{\infty} |a_{ij}|^2.$$

Furthermore, a simple calculation shows that

$$\int_a^b \int_a^b \left| k(x, \xi) - \sum_{i,j=1}^{n} a_{ij}\psi_i(x)\bar{\psi}_j(\xi) \right|^2 dx \, d\xi = \sum_{i,j=n+1}^{\infty} |a_{ij}|^2.$$

By choosing n sufficiently large, we can make this last sum as small as we please, say less than ε. With n so chosen, let $s_\varepsilon(x, \xi)$ stand for $\sum\limits_{i,j=1}^{n} a_{ij}\psi_i(x)\overline{\psi}_j(\xi)$, and let S_ε be the corresponding separable integral operator. By (3.3),

$$\|K - S_\varepsilon\|^2 \leq \int_a^b \int_a^b \left| k(x, \xi) - \sum_{i,j=1}^{n} a_{ij}\psi_i(x)\overline{\psi}_j(\xi) \right|^2 dx\, d\xi < \varepsilon.$$

Thus K can be approximated in norm by separable operators. Since separable operators are completely continuous, it follows from Theorem 3 of Section 2.10 that K is completely continuous.

The following are examples of H.-S. kernels:

1. Any bounded function $k(x, \xi)$ over the finite square $a \leq x, \xi \leq b$.
2. $1/|x - \xi|^\alpha$ over a finite square (with $\alpha < \frac{1}{2}$).
3. $e^{-(x^2 + \xi^2)}$ over the plane $-\infty < x, \xi < \infty$.

The H.-S. kernel $k(x, \xi)$ always generates a bounded, completely continuous operator, although $k(x, \xi)$ may be an unbounded function of x and ξ. It is essential that the theory should encompass such cases, as they frequently occur in applications (see Volume II).

Integral Equations

Consider the equations below, with μ and $f(x)$ given:

$$Ku = f; \qquad \text{that is,} \int_a^b k(x, \xi)u(\xi)d\xi = f(x), \qquad a \leq x \leq b. \tag{3.4}$$

$$Ku = \mu u; \qquad \text{that is,} \int_a^b k(x, \xi)u(\xi)d\xi = \mu u(x), \qquad a \leq x \leq b. \tag{3.5}$$

$$Ku = \mu u + f; \qquad \text{that is,} \int_a^b k(x, \xi)u(\xi)d\xi = \mu u(x) + f(x), \qquad a \leq x \leq b. \tag{3.6}$$

These equations are known as *Fredholm integral equations* [for the unknown function $u(x)$ appearing under the integral sign]. Equations (3.4) and (3.6) are inhomogeneous equations of the first and second kind, respectively. Although (3.4) can be obtained from (3.6) by setting $\mu = 0$, it has enough special features to warrant separate consideration. Equation (3.5) is a homogeneous equation and may be regarded as an eigenvalue problem: For most values of μ the unique solution is $u \equiv 0$; the special values of μ, for which nontrivial solutions $u(x)$ exist, are the eigenvalues; the corresponding solutions $u(x)$ are the eigenfunctions.

If, in any of the above equations, the upper limit of integration is x instead of b, the equation is known as a *Volterra equation*. Such an equation may be considered as a special case of a Fredholm equation with kernel

$$\tilde{k}(x, \xi) = \begin{cases} 0, & \xi > x; \\ k(x, \xi), & \xi < x. \end{cases}$$

As an immediate consequence of the linearity of K, the following properties hold true: (1) The inhomogeneous equation (3.6) has at most one solution unless the homogeneous equation (3.5) has a nontrivial solution; and (2) if u and v are two eigenfunctions corresponding to the same eigenvalue μ of (3.5), then $\alpha u + \beta v$ is also an eigenfunction corresponding to μ. Thus the eigenfunctions corresponding to a particular eigenvalue μ form a linear manifold.

EXAMPLES

All the examples below, except 6, deal with H.-S. kernels.
Example 1. $a = 0$, $b = 1$, $k(x, \xi) = x\xi$.

(a) The eigenvalue problem (3.5) becomes $\int_0^1 x\xi u(\xi)d\xi = \mu u(x)$. Since the left side is proportional to x, it follows that, for $\mu \neq 0$, the solution $u(x)$ must be of the form Cx. Substituting in the integral equation, we find $x\int_0^1 C\xi^2\, d\xi = \mu Cx$; therefore a nontrivial solution is possible only if $\mu = \int_0^1 \xi^2\, d\xi = \frac{1}{3}$. It is now easy to check that $\mu = \frac{1}{3}$, $u = Cx$, actually furnishes a solution of the problem. If $\mu = 0$, any function $u(x)$ with the property $\int_0^1 xu(x)dx = 0$ is a solution. Collecting the results, we have the following table:

Eigenvalues	Eigenfunctions
0	Any $u(x)$ such that $\int_0^1 xu\, dx = 0$
1/3	Cx

We note that there are infinitely many independent eigenfunctions corresponding to $\mu = 0$, but only one independent eigenfunction corresponding to $\mu = \frac{1}{3}$. We say that $\mu = 0$ is an eigenvalue of infinite multiplicity, whereas $\mu = \frac{1}{3}$ is a simple eigenvalue (that is, of multiplicity 1).

The set of all eigenfunctions is a complete set in the following sense: Every function $g(x)$ can be expanded in a component along the function x and a component orthogonal to the function x,

$$g(x) = \left[3\int_0^1 xg(x)dx\right]x + \left\{g(x) - \left[3\int_0^1 xg(x)dx\right]x\right\}.$$

We shall find that the eigenfunctions of any symmetric H.-S. kernel always form a complete set (as long as we make sure to include the eigenfunctions corresponding to $\mu = 0$).

(b) The inhomogeneous equation (3.6), for $\mu \neq 0$, becomes

$$\int_0^1 x\xi u(\xi)d\xi - f(x) = \mu u(x).$$

If a solution exists, it must be of the form $[Cx - f(x)]/\mu$.

Substituting in the integral equation, we obtain

$$C[\tfrac{1}{3} - \mu] = \int_0^1 \xi f(\xi)d\xi. \tag{3.7}$$

If $\mu \neq \tfrac{1}{3}$,

$$C = \frac{3}{1 - 3\mu}\int_0^1 \xi f(\xi)d\xi \quad \text{and} \quad u(x) = \frac{3x}{\mu(1 - 3\mu)}\int_0^1 \xi f(\xi)d\xi - \frac{f(x)}{\mu}.$$

If $\mu \neq \tfrac{1}{3}$ (and of course $\mu \neq 0$), the one and only solution of the inhomogeneous equation is the one given above. Note that even if $f(x)$ is discontinuous, the equation admits a solution. The solution u is then itself discontinuous but the quantity $\mu u(x) + f(x)$ is not! If $\mu = \tfrac{1}{3}$, and $f(x)$ is such that $\int_0^1 xf(x)dx \neq 0$, the equation has *no solution*, since the requirement (3.7) cannot possibly be satisfied. If $\mu = \tfrac{1}{3}$ and $\int_0^1 xf(x)dx = 0$, C in (3.7) is indeterminate, and the solution of (3.6) contains an arbitrary constant: $u(x) = Cx - 3f(x)$.

(c) If $\mu = 0$, we are dealing with the equation of the first kind,

$$\int_0^1 x\xi u(\xi)d\xi = f(x).$$

A solution is possible only if $f(x) = \alpha x$; if this condition is satisfied, there are many solutions, namely

$$u(x) = 2\alpha + u_0(x),$$

where $u_0(x)$ is any function such that $\int_0^1 xu_0(x)dx = 0$.

Example 2. $k(x, \xi) = \sin x \sin \xi + \theta \cos x \cos \xi$, $a = 0$, $b = \pi$, θ given $\neq 0$. We consider only the eigenvalue problem

$$\int_0^\pi k(x, \xi)u(\xi)d\xi = \mu u(x).$$

If $\mu \neq 0$, $u(x) = C_1 \sin x + C_2 \cos x$, and, on substitution.

$$\frac{\pi}{2}C_1 \sin x + \frac{\pi}{2}\theta C_2 \cos x = \mu C_1 \sin x + \mu C_2 \cos x.$$

Assuming $\theta \neq 1$, we have two possibilities for nontrivial solutions:

(a) $C_2 = 0$, $\quad \mu = \dfrac{\pi}{2}$, $\quad u(x) = C_1 \sin x$.

(b) $C_1 = 0$, $\quad \mu = \dfrac{\pi\theta}{2}$, $\quad u(x) = C_2 \cos x$.

If $\theta = 1$, we are left with the single eigenvalue $\mu = \pi/2$, which is now of multiplicity 2, since the eigenfunctions are $C_1 \sin x + C_2 \cos x$. If $\mu = 0$, any function $u(x)$ such that $\int_0^\pi u \sin x \, dx = \int_0^\pi u \cos x \, dx = 0$ is an eigenfunction. Collecting the results, we have the following table:

Eigenvalues	Eigenfunctions
0	Any u such that $\int_0^\pi u \sin x \, dx = \int_0^\pi u \cos x \, dx = 0$
$\pi/2$	$C_1 \sin x$
$\pi\theta/2$	$C_2 \cos x$

The set of all eigenfunctions is a complete set. If $\theta = 1$, the nonzero eigenvalues coalesce in the degenerate eigenvalue $\pi/2$ to which correspond the independent eigenfunctions $\sin x$ and $\cos x$.

Example 3. $k(x, \xi) = \sin x \cos \xi$; $a = 0$, $b = \pi$. The eigenvalue problem is

$$\int_0^\pi \sin x \cos \xi \, u(\xi) d\xi = \mu u(x).$$

If $\mu \neq 0$, $u(x)$ must be of the form $C \sin x$, but since $\int_0^\pi \cos \xi \sin \xi \, d\xi = 0$, no such solution is possible. If $\mu = 0$, we have as eigenfunctions all functions $u(x)$ such that $\int_0^\pi u(\xi) \cos \xi \, d\xi = 0$.

Eigenvalue	Eigenfunctions
0	Any $u(x)$ such that $\int_0^\pi u(x) \cos x \, dx = 0$.

We note that the eigenfunctions do not form a complete set (the function $\cos x$, for instance, cannot be expanded in the eigenfunctions!). This situation can occur only for a nonsymmetric kernel.

Example 4. $k(x, \xi) = \sum\limits_{i=1}^{n} p_i(x)\bar{q}_i(\xi)$; *separable kernel.*

The functions $p_i(x)$ are assumed linearly independent and the functions $q_i(x)$ are also assumed to form a linearly independent set $(a \leq x \leq b)$. If this assumption were not made, the kernel could be rewritten as a separable kernel with a smaller number of terms.

The eigenvalue problem is

$$\int_a^b \sum_{i=1}^n p_i(x)\bar{q}_i(\xi)u(\xi)d\xi = \mu u(x).$$

$$e_i = \langle u(x), g_i(x) \rangle$$

For $\mu \neq 0$, $u(x)$ must be of the form $\sum_{i=1}^n c_i p_i(x)$; hence

$$\sum_{i=1}^n p_i(x) \sum_{j=1}^n c_j \int_a^b \bar{q}_i(\xi)p_j(\xi)d\xi = \mu \sum_{i=1}^n c_i p_i(x)$$

and

$$\sum_{j=1}^n \alpha_{ij}c_j = \mu c_i, \qquad \text{where } \alpha_{ij} = \int_a^b \bar{q}_i(\xi)p_j(\xi)d\xi. \tag{3.8}$$

Consider the special case (symmetric case) when $q_i(x) = p_i(x)$; the matrix α_{ij} is then symmetric; that is, $\alpha_{ij} = \bar{\alpha}_{ji}$. Because the functions $p_i(x)$ are independent, the matrix eigenvalue problem (3.8) cannot have 0 as an eigenvalue. We therefore obtain n (not necessarily distinct) nonzero eigenvalues, with n independent eigenfunctions. Although $\mu = 0$ cannot be an eigenvalue of (3.8), it can still be an eigenvalue of the integral equation. In fact, for $\mu = 0$, we have a large number of eigenfunctions—those functions $u(x)$ such that

$$\int_a^b u(x)\bar{p}_i(x)dx = 0, \qquad \text{for } i = 1, \ldots, n.$$

In the symmetric case, the totality of eigenfunctions forms a complete set.

Example 5. Consider the eigenvalue problem

$$-\frac{d^2u}{dx^2} = \lambda u; \qquad u(0) = 0, \quad u(1) = 0. \tag{3.9}$$

Since $\lambda = 0$ is not an eigenvalue, we can construct the Green's function for $-d^2/dx^2$ with the above boundary conditions. This Green's function was found in Chapter 1:

$$k(x, \xi) = \begin{cases} x(1 - \xi), & 0 \leq x \leq \xi; \\ \xi(1 - x), & \xi \leq x \leq 1. \end{cases}$$

We have also shown that system (3.9) can be translated into the integral equation

$$u(x) = \lambda \int_0^1 k(x, \xi)u(\xi)d\xi. \tag{3.10}$$

It is left as an exercise to recover (3.9) from (3.10) by careful differentiation. Setting $\mu = 1/\lambda$, we obtain

$$\mu u(x) = \int_0^1 k(x, \xi)u(\xi)d\xi = Ku. \tag{3.11}$$

Equations (3.10) and (3.11) are equivalent except for the fact that $\mu = 0$ might be an eigenvalue of (3.11) [speaking loosely, this corresponds to the eigenvalue $\lambda = \infty$ for (3.10)]. Therefore, the nonzero eigenvalues of (3.11) are just the reciprocals of the eigenvalues of (3.9). The corresponding eigenfunctions are the same. The advantage of considering (3.11) instead of (3.9) lies in the fact that K is a bounded operator, whereas $-d^2/dx^2$ is not. That K is bounded (in fact, completely continuous) follows from its Hilbert-Schmidt status. On the other hand, we can exhibit functions u of unit norm for which $\| -d^2u/dx^2 \|$ is arbitrarily large: $\| \sqrt{2} \sin n\pi x \| = 1$, $\| -(d^2/dx^2)(\sqrt{2} \sin n\pi x) \| = n^2\pi^2$.

The eigenvalues of (3.9) are $\lambda_n = n^2\pi^2$; the eigenfunctions are $C \sin n\pi x$. The nonzero eigenvalues of (3.11) are therefore $\mu_n = 1/n^2\pi^2$, with eigenfunctions $C \sin n\pi x$; moreover, we now show that $\mu = 0$ is *not* an eigenvalue of (3.11) (although it is a limit point of eigenvalues). We claim that the only solution of $\int_0^1 k(x, \xi)u(\xi)d\xi = 0$ is $u \equiv 0$. To this end, consider the differential system $-d^2v/dx^2 = u$, $v(0) = v(1) = 0$, whose unique solution is

$$v(x) = \int_0^1 k(x, \xi)u(\xi)d\xi.$$

Since $-d^2v/dx^2 = u$, the assumption $v = 0$ leads to $u = 0$; hence $\mu = 0$ is not an eigenvalue of (3.11).

The reader may feel at this stage that we are going around in circles. We have solved (3.11) by reducing it to (3.9), whereas our aim is to throw light on (3.9) by studying (3.11). This sort of help is provided by Theorems 5 and 6 of Section 3.3, which guarantee that the eigenfunctions of (3.11) [and hence of (3.9)] form a complete set. Of course, for the particular case of the trigonometric functions $\sin n\pi x$, the result is obtainable without appealing to the theory of integral equations; for more complicated differential systems, the theory of integral equations provides the simplest proof of the completeness of the eigenfunctions.

Consider now the inhomogeneous equation [with μ and $f(x)$ given]

$$\mu u(x) + f(x) = \int_0^1 k(x, \xi)u(\xi)d\xi, \qquad (3.12)$$

or, in operator form,

$$(K - \mu I)u = f,$$

where I is the identity operator.

To solve this equation for u, we expand everything in sight in terms of the eigenfunctions $\sin n\pi x$ of the homogeneous equation. Thus, let $f(x) = \sum_{n=1}^{\infty} a_n \sin n\pi x$, with $a_n = 2\int_0^1 f(x) \sin n\pi x \, dx$. For $u(x)$ we have an expansion $\sum_{n=1}^{\infty} b_n \sin n\pi x$, with $b_n = 2\int_0^1 u(x) \sin n\pi x \, dx$. If we can find the coefficients b_n in terms of known quantities, we shall consider the problem solved.

Substituting the series in the integral equation, and recalling that

$$(1/n^2\pi^2) \sin n\pi x = \int_0^1 k(x, \xi) \sin n\pi\xi \, d\xi,$$

we obtain

$$\left(\frac{1}{n^2\pi^2} - \mu\right) b_n = a_n, \qquad n = 1, 2, 3, \ldots. \qquad (3.13)$$

Let us distinguish among three cases.

1. $\mu \neq 0$, $\mu \neq 1/n^2\pi^2$:

$$b_n = \frac{a_n}{-\mu + (1/n^2\pi^2)} \quad \text{and} \quad u(x) = \sum_{n=1}^{\infty} \frac{a_n \sin n\pi x}{-\mu + (1/n^2\pi^2)}. \qquad (3.13a)$$

The series can be shown to converge in the mean to the one and only solution of (3.12). For large n, the coefficients in the series for u are of the same order as the coefficients a_n of $f(x)$. Since $f(x)$ is arbitrary, we have little information about how fast the coefficients a_n approach 0.

The formula for u can be made more attractive by adopting a slightly different approach. We note that if the Fourier sine coefficients of $u(x)$ are b_n, the coefficients of $\int_0^1 k(x, \xi)u(\xi)d\xi$ are $b_n/n^2\pi^2$. Using (3.12),

$$u(x) = -\frac{f(x)}{\mu} + \sum_{n=1}^{\infty} \frac{a_n \sin n\pi x}{n^2\pi^2[-\mu + (1/n^2\pi^2)]}$$

$$= -\frac{f(x)}{\mu} + \sum_{n=1}^{\infty} \frac{a_n \sin n\pi x}{1 - n^2\pi^2\mu}. \qquad (3.14)$$

The terms of this last series are dominated for large n by A/n^2 and, therefore, the series converges uniformly and represents a continuous function. In a sense we have isolated the trouble-causing term, $-f(x)/\mu$, the remaining term being well behaved.

2. $\mu = 1/m^2\pi^2$ for an integer m. Then (3.13) is inconsistent and (3.12) has no solution unless $a_m = 0$. If the consistency condition

$$a_m = \int_0^1 f(x) \sin m\pi x \, dx = 0$$

is satisfied, b_m is arbitrary, but all other b_n are still given by (3.13a). The solution is no longer unique:

$$u(x) = -\frac{f(x)}{\mu} + \sum_{\substack{n=1 \\ n \neq m}}^{\infty} \frac{a_n \sin n\pi x}{1 - n^2\pi^2\mu} + C \sin m\pi x.$$

3. $\mu = 0$. The integral equation then becomes an equation of the first kind,

$$f(x) = \int_0^1 k(x, \xi)u(\xi)d\xi. \qquad (3.15)$$

Although $\mu = 0$ is not an eigenvalue, it is the limit point of eigenvalues, and in fact belongs to the continuous spectrum. Let us see what happens; apparently (3.13) can be solved for b_n, and $b_n = n^2\pi^2 a_n$. It appears that the solution of (3.12) (with $\mu = 0$) is

$$u(x) = \sum_{n=1}^{\infty} n^2\pi^2 a_n \sin n\pi x. \tag{3.16}$$

This is correct as long as the series in question converges in the mean, but, unfortunately, there are simple cases where this fails to happen. Suppose, for instance, that $f(x) = 1$, $0 < x < 1$. Then a simple computation yields $a_n = (2/\pi n)[1 - (-1)^n]$, and the series (3.16) fails to converge. The reason for the difficulty can be seen by returning to the differential system which corresponds to $f(x) = \int_0^1 k(x, \xi)u(\xi)d\xi$. We recall that $f(x)$ can be interpreted as the deflection of a string under the pressure $u(x)$, the ends of the string being fixed at $x = 0$, $x = 1$. It is clear that to every pressure corresponds a deflection, but an arbitrary function will not do as a deflection! Indeed, unless $f(x)$ has a continuous derivative, a piecewise continuous second derivative, and $f(0) = f(1) = 0$, it is not a possible deflection. Returning to (3.15), we can state that (3.16) furnishes the one and only solution if $\sum_{n=1}^{\infty} (n^2\pi^2|a_n|)^2$ converges. An interpretation can still be given for the "solution" (3.16) even if this criterion is not satisfied (see Exercise 3.7).

Example 6. Consider the differential expression $-(d^2/dx^2) + 1$ in $-\infty < x < \infty$. Its Green's function satisfies $-(d^2g/dx^2) + g = \delta(x - \xi)$; if we want g to belong to $\mathscr{L}_2(-\infty, \infty)$, we can readily calculate that

$$g(x\,|\,\xi) = \frac{e^{-|x-\xi|}}{2}.$$

The integral equation which corresponds to the eigenvalue problem $-(d^2u/dx^2) + u = \lambda u$ is, therefore,

$$u(x) = \lambda \int_{-\infty}^{\infty} \frac{e^{-|x-\xi|}}{2} u(\xi)d\xi.$$

Setting $\mu = 1/\lambda$,

$$\mu u(x) = \int_{-\infty}^{\infty} \frac{e^{-|x-\xi|}}{2} u(\xi)d\xi = Ku. \tag{3.17}$$

The eigenvalue differential equation can be recovered from (3.17) by differentiation.

The kernel $e^{-|x-\xi|}/2$ is *not* of the Hilbert-Schmidt type, since

$$\iint_{-\infty}^{\infty} \left[\frac{e^{-|x-\xi|}}{2}\right]^2 dx\,d\xi = \int_{-\infty}^{\infty} dx \int_{-\infty}^{\infty} \frac{e^{-2|t|}}{4} dt = \infty.$$

In spite of this, the integral operator K generated by the kernel is bounded. Indeed, let $z(x) = \int_{-\infty}^{\infty} (e^{-|x-\xi|}/2)f(\xi)d\xi$; then

$$|z^2(x)| = \iint_{-\infty}^{\infty} \frac{e^{-|x-\xi|}}{2} \frac{e^{-|x-t|}}{2} f(\xi)\bar{f}(t)d\xi\, dt$$

$$= \frac{1}{4} \iint_{-\infty}^{\infty} e^{-|v|}e^{-|w|}f(v+x)\bar{f}(w+x)dv\, dw.$$

It follows that

$$\|z\|^2 = \frac{1}{4} \int_{-\infty}^{\infty} dx \iint_{-\infty}^{\infty} e^{-|v|}e^{-|w|}f(v+x)\bar{f}(w+x)dv\, dw.$$

From Schwarz's inequality, $\left| \int_{-\infty}^{\infty} f(v+x)\bar{f}(w+x)dx \right| \leq \|f\|^2$; therefore,

$$\|z\|^2 \leq \frac{1}{4} \|f\|^2 \iint_{-\infty}^{\infty} e^{-|v|}e^{-|w|}dv\, dw = \|f\|^2.$$

We have shown that K is bounded and $\|K\| \leq 1$. It is left as an exercise to prove that $\|K\| = 1$. [HINT: Consider the function

$$u(x) = \begin{cases} 1, & |x| < A; \\ 0, & |x| \geq A, \end{cases}$$

and show that for A large, $\|Ku\| \sim \|u\|$.]

We return to (3.17) and make the claim that no eigenvalues exist. In fact, (3.17) corresponds to the differential equation $-(d^2u/dx^2) + u = \lambda u$, whose general solution is $u = A \exp(\sqrt{1-\lambda}\, x) + B \exp(-\sqrt{1-\lambda}\, x)$ (unless $\lambda = 1$, in which case $u = A + Bx$); no matter how λ is chosen in the complex plane, there is no nontrivial solution with $\int_{-\infty}^{\infty} |u|^2\, dx < \infty$. This is hardly the end of the story. We continue our analysis by investigating the inhomogeneous integral equation

$$Ku = \mu u + f, \tag{3.18}$$

where f is a given element in $\mathscr{L}_2^{(c)}(-\infty, \infty)$, and μ is a fixed complex number. Let us apply the operator $L = -(d^2/dx^2) + 1$ to both sides of the integral equation (this is permissible, since Ku is twice-differentiable). Then

$$LKu = L(\mu u + f),$$

and, since $LK = I$,

$$u(x) = -z'' + z, \tag{3.19}$$

where

$$z(x) = \mu u(x) + f.$$

Rewriting (3.19) in terms of z, we have (for $\mu \neq 0$)

$$\frac{z-f}{\mu} = -z'' + z$$

or

$$z'' - \left(1 - \frac{1}{\mu}\right)z = \frac{f}{\mu}. \tag{3.20}$$

We are looking for an $\mathscr{L}_2$ solution of (3.20). We construct the Green's function which satisfies

$$\frac{d^2g}{dx^2} - \left(1 - \frac{1}{\mu}\right)g = \delta(x - \xi).$$

Let $\sqrt{1 - (1/\mu)}$ be the square root with positive real part. Such a square root always exists when μ is *not* on the *real* interval $0 \leq \mu \leq 1$. The requirement of square integrability for g is then satisfied by the choice

$$g(x \mid \xi) = \begin{cases} A \exp[-\sqrt{1 - (1/\mu)}x], & x > \xi; \\ B \exp[\sqrt{1 - (1/\mu)}x], & x < \xi. \end{cases}$$

The usual matching conditions at $x = \xi$ yield

$$g(x \mid \xi) = -\frac{1}{2\sqrt{1 - (1/\mu)}} \exp[-\sqrt{1 - (1/\mu)} \, |x - \xi|]. \tag{3.21}$$

Thus, if μ is *not* in $0 \leq \mu \leq 1$, the one and only $\mathscr{L}_2$ solution of (3.20) is

$$z(x) = \frac{1}{\mu} \int_{-\infty}^{\infty} g(x \mid \xi) f(\xi) d\xi.$$

Therefore the one and only $\mathscr{L}_2$ solution of (3.18) is

$$u(x) = \frac{z - f}{\mu} = -\frac{f}{\mu} + \frac{1}{\mu^2} \int_{-\infty}^{\infty} g(x \mid \xi) f(\xi) d\xi,$$

where $g(x \mid \xi)$ is given by (3.21).

In spectral terminology (see Chapter 2) it has been shown that (a) the point spectrum of K is empty, and (b) all values of μ except $0 \leq \mu \leq 1$ are regular values of K. By refining our analysis, we can show that the values $0 \leq \mu \leq 1$ are in the continuous spectrum of K.

EXERCISES

3.1 $k(x, \xi) = x - \xi$, $a = 0$, $b = 1$. Find the eigenvalues and eigenfunctions. Note that the eigenvalues are purely imaginary. Find the consistency conditions (if any) for the solution of the ~~homogeneous~~ *inhomogeneous* equations (3.4) and (3.6).

3.2 $k(x, \xi) = \sin x \sin \xi + \cos x \cos \xi$, $a = 0$, $b = \pi$. This is Example 2 with $\theta = 1$. Discuss the inhomogeneous equations (3.4) and (3.6).

3.3 $k(x, \xi) = 1 - |x - \xi|$, $a = -1$, $b = 1$. Consider the eigenvalue problem (3.5). Differentiate correctly under the integral sign to obtain the corresponding differential equation and boundary conditions. Determine all eigenvalues and eigenfunctions.

3.4 $k(x, \xi) = e^{-|x-\xi|}$, $a = 0$, $b = 1$. Same question as in Exercise 3.3.

3.5 **(a)** Find the eigenvalues and eigenfunctions of the system

$$-i\frac{du}{dx} = \lambda u, \qquad u(0) = u(1).$$

(b) Construct the Green's function

$$-i\frac{dg}{dx} - \theta g = \delta(x - \xi), \qquad g(0 \mid \xi) = g(1 \mid \xi),$$

where θ is not an eigenvalue of **(a)**.

(c) Using the Green's function of **(b)**, translate the system in **(a)** into an integral equation.

3.6 In the study of vibrations of a simply supported beam, the following system is encountered

$$\frac{d^4u}{dx^4} - \lambda u = 0, \qquad 0 \le x \le 1, \qquad u(0) = u''(0) = u(1) = u''(1) = 0.$$

Show that $\lambda = 0$ is not an eigenvalue. Show that the Green's function satisfying

$$\frac{d^4g}{dx^4} = \delta(x - \xi), \qquad g(0 \mid \xi) = g''(0 \mid \xi) = g(1 \mid \xi) = g''(1 \mid \xi) = 0$$

is

$$g(x \mid \xi) = \begin{cases} \dfrac{x(\xi - 1)}{6}(x - \xi)^2, & 0 \le x \le \xi; \\[2mm] \dfrac{\xi(x - 1)}{6}(x - \xi)^2, & \xi \le x \le 1. \end{cases}$$

Translate the eigenvalue problem into an integral equation.

3.7 Consider the Fredholm equation of the first kind in Example 5: $f(x) = \int_0^1 k(x, \xi)u(\xi)d\xi$ with

$$k(x, \xi) = \begin{cases} x(1 - \xi), & 0 \le x \le \xi; \\ \xi(1 - x), & \xi \le x \le 1. \end{cases}$$

The interpretation is that $f(x)$ is the given deflection of a string (with fixed ends) under the unknown pressure $u(x)$. Suppose that

$$f(x) = \begin{cases} \dfrac{x}{2}, & 0 \le x \le \tfrac{1}{2}; \\ \dfrac{1-x}{2}, & \tfrac{1}{2} \le x \le 1. \end{cases}$$

Show by substitution that $u(x) = \delta(x - \tfrac{1}{2})$ formally satisfies the integral equation. Explain the physical significance. Show that the solution (3.16) yields a diverging series which can be interpreted by the methods of Chapter 1 as $\delta(x - \tfrac{1}{2})$.

3.2 THE NEUMANN SERIES (METHOD OF SUCCESSIVE APPROXIMATIONS)

Consider the inhomogeneous integral equation (3.6) for $\mu \ne 0$. Setting $\lambda = 1/\mu$ and redefining f in a suitable manner, we obtain

$$u = \lambda K u + f, \quad \text{that is, } u(x) = \lambda \int_a^b k(x, \xi)u(\xi)d\xi + f(x). \quad (3.22)$$

We now describe a simple (but nevertheless effective) attempt at solving (3.22). On the right side of (3.22) let us substitute $\lambda K u + f$ for u. This yields

$$u = \lambda K\{\lambda K u + f\} + f = \lambda^2 K^2 u + \lambda K f + f$$

Successive substitutions give

$$u = \lambda^n K^n u + \lambda^{n-1} K^{n-1} f + \cdots + \lambda K f + f, \quad (3.23)$$

where

$$K^n f = \underbrace{K \cdots K}_{n \text{ times}} f = \int_a^b k(x, \xi_{n-1})d\xi_{n-1} \cdots \int_a^b k(\xi_2, \xi_1)d\xi_1 \int_a^b k(\xi_1, \xi)f(\xi)d\xi$$

$$= \int_a^b f(\xi)d\xi \left\{ \int_a^b \cdots \int_a^b k(x, \xi_{n-1})k(\xi_{n-1}, \xi_{n-2}) \cdots k(\xi_1, \xi)d\xi_1 \cdots d\xi_{n-1} \right\}$$

$$= \int_a^b k_n(x, \xi)f(\xi)d\xi.$$

The iterated transformation K^n is therefore an integral transformation generated by the kernel $k_n(x, \xi)$, the so-called nth iterated kernel:

$$k_n(x, \xi) = \underbrace{\int_a^b \cdots \int_a^b}_{n-1 \text{ times}} k(x, \xi_{n-1})k(\xi_{n-1}, \xi_{n-2}) \cdots k(\xi_1, \xi)d\xi_1 \cdots d\xi_{n-1}. \quad (3.24)$$

For large n we can hope that $\lambda^n K^n u$ is small enough to be neglected in (3.23). This leads to the following candidate (known as the *Neumann series*) for the solution of (3.22):

$$u = f + \sum_{n=1}^{\infty} \lambda^n K^n f. \tag{3.25}$$

Theorem.   *If the series (3.25) converges (in the mean), it is a solution to (3.22).*

Proof.   Let $u = f + \sum_{n=1}^{\infty} \lambda^n K^n f$. Since K is a continuous operator,

$$\lambda K u = \lambda K f + \sum_{n=1}^{\infty} \lambda^{n+1} K^{n+1} f = \sum_{n=1}^{\infty} \lambda^n K^n f = u - f,$$

so that $f + \sum_{n=1}^{\infty} \lambda^n K^n f$ is indeed a solution of (3.22).

Next we determine conditions for which the Neumann series converges. We have

$$\left\| \sum_{n=i}^{m} \lambda^n K^n f \right\| \le \sum_{n=i}^{m} |\lambda|^n \|K^n f\| = \sum_{n=i}^{m} |\lambda|^n \|\underbrace{K \cdots K}_{n \text{ times}} f\| \le \sum_{n=i}^{m} |\lambda|^n \|K\|^n \|f\|.$$

The last sum is part of a geometric series with ratio $|\lambda| \, \|K\|$. If $|\lambda| \, \|K\| < 1$, $\lim_{i,\, m \to \infty} \sum_{n=i}^{m} |\lambda|^n \|K\|^n \|f\| = 0$; therefore $\lim_{i,\, m \to \infty} \left\| \sum_{n=i}^{m} \lambda^n K^n f \right\| = 0$, and $\sum_{n=1}^{\infty} \lambda^n K^n f$ converges. Thus (3.25) is a solution of (3.22) whenever $|\lambda| < 1/\|K\|$. For an H.-S. kernel $\|K\|^2 \le \int_a^b \int_a^b |k(x, \xi)|^2 dx \, d\xi$, so that the solution (3.25) is surely valid whenever

$$|\lambda| < \left[\int_a^b \int_a^b |k(x, \xi)|^2 dx \, d\xi \right]^{-1/2}.$$

We assert that the solution (3.25) is unique. Indeed, if u_1 and u_2 are solutions of (3.22), we infer that $u_1 - u_2 = \lambda K(u_1 - u_2)$ or

$$\|u_1 - u_2\| \le |\lambda| \, \|K\| \, \|u_1 - u_2\|.$$

Since $|\lambda| \, \|K\| < 1$, we conclude that $\|u_1 - u_2\| = 0$ or $u_1 = u_2$.

We consolidate our results in the following theorem.

Theorem.   *If $|\lambda| < 1/\|K\|$, (3.22) has one and only one solution given by the Neumann series (3.25). (In particular, if $f = 0$, the only solution is $u = 0$, and therefore every eigenvalue of (3.5) satisfies the condition $|\mu| \le \|K\|$.)*

There are two serious drawbacks to the Neumann series: (a) the explicit calculations of the iterated kernels required in (3.25) are usually very cumbersome, and (b) a solution of the integral equation (3.22) may exist even if

$|\lambda| > 1/\|K\|$, but the Neumann series does not converge, so that it does not provide the desired solution (see Example 1 below for further comments on this point).

In the next sections we shall obtain the solution of the inhomogeneous equation as an expansion in the eigenfunctions of the homogeneous equation; this new form of the solution will shed considerable light not only on the questions we have raised above but also on the whole subject of integral equations and differential equations.

EXAMPLES

Example 1. $k(x, \xi) = x\xi$, $0 \le x, \xi \le 1$. We have

$$\|K\| \le \left[\int_0^1 \int_0^1 x^2 \xi^2 \, dx \, d\xi \right]^{1/2} = \tfrac{1}{3}.$$

$$= \int_0^1 \int_0^1 |K(x,\xi)|^2 \, dx \, d\xi$$

In this problem the inequality can be shown to be unnecessary, that is, $\|K\| = \tfrac{1}{3}$. The iterated kernels are easily calculated,

$$k_2(x, \xi) = \int_0^1 x\xi_1 \xi_1 \xi \, d\xi_1 = \frac{x\xi}{3}, \quad = \int_0^1 K(x,\xi_1)K(\xi_1,\xi)\,d\xi_1$$

$$= \int_0^1 (x\xi_1)(\xi_1\xi)\,d\xi_1$$

$$k_3(x, \xi) = \int_0^1 \int_0^1 x\xi_1 \xi_1 \xi_2 \xi_2 \xi \, d\xi_1 \, d\xi_2 = x\xi(\tfrac{1}{3})^2,$$

$$\vdots$$

$$k_n(x, \xi) = x\xi(\tfrac{1}{3})^{n-1}.$$

$$\vdots$$

When $|\lambda| < 3$, the solution of $u(x) = \lambda \int_0^1 x\xi u(\xi)d\xi + f(x)$ is

$$u(x) = f(x) + \sum_{n=1}^{\infty} \frac{\lambda^n}{3^{n-1}} \int_0^1 x\xi f(\xi)d\xi = f(x) + 3x \sum_{n=1}^{\infty} \left(\frac{\lambda}{3}\right)^n \int_0^1 \xi f(\xi)d\xi. \qquad (3.26)$$

The series converges for $|\lambda| < 3$, but does not converge for $|\lambda| > 3$. In our simple problem, the sum can be calculated explicitly,

$$\sum_{n=1}^{\infty} \left(\frac{\lambda}{3}\right)^n = \frac{1}{1 - (\lambda/3)} - 1 = \frac{\lambda}{3 - \lambda}$$

and, therefore,

$$u(x) = f(x) + \frac{3\lambda x}{3 - \lambda} \int_0^1 \xi f(\xi)d\xi. \qquad (3.27)$$

The Neumann-series approach only tells us that this is the solution for $|\lambda| < 3$, but it is easy to verify (as in Section 3.1, Example 1) that the expression (3.27) furnishes the solution for all $\lambda \ne 3$. Formula (3.27) [which is the analytic continuation of the series in (3.26)] provides the solution even for those λ which are outside the circle of convergence of the series!

Example 2. *The Volterra equation.* **(a)** For $\mu \neq 0$, the homogeneous equation can be written in either of two forms:

$$\mu u(x) = \int_a^x k(x, \xi)u(\xi)d\xi, \tag{3.28}$$

$$u(x) = \lambda \int_a^x k(x, \xi)u(\xi)d\xi, \qquad \lambda = \frac{1}{\mu}. \tag{3.29}$$

The lower limit a is finite, and we are interested in solutions for $x > a$. It is convenient to introduce a finite right end point b which will disappear in the final results. For simplicity we assume that $k(x, \xi)$ is a bounded function of the two variables x and ξ, so that $|k| \leq M$ over the square $a \leq x, \xi \leq b$.

We show that, for any λ, (3.29) has only the trivial solution. We are looking for solutions $u(x)$ which are in $\mathcal{L}_2^{(c)}(a, b)$, that is, solutions such that $\int_a^b |u|^2 \, dx$ is finite; since the interval is finite, this implies that $\int_a^b |u| dx$ is also finite. Setting $\int_a^b |u| dx = p$, we find from (3.29) that

$$|u| \leq |\lambda| \int_a^x |k| \, |u| d\xi \leq |\lambda| M p, \qquad \text{for } a \leq x \leq b.$$

Using the integral equation again,

$$|u| \leq |\lambda| \int_a^x |k| \, |\lambda| M p \, d\xi \leq |\lambda|^2 M^2 p(x - a), \qquad \text{for } a \leq x \leq b.$$

In a similar fashion,

$$|u| \leq |\lambda|^n M^n p \frac{(x - a)^{n-1}}{(n - 1)!}, \qquad \text{for } a \leq x \leq b.$$

The last inequality holds for any n, and the right side can be made as small as we wish by choosing n sufficiently large. It follows therefore that $u \equiv 0$, $a \leq x \leq b$. Since b is arbitrary, the result holds for $x \geq a$. A slightly more delicate method of estimation shows that the result also holds under the less restrictive assumption that k is an H.-S. kernel.[†] Hence (3.29) has no eigenvalues and no eigenfunctions.[‡] We can therefore state that (3.28) has no eigenvalues except possibly $\mu = 0$. This case is disposed of below.

(b) Consider the homogeneous equation with $\mu = 0$; that is,

$$\int_a^x k(x, \xi)u(\xi)d\xi = 0. \tag{3.30}$$

---

† See F. Smithies, *Integral Equations*, Cambridge University Press, Cambridge, 1958.

‡ It is understood that we are talking about $\mathcal{L}_2$ eigenfunctions. It may be possible for (3.29) to have eigenfunctions not in $\mathcal{L}_2$ on any finite interval.

We can reduce this to an equation of the form (3.26) by differentiating with respect to x,

$$\int_a^x \frac{\partial k}{\partial x} u(\xi)d\xi + k(x, x)u(x) = 0. \tag{3.31}$$

If $k(x, x) \neq 0$, (3.31) is just of the type (3.29), and therefore has only the trivial solution. If, on the other hand, $k(x, x) = 0$ at some point x, the preceding result no longer holds. As an example we note that $\varphi(x) = x^2$ is a solution of $\int_0^x (x - \frac{4}{3}\xi)\varphi(\xi)d\xi = 0$. This phenomenon is related to singular points for differential equations (see Exercise 3.10).

(c) The inhomogeneous equation (for $\mu \neq 0$) may be written

$$u(x) = \lambda \int_a^x k(x, \xi)u(\xi)d\xi + f(x), \quad a \leq x \leq b; \qquad \lambda = \frac{1}{\mu}. \tag{3.32}$$

It is convenient to extend the definition of $k(x, \xi)$ so that k vanishes identically for $x < \xi$. Equation (3.32) then takes the form of a Fredholm equation (3.22), namely,

$$u(x) = \lambda \int_a^b k(x, \xi)u(\xi)d\xi + f(x).$$

Retaining the assumptions of part **(a)**, and setting $m = \int_a^b |f| dx$, we have

$$|Kf| = \int_a^x |k| \, |f| d\xi \leq Mm;$$

$$|K^2f| = \int_a^x |k| \, |Kf| d\xi \leq M^2 m(x - a);$$

$$\vdots$$

$$|K^n f| \leq M^n m \frac{(x - a)^{n-1}}{(n-1)!}.$$

The corresponding Neumann series [see (3.25)] is

$$f + \sum_{n=1}^{\infty} \lambda^n K^n f, \tag{3.33}$$

where $\sum_{n=1}^{\infty} \lambda^n K^n f$ is dominated by $\sum_{n=1}^{\infty} M^n |\lambda|^n m [(x-a)^{n-1}/(n-1)!]$.

For any λ and x, the ratio of two successive terms for this last series approaches zero as $n \to \infty$, so that (3.33) certainly converges in the sense of ordinary convergence. Moreover for any λ we see that (3.33) converges uniformly over $a \leq x \leq b$, hence surely converges in the mean. From our previous discussion of Neumann series, we can conclude that (3.33) furnishes a solution of (3.32) for any value of λ. Furthermore, it is the only solution, since it was shown in part (a) that the homogeneous equation has only the trivial solution. The result can again be extended to the more general case of an H.-S. kernel.

EXERCISES

3.8 $k(x, \xi) = \sin x \cos \xi$; $a = 0$, $b = \pi$. Show that the Neumann series converges in the whole plane. Check that your solution satisfies the integral equation.

3.9 $k(x, \xi) = e^{x-\xi}$; $a = 0$, $b = 1$. Solve the inhomogeneous equation (3.6) by elementary considerations as in Section 3.1 and then by a Neumann series; show that the two solutions are identical.

3.10 *Existence and uniqueness for the initial value problem of linear differential equations.* Consider the second-order linear differential equation

$$a_0(x)u''(x) + a_1(x)u'(x) + a_2(x)u(x) = f(x),$$

with $u(a) = k_1$, $u'(a) = k_2$. We assume that a_0, a_1, a_2 are continuous and that f is piecewise continuous. For any function u with a piecewise continuous second derivative (a requirement which must be met by any solution of the differential equation), we have

$$u'(x) = u'(a) + \int_a^x u''(\xi)d\xi,$$

$$u(x) = u(a) + (x - a)u'(a) + \int_a^x (x - \xi)u''(\xi)d\xi.$$

Substituting in the differential equation, we obtain

$$u''(x) = \int_a^x k(x, \xi)u''(\xi)d\xi + F(x),$$

where

$$k(x, \xi) = -\frac{[(x - \xi)a_2(x) + a_1(x)]}{a_0(x)}$$

and

$$a_0(x)F(x) = f(x) - k_2(x - a)a_2(x) - k_2 a_1(x) - k_1 a_2(x).$$

The differential equation has been reduced to a Volterra equation of the second kind for $u''(x)$. As long as $a_0(x) \neq 0$, the kernel satisfies all the requirements of Example 2. Therefore, there is exactly one solution for the unknown $u''(x)$. From the preceding formulas for $u'(x)$ and $u(x)$ we see that $u(x)$ can be uniquely determined from $u''(x)$.

The same method can be used with slight modifications for linear equations of the nth order.

3.3 THE SPECTRUM OF A SELF-ADJOINT HILBERT-SCHMIDT OPERATOR

The Adjoint of a Bounded Integral Operator

Let K be a bounded linear integral operator. Whenever u belongs to $\mathscr{L}_2^{(c)}(a, b)$, the transformed function $Ku = \int_a^b k(x, \xi)u(\xi)d\xi$ also belongs to $\mathscr{L}_2^{(c)}(a, b)$. The adjoint operator is introduced according to the scheme of Chapter 2. The inner product of Ku and v exists, and

$$\langle Ku, v \rangle = \int_a^b \bar{v}Ku \, dx = \int_a^b \int_a^b \bar{v}(x)k(x, \xi)u(\xi)dx \, d\xi.$$

If this expression can be rewritten, for all u and v, in the form $\langle u, K^*v \rangle$, K^* will be the adjoint operator. Its explicit determination follows:

$$\langle Ku, v \rangle = \int_a^b \int_a^b \bar{v}(x)k(x, \xi)u(\xi)dx \, d\xi = \int_a^b \int_a^b \bar{v}(\xi)k(\xi, x)u(x)d\xi \, dx$$

$$= \int_a^b u\overline{K^*v} \, dx = \langle u, K^*v \rangle,$$

where

$$K^*v = \int_a^b \bar{k}(\xi, x)v(\xi)d\xi.$$

The adjoint of an integral operator is itself an integral operator generated by the transposed kernel $\bar{k}(\xi, x)$. For all u and v, we have

$$\langle Ku, v \rangle = \langle u, K^*v \rangle.$$

A kernel $k(x, \xi)$ is *symmetric* if $k(x, \xi) = \bar{k}(\xi, x)$. The corresponding integral operator K satisfies the relation $K = K^*$, and is, therefore, *self-adjoint*. For such an operator, we have $\langle Ku, v \rangle = \langle u, Kv \rangle$ for all u and v. We also note that for a symmetric kernel, $\langle Ku, u \rangle$ is always *real*. Moreover, if $\langle Ku, u \rangle$ is real for all u, then K is symmetric [see Exercise 2.35(a)].

Properties of Eigenvalues and Eigenfunctions of Symmetric Kernels

The eigenvalue problem is

$$Ku = \mu u \quad \text{or} \quad \int_a^b k(x, \xi)u(\xi)d\xi = \mu u(x); \qquad k(x, \xi) = \bar{k}(\xi, x). \qquad (3.34)$$

A value of μ, for which there exists a nontrivial solution $u(x)$, (that is, $\int_a^b |u|^2 \, dx > 0$), is said to be an *eigenvalue* of K. Any corresponding nontrivial solution $u(x)$ is an eigenfunction of K. We have already noted that the eigen-functions, corresponding to a particular eigenvalue, form a linear manifold. The dimension of this manifold is the multiplicity of the eigenvalue. This multiplicity is therefore equal to the largest number of independent eigen-functions corresponding to that eigenvalue. An eigenvalue is *simple* if there is only one corresponding independent eigenfunction; otherwise, the eigen-value is *degenerate*. The *point spectrum* of K is the set of all eigenvalues.

We now list some important properties of (3.34). These properties are special cases of the general theorems of Chapter 2, but we prefer to give direct proofs.

1. *The Eigenvalues Are Real.* Let μ be an eigenvalue of K with corresponding eigenfunction $u(x)$,

$$\int_a^b k(x, \xi)u(\xi)d\xi = \mu u(x).$$

Taking complex conjugates,

$$\int_a^b \bar{k}(x, \xi)\bar{u}(\xi)d\xi = \overline{\mu u}(x).$$

Multiply the first equation by $\bar{u}(x)$, the second by $u(x)$, subtract, and integrate from a to b,

$$\int_a^b \int_a^b \bar{u}(x)k(x, \xi)u(\xi)d\xi\, dx - \int_a^b \int_a^b u(x)\bar{k}(x, \xi)\bar{u}(\xi)d\xi\, dx = (\mu - \bar{\mu})\int_a^b \bar{u}(x)u(x)dx.$$

Since $k(x, \xi) = \bar{k}(\xi, x)$, the double integrals cancel. Because u is an eigen-function, we must have $\int_a^b |u|^2\, dx > 0$; hence $\mu = \bar{\mu}$.

2. *The Eigenfunctions Corresponding to Different Eigenvalues Are Ortho-gonal.* If u and v are eigenfunctions corresponding, respectively, to the eigen-values μ and γ, we have

$$\int_a^b k(x, \xi)u(\xi)d\xi = \mu u(x),$$

$$\int_a^b k(x, \xi)v(\xi)d\xi = \gamma v(x).$$

Since γ is real, this second equation may be rewritten $\int_a^b \bar{k}(x, \xi)\bar{v}(\xi)d\xi = \gamma\bar{v}(x)$. It follows that

$$\int_a^b \int_a^b \bar{v}(x)k(x, \xi)u(\xi)d\xi\, dx - \int_a^b \int_a^b u(x)\bar{k}(x, \xi)\bar{v}(\xi)d\xi\, dx = (\mu - \gamma)\int_a^b u\bar{v}\, dx.$$

Because $k(x, \xi) = \bar{k}(\xi, x)$, the integrals cancel and, if $\mu \neq \gamma$, $\int_a^b u\bar{v}\, dx = 0$.

For a Hilbert-Schmidt kernel, we can add the following two pivotal properties.

3. *The Multiplicity of Any Nonzero Eigenvalue Is Finite.* Let μ be an eigen-value with corresponding linearly independent eigenfunctions $u_{1\mu}(x), \ldots,$ $u_{n\mu}(x), \ldots$. By the Gram-Schmidt process we can find linear combinations of these which form an orthonormal set $\varphi_{1\mu}(x), \ldots, \varphi_{n\mu}(x), \ldots$. The complex conjugates $\bar{\varphi}_{n\mu}(x)$ also form an orthonormal set.

Consider the series in $\bar{\varphi}_{n\mu}(\xi)$ associated with $k(x, \xi)$ for a fixed value of x:

$$k(x, \xi) \sim \sum_i c_i \bar{\varphi}_{i\mu}(\xi), \qquad \text{with } c_i = \int_a^b k(x, \xi)\varphi_{i\mu}(\xi)d\xi = \mu \varphi_{i\mu}(x).$$

Bessel's inequality yields

$$\int_a^b |k^2(x, \xi)|d\xi \geq \sum_i \mu^2 |\varphi_{i\mu}(x)|^2.$$

Integrating with respect to x, we obtain

$$\int_a^b \int_a^b |k^2(x, \xi)|d\xi \, dx \geq \sum_i \mu^2.$$

The right side is $p\mu^2$, where p is the multiplicity of μ. By the H.-S. property, the left side is finite, so that the multiplicity p must be finite (as long as μ is a nonzero eigenvalue).

4. *The Number of Eigenvalues Is Either Finite, or, If Infinite, the Only Limit Point of the Eigenvalues Is* $\mu = 0$. The proof is similar to that of property 3. Let $\varphi_i(x)$ be the orthonormal eigenfunctions corresponding to the different eigenvalues μ_i. The set $\bar{\varphi}_i(x)$ is also an orthonormal set. By Bessel's inequality,

$$\sum_i \mu_i^2 \leq \int_a^b \int_a^b |k^2(x, \xi)|dx \, d\xi < \infty.$$

Therefore, if there exist infinitely many μ_i, we must have $\sum_{i=1}^{\infty} \mu_i^2 < \infty$; hence $\lim_{i \to \infty} \mu_i = 0$, and 0 is the only limit point of the eigenvalues.

The Existence of a Nonzero Eigenvalue for a Symmetric Hilbert-Schmidt Operator

We wish to characterize the eigenvalues and eigenfunctions of the operator K. An upper bound for the eigenvalues is immediately available from (3.34); since

$$\langle Ku, u \rangle = \mu \langle u, u \rangle = \mu \|u\|^2,$$

we have

$$|\mu| \|u\|^2 = |\langle Ku, u \rangle| \leq \|Ku\| \|u\| \leq \|K\| \|u\|^2$$

and

$$|\mu| \leq \|K\|. \tag{3.35}$$

If $k(x, \xi)$ is an H.-S. kernel, (3.3) yields

$$|\mu| \leq \left[\int_a^b \int_a^b |k^2(x, \xi)| dx \, d\xi \right]^{1/2}. \tag{3.36}$$

If we assume further that $k(x, \xi)$ is a symmetric H.-S. kernel, then theorem 6, Section 2.11, guarantees that at least one of the two numbers $\|K\|$ and $-\|K\|$ is an eigenvalue of K. The reader is warned that the last statement does not hold if $k(x, \xi)$ fails to have either the symmetry or the H.-S. property. In fact, Example 3 of section 3.1 shows an H.-S. kernel (unsymmetric) for which $\|K\| \neq 0$, yet $\mu = 0$ is the only eigenvalue, whereas the kernel in Example 6 of that section is symmetric (but not H.-S.) with $\|K\| = 1$ and has no eigenvalue.

We collect our results in:

Theorem 1. *Let K be a symmetric Hilbert-Schmidt operator. The extremal problem,*

$$\max |\langle Ku, u \rangle| \text{ subject to } \|u\| = 1,$$

has solutions. Any solution is a normalized eigenfunction of K, corresponding to an eigenvalue μ, whose absolute value is just the maximum in question. Thus

$$\left.\begin{aligned} |\mu_1| &= \max_{\|u\|=1} |\langle Ku, u \rangle|; \\ |\mu_1| &= \|K\|; \end{aligned}\right\} \text{ for any element } f, \ \|Kf\| \leq |\mu_1| \, \|f\|.$$

COROLLARY. *Every nontrivial $(\|K\| \neq 0)$ symmetric Hilbert-Schmidt operator has at least one nonzero eigenvalue.*

Let us now fix our attention on a particular solution φ_1 of the extremal problem in Theorem 1. Thus φ_1 is a normalized eigenfunction of K corresponding to the eigenvalue μ_1, with $|\mu_1| = \|K\|$. We wish to proceed from φ_1 to construct other eigenfunctions and eigenvalues of K (actually the method will yield *all* other eigenfunctions corresponding to nonzero eigenvalues; in particular, if μ_1 is degenerate, we shall also obtain the other eigenfunctions corresponding to μ_1). Consider the symmetric H.-S. kernel

$$k^{(2)}(x, \xi) = k(x, \xi) - \mu_1 \varphi_1(x) \bar{\varphi}_1(\xi), \tag{3.37}$$

which generates the integral operator

$$
\begin{aligned}
K^{(2)}u &= \int_a^b k^{(2)}(x, \xi) u(\xi) d\xi \\
&= \int_a^b k(x, \xi) u(\xi) d\xi - \mu_1 \varphi_1(x) \int_a^b u(\xi) \bar{\varphi}_1(\xi) d\xi \\
&= Ku - \mu_1 \varphi_1 \langle u, \varphi_1 \rangle. \tag{3.38}
\end{aligned}
$$

We observe four properties of $K^{(2)}$:

(a) If $\langle u, \varphi_1 \rangle = 0$, $K^{(2)}u = Ku$.

(b) If $u = c\varphi_1$, $K^{(2)}u = 0$.

(c) The range of $K^{(2)}$ is orthogonal to φ_1. Indeed, for any u, it follows from (3.38) that $\langle K^{(2)}u, \varphi_1 \rangle = \langle Ku, \varphi_1 \rangle - \mu_1 \langle u, \varphi_1 \rangle$. Since

$$\langle Ku, \varphi_1 \rangle = \langle u, K\varphi_1 \rangle = \mu_1 \langle u, \varphi_1 \rangle, \qquad \langle K^{(2)}u, \varphi_1 \rangle = 0.$$

(d) If u is an eigenfunction of $K^{(2)}$ corresponding to a nonzero eigenvalue, it is also an eigenfunction of K corresponding to the same eigenvalue. Indeed, if $\mu \neq 0$ and $K^{(2)}u = \mu u$, we have $K^{(2)}(u/\mu) = u$ and u is in the range of $K^{(2)}$ so that, by (c), $\langle u, \varphi_1 \rangle = 0$. It follows from (a) that $K^{(2)}u = Ku$; hence $Ku = \mu u$. Thus $K^{(2)}$ essentially differs from K only in that the eigenfunction φ_1 has been demoted to an eigenfunction corresponding to the zero eigenvalue.

From Theorem 1 and the four properties of $K^{(2)}$ we infer the following theorem.

Theorem 2. *The extremal problem*

$$\max |\langle K^{(2)}u, u \rangle| \text{ subject to } \|u\| = 1,$$

has solutions. Any solution is a normalized eigenfunction φ_2 of $K^{(2)}$ corresponding to an eigenvalue μ_2 whose absolute value is just the maximum in question. Moreover, $|\mu_2| \leq |\mu_1|$ and, for any element f, $\|K^{(2)}f\| \leq |\mu_2| \|f\|$. If $\mu_2 \neq 0$ then $\langle \varphi_2, \varphi_1 \rangle = 0$ and φ_2 is also an eigenfunction of K corresponding to the eigenvalue μ_2.

If $\mu_2 \neq 0$, the function u for which the maximum in Theorem 2 is attained satisfies the condition $\langle u, \varphi_1 \rangle = 0$. If $\mu_2 = 0$ then $K^{(2)}$ is the 0 operator, and therefore every function u yields a maximum for $|\langle K^{(2)}u, u \rangle|$, namely 0; we can therefore surely find a maximizing function u with the additional property $\langle u, \varphi_1 \rangle = 0$. Thus the condition $\langle u, \varphi_1 \rangle = 0$ can be included as an additional constraint in the statement of the extremal principle 2 without affecting any of the conclusions. Moreover from property (a), if $\langle u, \varphi_1 \rangle = 0$, then $\langle K^{(2)}u, u \rangle = \langle Ku, u \rangle$. We can therefore reformulate principle 2 without reference to $K^{(2)}$.

Theorem 2A. *The extremal problem*

$$\max |\langle Ku, u \rangle| \text{ subject to } \|u\| = 1 \text{ and } \langle u, \varphi_1 \rangle = 0$$

has solutions. Each solution is a normalized eigenfunction φ_2 of K corresponding to an eigenvalue μ_2 whose absolute value is just the maximum in question. Thus

(a) $\displaystyle \max_{\|u\|=1, \langle u,\varphi_1 \rangle = 0} |\langle Ku, u \rangle| = |\mu_2|.$

(b) $|\mu_2| \leq |\mu_1|.$

(c) $\langle \varphi_2, \varphi_1 \rangle = 0.$

(d) $\|Kf\| \leq |\mu_2| \|f\|$, *for every f satisfying $\langle f, \varphi_1 \rangle = 0$.*

All these theorems can be restated in a scale-independent form. We can maximize the quotient $|\langle Ku, u\rangle|/\|u\|^2$ and remove the restriction $\|u\| = 1$ without affecting the correctness of any of the extremum principles.

By a procedure similar to that used to obtain Theorems 2 and 2A, we have the further principles:

Theorem 3

$$\max \frac{|\langle K^{(n+1)}u, u\rangle|}{\|u\|^2} = |\mu_{n+1}|,$$

where $K^{(n+1)}$ is the operator associated with the kernel

$$k^{(n+1)}(x, \xi) = k(x, \xi) - \sum_{i=1}^{n} \mu_i \varphi_i(x) \bar{\varphi}_i(\xi).$$

Theorem 3A

$$\max_{\substack{\langle u, \varphi_1\rangle = 0 \\ \vdots \\ \langle u, \varphi_n\rangle = 0}} \frac{|\langle Ku, u\rangle|}{\|u\|^2} = |\mu_{n+1}|.$$

The function φ_{n+1} which maximizes this quotient is an eigenfunction of K, $K\varphi_{n+1} = \mu_{n+1}\varphi_{n+1}$, with $|\mu_{n+1}| \le |\mu_n|$. In addition, if u is a function satisfying $\langle u, \varphi_1\rangle = \cdots = \langle u, \varphi_n\rangle = 0$, we have $\|Ku\| \le |\mu_{n+1}| \|u\|$.

There are only two possible outcomes for this process of constructing eigenfunctions:

1. The process essentially ends after a finite number of steps m, that is, $\mu_{m+1} = 0$ and therefore $k^{(m+1)}(x, \xi) = 0$. As we continue to apply the extremal principle, we only generate additional eigenfunctions corresponding to $\mu = 0$ (in other words, we sweep out the null space of K). We observe that $|\mu_1| \ge |\mu_2| \ge \cdots \ge |\mu_m|$, and that the eigenfunctions $\varphi_1, \ldots, \varphi_m$ form an orthonormal set.

2. The process continues indefinitely and an infinite sequence of orthonormal eigenfunctions (corresponding to nonzero eigenvalues) is generated. Again we have $|\mu_1| \ge |\mu_2| \ge \cdots \ge |\mu_m| \ge \cdots$.

Two essential questions must be answered:

1. Are all nonzero eigenvalues and corresponding eigenfunctions constructed by this procedure? As we shall see in what follows, the answer is affirmative.

2. Does the set of *all* eigenfunctions of K form a complete set? Again the answer is affirmative, but we must remember to include the eigenfunctions corresponding to $\mu = 0$. It is frequently important to determine if the eigenfunctions corresponding to nonzero eigenvalues (that is, the set $\{\varphi_k\}$) form a complete set by themselves. This will be the case if and only if $Ku = 0$ implies $u = 0$, in other words, if and only if $\mu = 0$ is not an eigenvalue of K.

Let $\{\varphi_k\}$ be the *orthonormal* set of eigenfunctions generated by the preceding extremal principles. We have $K\varphi_k = \mu_k \varphi_k$, with $\mu_k \neq 0$, and $|\mu_{k+1}| \leq |\mu_k|$. Consider the Fourier series in the $\{\varphi_k\}$ associated with the arbitrary function f:

$$f(x) \sim \sum_{k=1}^{n} c_k \varphi_k(x) \qquad \text{with } c_k = \langle f, \varphi_k \rangle.$$

Even if the index n is allowed to go to infinity, the Fourier series may not represent f, since the set $\{\varphi_k\}$ is not necessarily complete. We now show that every function in the range of K (that is, every function of the form Kf for some f in $\mathscr{L}_2$) is represented by its Fourier series in $\{\varphi_k\}$.

We first note that for an arbitrary f, $f - \sum_{k=1}^{n} c_k \varphi_k$ is orthogonal to $\varphi_1, \ldots, \varphi_n$. Therefore, by the last line of Theorem 3A,

$$\left\| K\left(f - \sum_{k=1}^{n} c_k \varphi_k\right) \right\|^2 \leq |\mu_{n+1}|^2 \left\| f - \sum_{k=1}^{n} c_k \varphi_k \right\|^2 = |\mu_{n+1}|^2 \left\{ \|f\|^2 - \sum_{k=1}^{n} |c_k|^2 \right\}.$$

It follows that

$$\left\| K\left(f - \sum_{k=1}^{n} c_k \varphi_k\right) \right\| \leq |\mu_{n+1}| \, \|f\|. \tag{3.39}$$

If there are only m nonzero eigenvalues, $|\mu_{m+1}| = 0$, and we have from (3.39),

$$Kf = \sum_{k=1}^{m} c_k K\varphi_k = \sum_{k=1}^{m} \mu_k c_k \varphi_k = \sum_{k=1}^{m} \mu_k \langle f, \varphi_k \rangle \varphi_k = \sum_{k=1}^{m} \langle Kf, \varphi_k \rangle \varphi_k.$$

In the case of an infinite number of nonzero eigenvalues, we must have $\lim_{n \to \infty} \mu_n = 0$. We obtain from (3.39) in the sense of convergence in the mean,

$$Kf = \sum_{k=1}^{\infty} c_k K\varphi_k = \sum_{k=1}^{\infty} \mu_k \langle f, \varphi_k \rangle \varphi_k = \sum_{k=1}^{\infty} \langle Kf, \varphi_k \rangle \varphi_k.$$

Theorem 4. *Every function of the form Kf can be expanded in a Fourier series in the eigenfunctions of K corresponding to nonzero eigenvalues. Thus the set $\{\varphi_k\}$ forms an orthonormal basis for the range of K.*

We can now show that the extremal principles yield all the nonzero eigenvalues (and their corresponding eigenfunctions). Suppose there existed an eigenfunction ψ with corresponding eigenvalue $\alpha \neq 0$, not listed among the μ_k. Then $K\psi = \alpha\psi$, and by the expansion theorem,

$$K\psi = \sum_{k=1}^{\infty} \langle K\psi, \varphi_k \rangle \varphi_k = \alpha \sum_{k=1}^{\infty} \langle \psi, \varphi_k \rangle \varphi_k.$$

But ψ is orthogonal to all the φ_k, which yields $K\psi = 0$, which contradicts the assumption that ψ is an eigenfunction corresponding to a nonzero eigenvalue.

Now suppose that f is an arbitrary function. Since f is not necessarily in the range of K, there is no guarantee that its Fourier series $\sum \langle f, \varphi_k \rangle \varphi_k$ converges to f. On the other hand the Riesz-Fischer theorem states that $\sum \langle f, \varphi_k \rangle \varphi_k$ converges to some element, say g, in $\mathscr{L}_2$. Clearly the functions Kf and Kg have the same expansion $\sum \mu_k \langle f, \varphi_k \rangle \varphi_k$, and therefore $K(g - f) = 0$, so that the function $h = g - f$ has the property $Kh = 0$. Thus an arbitrary function f can decomposed in an unambiguous manner as

$$f = h + \sum \langle f, \varphi_k \rangle \varphi_k, \qquad \text{with } Kh = 0. \tag{3.40}$$

We can restate the content of the equality (3.40) as:

Theorem 5.   *The set of all eigenfunctions of K (including the eigenfunctions corresponding to $\mu = 0$) forms a complete set.*

As an immediate corollary, we have:

Theorem 5A.   *The set $\{\varphi_n\}$ of eigenfunctions corresponding to nonzero eigenvalues forms a complete set if and only if $\mu = 0$ is not an eigenvalue of K.*

The most important application of Theorem 5A is in connection with self-adjoint differential systems of the second order. Let L with the boundary conditions $B_1 = 0$, $B_2 = 0$ be such a system. The related eigenvalue problem is

$$Ly = \lambda y; \qquad B_1(y) = 0, \quad B_2(y) = 0. \tag{3.41}$$

This system generates a set of eigenvalues $\{\lambda_k\}$ and corresponding normalized eigenfunctions $\{y_k\}$. To avoid the complications that arise if $\lambda = 0$ is an eigenvalue of (3.41), we introduce the slightly different system

$$My = \theta y; \qquad B_1(y) = 0, \quad B_2(y) = 0, \tag{3.42}$$

where $\theta = \lambda - \lambda^*$, $M = L - \lambda^* I$, and λ^* is a fixed real value of λ which is *not* an eigenvalue of (3.41). It is clear that (3.42) has exactly the same eigenfunctions as (3.41), but its eigenvalues are given by $\theta_k = \lambda_k - \lambda^*$, so that 0 is not an eigenvalue of (3.42).

The system (3.42) can be translated into the equivalent integral equation

$$y(x) = \theta \int_a^b g(x, \xi) y(\xi) d\xi, \tag{3.42a}$$

using the unique Green's function $g(x, \xi)$ of M with the boundary conditions $B_1 g = 0$ and $B_2 g = 0$. The integral operator G corresponding to $g(x, \xi)$ is a symmetric H.-S. operator. It is clear that the equation (3.42a) has exactly the same eigenfunctions as

$$Gy = \int_a^b g(x, \xi) y(\xi) d\xi = \mu y(x), \tag{3.42b}$$

as long as we can assert that $\mu = 0$ is *not* an eigenvalue of G. To prove this assertion, we must establish that $u = 0$ is the only solution of

$$\int_a^b g(x, \xi)u(\xi)d\xi = 0.$$

To this end, consider the system

$$Mz = u; \qquad B_1(z) = 0, \quad B_2(z) = 0,$$

which, by the theory of Chapter 1, has the unique solution $z = \int_a^b g(x, \xi)u(\xi)d\xi$. If $\int_a^b g(x, \xi)u(\xi)d\xi = 0$, then $z = 0$ and $Mz = 0$, so that $u = 0$. Thus $\mu = 0$ is not an eigenvalue of G. Theorem 5A guarantees that the eigenfunctions of G [hence those of (3.42a), (3.42), and (3.41)] form a complete orthonormal set. We have the result:

Theorem 6.   *The eigenfunctions of any self-adjoint differential system of the second order form a complete orthonormal set.*

3.4   THE SOLUTION OF THE INHOMOGENEOUS EQUATION WITH A SYMMETRIC HILBERT-SCHMIDT KERNEL

Consider the inhomogeneous integral equation

$$Ku = \mu u + f. \tag{3.43}$$

For $\mu \neq 0$ the equation is of the second kind, whereas for $\mu = 0$ it is of the first kind. Let $\{\varphi_k\}$ be the normalized eigenfunctions of K corresponding to nonzero eigenvalues. The eigenvalues are indexed in order of decreasing magnitude, $|\mu_{k+1}| \leq |\mu_k|$; a degenerate eigenvalue is listed as often as its multiplicity. Since K is symmetric, all eigenvalues are real.

To solve (3.43) we use an expansion in the set $\{\varphi_k\}$. The series associated with u and f are, respectively, $\sum_k a_k\varphi_k$ and $\sum_k b_k\varphi_k$, where $a_k = \langle u, \varphi_k \rangle$ and $b_k = \langle f, \varphi_k \rangle$; since there is no reason to believe that the set $\{\varphi_k\}$ is complete, the series may not represent the functions with which they are associated. In spite of this, if (3.43) possesses a solution u, Theorem 4 guarantees that $\mu u + f$ can be represented by its Fourier series in $\{\varphi_k\}$. Thus $\mu u + f = \sum (\mu a_k + b_k)\varphi_k = \sum \mu_k a_k \varphi_k$, and

$$a_k(\mu_k - \mu) = b_k, \qquad k = 1, \ldots, n, \ldots. \tag{3.44}$$

If (3.43) has a solution, the equations (3.44) *must* be satisfied,

Case 1. $\mu \neq 0$, *and* μ *does not coincide with any of the eigenvalues of* K. For every k, (3.44) can be solved for a_k, and

$$a_k = \frac{b_k}{\mu_k - \mu}.$$

If (3.43) has a solution, it is unique and is given by

$$u = -\frac{f}{\mu} + \frac{1}{\mu} Ku = -\frac{f}{\mu} + \sum_k \frac{\mu_k b_k}{\mu(\mu_k - \mu)} \varphi_k. \tag{3.45}$$

It remains to show that (3.45) actually satisfies (3.43). Since $\sum |b_k|^2$ converges, and since the only possible limit point of $\{\mu_k\}$ is 0, it follows that

$$\sum \frac{|\mu_k|^2 |b_k|^2}{|\mu|^2 |\mu_k - \mu|^2} \qquad \text{and hence} \qquad \sum \frac{\mu_k b_k}{\mu(\mu_k - \mu)} \varphi_k$$

converge. Substituting (3.45) in (3.43), and appealing to the continuity of K, we are led to an identity.

Theorem. *If $\mu \neq 0$ and μ is not an eigenvalue of K, (3.43) has one and only one solution, given by* (3.45).

Case 2. $\mu \neq 0$, $\mu = \mu_m$ *for some fixed index m.* Assuming first that μ_m is a simple eigenvalue, (3.44) presents difficulties only when $k = m$.

(a) If $b_m \neq 0$, there is no solution of (3.44) for $k = m$. Therefore, the integral equation has *no solution*.

(b) If $b_m = 0$, a_m is indeterminate and $a_k = b_k/(\mu_k - \mu)$ for $k \neq m$. The integral equation has infinitely many solutions:

$$u = -\frac{f}{\mu} + c\varphi_m + \sum_{k \neq m} \frac{\mu_k b_k}{\mu(\mu_k - \mu)} \varphi_k. \tag{3.46}$$

In the above solution, c is an arbitrary constant. The solution (3.46) is possible only if the *consistency* condition $\langle f, \varphi_m \rangle = 0$ is satisfied.

If the eigenvalue μ_m is degenerate, say $\mu_m = \mu_{m+1} = \cdots = \mu_{m+i}$, a solution is possible only if the consistency conditions $\langle f, \varphi_m \rangle = \langle f, \varphi_{m+1} \rangle = \cdots = \langle f, \varphi_{m+i} \rangle = 0$ are satisfied. The solution of the integral equation becomes

$$u = -\frac{f}{\mu} + c_0 \varphi_m + c_1 \varphi_{m+1} + \cdots + c_i \varphi_{m+i} + \sum_{k \neq m, \, m+1, \ldots, \, m+i} \frac{\mu_k b_k}{\mu(\mu_k - \mu)} \varphi_k,$$

where $c_0, c_1, \ldots, c_i$ are arbitrary constants. Our result is another illustration of the alternative theorems discussed in Chapters 1 and 2.

Case 3. $\mu = 0$, *and 0 is not an eigenvalue of K.* If there is a solution of the integral equation $Ku = f$, the solution must be $\sum (b_k/\mu_k)\varphi_k$. The difficulty here is that the series may not converge, since $\{\mu_k\}$ can have 0 as a limit point. If the series $\sum |b_k|^2/|\mu_k|^2$ converges, then $\sum (b_k/\mu_k)\varphi_k$ converges and furnishes the one and only solution of $Ku = f$. If $\sum |b_k|^2/|\mu_k|^2$ diverges, no strict solution is possible, but a distributional solution may exist (see Exercise 3.7).

Case 4. $\mu = 0$, *and 0 is an eigenvalue of K.*

The consistency condition(s) $\langle f, \varphi_0 \rangle = 0$ must be satisfied for $Ku = f$ to have a solution. Here φ_0 stands for any eigenfunction associated with $\mu = 0$. In addition, we still must require $\sum |b_k|^2 / |\mu_k|^2 < \infty$.

EXERCISES

3.11 Solve the inhomogeneous integral equations of the first and second kind associated with the kernels of Examples 1, 2, and 5 and Exercises 3.2, 3.3, 3.4, and 3.5.

3.12 Consider the kernel $k(x, \xi) = \log [1 - \cos (x - \xi)]$, $0 \leq x, \xi \leq 2\pi$. (This kernel arises in potential theory; see Volume II.)

    (a) Show that this is a symmetric H.-S. kernel.

    (b) Prove that

$$k(x, \xi) = - \log 2 + 2 \operatorname{Re} \log [1 - e^{i(x - \xi)}];$$

hence

$$k(x, \xi) = - \log 2 - 2 \sum_{n=1}^{\infty} \frac{\cos nx \cos n\xi}{n} - 2 \sum_{n=1}^{\infty} \frac{\sin nx \sin n\xi}{n}.$$

    (c) Prove that the eigenvalues of $\int_0^{2\pi} k(x, \xi)u(\xi)d\xi = \mu u(x)$ are $\mu_0 = - 2\pi \log 2$, $\mu_n = -2\pi/n$, $n = 1, 2, \ldots$, with eigenfunctions $\varphi_0(x) = c$, $\varphi_n(x) = A \cos nx + B \sin nx$.

    (d) Discuss the inhomogeneous Fredholm equations of the first and second kind.

3.13 Let ρ be fixed, $0 < \rho < 1$. Consider the kernel

$$k(x, \xi) = [(1 - \rho^2)/2\pi][1 - 2\rho \cos (x - \xi) + \rho^2]^{-1}, \qquad 0 \leq x, \xi \leq 2\pi.$$

This kernel also arises in potential theory, and it is shown in Volume II that k can be written in the form

$$k(x, \xi) = \frac{1}{2\pi} + \frac{1}{\pi} \sum_{n=1}^{\infty} \rho^n \cos n(x - \xi).$$

    (a) Find the eigenvalues and eigenfunctions of

$$Ku = \mu u.$$

    (b) Solve the inhomogeneous Fredholm equation of the second kind.

3.14 Consider $k(x, \xi) = 1/|x - \xi|^\alpha$, $a \leq x, \xi \leq b$; $\alpha < 1$. The values of a and b are finite.

    (a) Show that K is H.-S. only for $\alpha < \frac{1}{2}$, but is completely continuous for $\alpha < 1$ (see Section 2.10).

    (b) Show that the iterated kernel $k_2(x, \xi)$ is bounded for $\alpha < \frac{1}{2}$ and satisfies $|k_2| \leq c/|x - \xi|^{2\alpha - 1}$ for $\frac{1}{2} < \alpha < 1$.

    (c) Let $h(x, \xi) = [h_1(x, \xi)/|x - \xi|^\alpha] + h_2(x, \xi)$, $\alpha < 1$, h_1 and h_2 continuous on $a \leq x, \xi \leq b$. Show that H is completely continuous.

3.15 Consider the kernel

$$k(x, \xi) = \sum_{n=1}^{\infty} \frac{\sin(n+1)x \sin n\xi}{n^2}, \qquad 0 \le x, \xi \le \pi.$$

Show that this is a H.-S. kernel (unsymmetric) and that the corresponding integral operator K has *no* eigenvalue (not even 0!). Compute $\|K\|$. Show that, if $\mu \ne 0$, $Ku = \mu u + f$ has a unique solution for each f and that $(K - \mu I)^{-1}$ is bounded. Hence every value of μ except 0 is a regular value of K. Show that $\mu = 0$ is in the residual spectrum of K (see Section 2.9). Note that K is a modified shift operator as in Example 6 of Section 2.8.

3.5 EXTREMAL PRINCIPLES

We have seen in Section 3.3 that the nonzero eigenvalues $\{\mu_k\}$ and the corresponding eigenfunctions $\{\varphi_k\}$ of a symmetric H.-S. operator can be characterized by extremal principles. It is of interest to develop separate principles for eigenvalues of opposite sign. Let the positive eigenvalues (in decreasing order) be denoted by $\mu_1^+, \mu_2^+, \ldots$, with $\mu_{n+1}^+ \le \mu_n^+$. The corresponding normalized eigenfunctions are $\varphi_1^+, \varphi_2^+, \ldots$. The negative eigenvalues (in order of decreasing *absolute value*) are denoted by $\mu_1^-, \mu_2^-, \ldots$, with $|\mu_{n+1}^-| \le |\mu_n^-|$. The corresponding normalized eigenfunctions are $\varphi_1^-, \varphi_2^-, \ldots$.

Consider the quadratic form $\langle Ku, u \rangle$. By the expansion theorem (4),

$$\langle Ku, u \rangle = \left\langle \sum \mu_i \langle u, \varphi_i \rangle \varphi_i, u \right\rangle = \sum \mu_i |\langle u, \varphi_i \rangle|^2$$

$$= \sum \mu_i^+ |\langle u, \varphi_i^+ \rangle|^2 + \sum \mu_i^- |\langle u, \varphi_i^- \rangle|^2$$

$$\le \sum \mu_i^+ |\langle u, \varphi_i^+ \rangle|^2 \le \mu_1^+ \|u\|^2.$$

Therefore,

$$\frac{\langle Ku, u \rangle}{\|u\|^2} \le \mu_1^+, \qquad \text{for all } u \ne 0.$$

With $u = c\varphi_1^+$ the above inequality becomes an equality, so that

$$\max \frac{\langle Ku, u \rangle}{\|u\|^2} = \mu_1^+; \tag{3.47}$$

the function yielding the maximum is proportional to φ_1^+. Similarly,

$$\max_{\substack{\langle u, \varphi^+_1 \rangle = 0 \\ \vdots \\ \langle u, \varphi^+_n \rangle = 0}} \frac{\langle Ku, u \rangle}{\|u\|^2} = \mu_{n+1}^+; \tag{3.48}$$

the function yielding the maximum is proportional to φ_{n+1}^+.

If there are only a finite number m of positive eigenvalues, the above procedure terminates after m steps; otherwise it goes on indefinitely and generates all the positive eigenvalues and their corresponding eigenfunctions.

To characterize the negative eigenvalues we note that

$$\langle Ku, u \rangle = \sum \mu_i |\langle u, \varphi_i \rangle|^2 \geq \sum \mu_i^- |\langle u, \varphi_i^- \rangle|^2 \geq \mu_1^- \|u\|^2.$$

Therefore,

$$\frac{\langle Ku, u \rangle}{\|u\|^2} \geq \mu_1^-, \qquad \text{for all } u \neq 0.$$

With $u = c\varphi_1^-$ the above inequality becomes an equality, so that

$$\min \frac{\langle Ku, u \rangle}{\|u\|^2} = \mu_1^-; \tag{3.49}$$

the function yielding the minimum is proportional to φ_1^-. It can be shown
that

$$\min_{\substack{\langle u, \varphi^-_1 \rangle = 0 \\ \vdots \\ \langle u, \varphi^-_n \rangle = 0}} \frac{\langle Ku, u \rangle}{\|u\|^2} = \mu_{n+1}^-; \tag{3.50}$$

the function yielding the minimum is proportional to φ_{n+1}^-.

In many applications the nonzero eigenvalues of K will all be positive or
else all negative.

DEFINITION.   (See Exercises 2.35, 2.36, and 2.37 for similar definitions
on $E_n^{(c)}$.) An operator K is said to be *nonnegative* if $\langle Ku, u \rangle \geq 0$ for every u.
It is easy to see that the eigenvalues of K must be nonnegative, and, con-
versely, if the eigenvalues of K are nonnegative, K is a nonnegative operator.

DEFINITION.   An operator K is said to be *positive* if $\langle Ku, u \rangle > 0$ for
every $u \neq 0$. It follows that the eigenvalues of K are all *positive*, and conversely,
if the eigenvalues of K are all positive, K is a positive operator.

The definitions of a negative operator and of a nonpositive operator
follow in an obvious manner. The reader should note that operators in any of
these four categories are necessarily symmetric. A symmetric operator which
does not fall in any of these four categories is called *indefinite*. An indefinite
operator will have some positive and some negative eigenvalues, and $\langle Ku, u \rangle$
will be positive for some u, negative for other u.

If $k(x, \xi)$ is a real function, some additional simplifications can be made.
Suppose that $k(x, \xi)$ is real and symmetric; not only are the eigenvalues of K
real but the eigenfunctions are "essentially" real. To elaborate on this
statement, let $u(x)$ be a complex eigenfunction corresponding to the eigen-
value μ. Writing $u(x) = \alpha(x) + i\beta(x)$, where $\alpha(x)$ and $\beta(x)$ are real, we obtain
the *separate* equations $K\alpha = \mu\alpha$, $K\beta = \mu\beta$. Thus both $\alpha(x)$ and $\beta(x)$ are

separately eigenfunctions of K corresponding to μ. It follows that any eigen-function of a real symmetric kernel is a linear combination (possibly with complex coefficients) of real eigenfunctions. For such a kernel, the basic set of eigenfunctions $\varphi_1(x), \dots, \varphi_n(x), \dots$ can always be chosen to contain only real-valued functions. (Contrast this with Exercise 3.5, where $e^{i2\pi nx}$ is an eigenfunction, but neither $\cos 2\pi nx$ nor $\sin 2\pi nx$ is an eigenfunction.)

If u and v are real functions and k is a real symmetric kernel, we have $\langle Ku, v \rangle = \langle u, Kv \rangle = \langle Kv, u \rangle = \langle v, Ku \rangle$.

An operator K is said to be *real* if Ku is a real function for all real functions $u(x)$. An integral operator is real if and only if $k(x, \xi)$ is real.

Although many of the following theorems can be suitably reformulated for other operators, we restrict ourselves to *real, symmetric, nonnegative operators*. For such an operator we have the extremal principles:

$$\max \frac{\langle Ku, u \rangle}{\|u\|^2} = \mu_1; \tag{3.51}$$

maximizing function is $c\varphi_1$.

$$\max_{\substack{\langle u, \varphi_1 \rangle = 0 \\ \vdots \\ \langle u, \varphi_n \rangle = 0}} \frac{\langle Ku, u \rangle}{\|u\|^2} = \mu_{n+1}; \tag{3.52}$$

maximizing function is $c\varphi_{n+1}$. We can also characterize the higher eigenvalues without referring to lower-order eigenfunctions. This is the *Courant minimax principle*.

Theorem. *Consider the maximum over all possible u of $\langle Ku, u \rangle / \|u\|^2$ subject to the constraints $\langle u, \psi_1 \rangle = \cdots = \langle u, \psi_n \rangle = 0$, where $\psi_1, \dots, \psi_n$ are arbitrary functions. This maximum is a number v_{n+1} which depends solely on $\psi_1, \dots, \psi_n$. We have the theorem*

$$\min_{\substack{\text{over all possible} \\ \psi_1, \dots, \psi_n}} v_{n+1} = \mu_{n+1},$$

which restated in one line becomes

$$\min_{\text{over } \psi_1, \dots, \psi_n} \left\{ \max_{\substack{\text{over } u \text{ with} \\ \langle u, \psi_1 \rangle = \cdots = \langle u, \psi_n \rangle = 0}} \frac{\langle Ku, u \rangle}{\|u\|^2} \right\} = \mu_{n+1}.$$

Proof. If $\psi_1, \dots, \psi_n$ are chosen to be $\varphi_1, \dots, \varphi_n$, the correct first n eigenfunctions of K, then the corresponding v_{n+1} is μ_{n+1} by (3.52). Therefore, the minimum of v_{n+1} over all possible choices of the $\{\psi_k\}$ must be no greater than μ_{n+1}; that is, $\min v_{n+1} \leq \mu_{n+1}$. It remains to show that the opposite inequality also holds. For each set $\{\psi_k\}$, we shall exhibit a function u with $\langle u, \psi_1 \rangle = \cdots = \langle u, \psi_n \rangle = 0$, such that $\langle Ku, u \rangle / \|u\|^2 \geq \mu_{n+1}$. It follows there-fore that for each set $\{\psi_k\}$, the corresponding v_{n+1} is $\geq \mu_{n+1}$. Therefore, the minimum of v_{n+1} over all possible choices of the set $\{\psi_k\}$ must be $\geq \mu_{n+1}$. To construct the function u in question, we consider the linear combination $u = \sum_{i=1}^{n+1} c_i \varphi_i$ and choose the $\{c_i\}$ such that $\sum_{i=1}^{n+1} c_i \varphi_i$ is orthogonal to each member of the given set $\{\psi_k\}$. Since there are only n functions in the set, such constants $c_1, \ldots, c_{n+1}$ will surely exist. With the $\{c_i\}$ so determined, we have

$$\frac{\langle Ku, u \rangle}{\|u\|^2} = \frac{\left\langle \sum_{i=1}^{n+1} c_i K\varphi_i, \sum_{i=1}^{n+1} c_i \varphi_i \right\rangle}{\sum_{i=1}^{n+1} c_i^2} = \frac{\sum_{i=1}^{n+1} c_i^2 \mu_i}{\sum_{i=1}^{n+1} c_i^2} \geq \mu_{n+1} \frac{\sum_{i=1}^{n+1} c_i^2}{\sum_{i=1}^{n+1} c_i^2} = \mu_{n+1}.$$

We have thus exhibited, for *each* set $\{\psi_k\}$, a function u orthogonal to each member of the set $\{\psi_k\}$ and such that $\langle Ku, u \rangle / \|u\|^2 \geq \mu_{n+1}$. Therefore for each set $\{\psi_k\}$, $v_{n+1} \geq \mu_{n+1}$, and $\min v_{n+1} \geq \mu_{n+1}$. Combining with $\min v_{n+1} \leq \mu_{n+1}$, we have $\min v_{n+1} = \mu_{n+1}$, which completes the proof.

3.6 APPROXIMATIONS BASED ON EXTREMAL PRINCIPLES

Introduction

For a real, nonnegative, symmetric, Hilbert-Schmidt operator K, the largest eigenvalue μ_1 can be characterized by the extremal or variational principle

$$\max \frac{\langle Ku, u \rangle}{\|u\|^2} = \mu_1. \tag{3.53}$$

Assume for simplicity that μ_1 is not degenerate. The functions which yield the maximum in (3.53) are all of the form $c\varphi_1(x)$, where $\varphi_1(x)$ is an eigenfunction of K corresponding to the value μ_1. $\varphi_1(x)$ is not necessarily normalized. The ratio $R(u) = \langle Ku, u \rangle / \|u\|^2$ is known as the Rayleigh quotient, and

$$\mu_1 = R(\varphi_1) = \frac{\langle K\varphi_1, \varphi_1 \rangle}{\|\varphi_1\|^2}.$$

There are many other formulas which relate μ_1 and φ_1. Consider, for instance, the expressions

$$V(u) = \frac{\int_a^b Ku \, dx}{\int_a^b u \, dx} \quad \text{and} \quad W(u) = \frac{\int_a^b f Ku \, dx}{\int_a^b fu \, dx},$$

where $f(x)$ is an arbitrary fixed function. Starting from the integral equation $K\varphi_1 = \mu_1 \varphi_1$, it is easy to see that $W(\varphi_1) = V(\varphi_1) = \mu_1$. Besides $R(u)$, $V(u)$, and $W(u)$, there are many functionals of u which will reduce to the value μ_1, when φ_1 is substituted for u. We contend that, among these functionals, $R(u)$ is particularly useful for estimating μ_1. The reason is that $R(u)$ is stationary about $u = \varphi_1$, whereas $V(u)$ and $W(u)$ are not. Suppose that we substitute for u the approximate eigenfunction $u = \varphi_1(x) + \varepsilon\eta(x)$, where $\eta(x)$ is a fixed arbitrary function and ε is a small, real parameter. Then $R(\varphi_1 + \varepsilon\eta)$ depends only on ε, and we write $R(\varphi_1 + \varepsilon\eta) = R(\varepsilon)$. The crucial point is that $R(\varepsilon)$ differs from μ_1 only by terms of the *second order* in ε, whereas $V(\varepsilon) = V(\varphi_1 + \varepsilon\eta)$ and $W(\varepsilon) = W(\varphi_1 + \varepsilon\eta)$ differ from μ_1 by terms of the *first order* in ε. We can therefore expect that for small ε, $R(\varepsilon)$ will be closer to μ_1 than either $V(\varepsilon)$ or $W(\varepsilon)$. The situation is illustrated in Figure 3.1.

The proof that $R(u)$ is stationary about $u = \varphi_1$ is very simple. We have

$$R(\varphi_1 + \varepsilon\eta) = R(\varepsilon) = \frac{\langle K(\varphi_1 + \varepsilon\eta), \varphi_1 + \varepsilon\eta \rangle}{\langle \varphi_1 + \varepsilon\eta, \varphi_1 + \varepsilon\eta \rangle}$$

$$= \frac{\langle K\varphi_1, \varphi_1 \rangle + 2\varepsilon\langle \eta, K\varphi_1 \rangle + \varepsilon^2\langle \eta, K\eta \rangle}{\langle \varphi_1, \varphi_1 \rangle + 2\varepsilon\langle \varphi_1, \eta \rangle + \varepsilon^2\langle \eta, \eta \rangle}.$$

For small ε we may expand $R(\varepsilon)$ in a Taylor series about $\varepsilon = 0$,

$$R(\varepsilon) = R(0) + \varepsilon \left.\frac{dR}{d\varepsilon}\right|_{\varepsilon=0} + \varepsilon^2 \left.\frac{d^2R}{d\varepsilon^2}\right|_{\varepsilon=0} + \cdots.$$

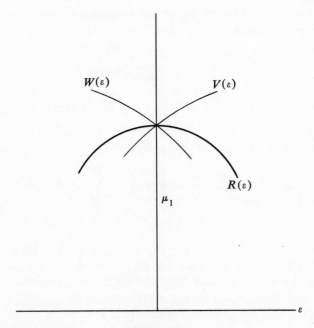

FIGURE 3.1

Straightforward differentiation yields

$$\left.\frac{dR}{d\varepsilon}\right|_{\varepsilon=0} = \frac{\langle \varphi_1, \varphi_1 \rangle [2\langle \eta, K\varphi_1 \rangle] - \langle K\varphi_1, \varphi_1 \rangle [2\langle \varphi_1, \eta \rangle]}{\langle \varphi_1, \varphi_1 \rangle^2}$$

$$= \frac{2}{\langle \varphi_1, \varphi_1 \rangle} \left[\langle \eta, K\varphi_1 \rangle - \frac{\langle K\varphi_1, \varphi_1 \rangle}{\langle \varphi_1, \varphi_1 \rangle} \langle \varphi_1, \eta \rangle \right].$$

Since

$$K\varphi_1 = \mu_1 \varphi_1 \qquad \text{and} \qquad \frac{\langle K\varphi_1, \varphi_1 \rangle}{\langle \varphi_1, \varphi_1 \rangle} = R(0) = \mu_1,$$

it follows that $dR/d\varepsilon|_{\varepsilon=0} = 0$, and, for small ε, $R(\varepsilon) \cong \mu_1 + \varepsilon^2 (d^2R/d\varepsilon^2)|_{\varepsilon=0}$, as predicted. Similar considerations show that neither V nor W is stationary about $u = \varphi_1$.

REMARKS.   1. $R(u)$ is also stationary about $u = \varphi_k$, with $R(\varphi_k) = \mu_k$.
2. Of these stationary values only μ_1 is a relative maximum. From (3.53), we know μ_1 is a global maximum.

The Rayleigh-Ritz Procedure

We now use (3.53) to obtain an approximation to μ_1. It will turn out that the procedure, known as the *Rayleigh-Ritz procedure*, will also yield approximations to $\varphi_1(x)$ and to some higher-order eigenvalues and eigenfunctions.

For any *trial* function $u(x)$, we have from (3.53),

$$R(u) = \frac{\langle Ku, u \rangle}{\|u\|^2} \leq \mu_1.$$

Consider a special class of trial functions of the form $\sum_{i=1}^{n} c_i v_i(x)$, where $\{v_i(x)\}$ is a given set of real linearly independent functions, and the $\{c_i\}$ are real numbers. For all values of the coefficients $\{c_i\}$,

$$R(c_1, \ldots, c_n) = \frac{\left\langle \sum_{i=1}^{n} c_i K v_i, \sum_{i=1}^{n} c_i v_i \right\rangle}{\left\langle \sum_{i=1}^{n} c_i v_i, \sum_{i=1}^{n} c_i v_i \right\rangle} = \frac{\sum_{i,k=1}^{n} c_i c_k \langle K v_i, v_k \rangle}{\sum_{i,k=1}^{n} c_i c_k \langle v_i, v_k \rangle} \leq \mu_1.$$

Clearly $\langle v_i, v_k \rangle = \langle v_k, v_i \rangle$, and $\langle K v_i, v_k \rangle = \langle v_i, K v_k \rangle = \langle v_k, K v_i \rangle = \langle K v_k, v_i \rangle$ because K is symmetric and real. We denote $\langle v_i, v_k \rangle$ by α_{ik} and $\langle K v_i, v_k \rangle$ by K_{ik}. The numbers $\{\alpha_{ik}\}$ and $\{K_{ik}\}$ can be computed at the start of the procedure and are regarded as *known*. If we choose the coefficients $\{c_i\}$ so that the left side of the preceding inequality is as large as possible, we can reasonably expect to obtain a close lower bound to μ_1. To obtain the maximum of $R(c_1, \ldots, c_n)$, we differentiate with respect to each coefficient c_m and equate the result to 0. This yields the n equations

$$\frac{\left(\sum\limits_{i,k=1}^{n} \alpha_{ik}c_ic_k\right)\left(2\sum\limits_{i=1}^{n} K_{mi}c_i\right) - \left(\sum\limits_{i,k=1}^{n} K_{ik}c_ic_k\right)\left(2\sum\limits_{i=1}^{n} \alpha_{mi}c_i\right)}{\left(\sum\limits_{i,k=1}^{n} \alpha_{ik}c_ic_k\right)^2} = 0,$$

which in turn can be reduced to

$$\sum_{i=1}^{n} K_{mi}c_i - \left(\frac{\sum\limits_{i,k=1}^{n} K_{ik}c_ic_k}{\sum\limits_{i,k=1}^{n} \alpha_{ik}c_ic_k}\right)\sum_{i=1}^{n} \alpha_{mi}c_i = 0, \qquad m = 1, 2, \ldots, n.$$

The quantity in parentheses is just the extremal value of $R(c_1, \ldots, c_n)$, which we denote by R^* (of course R^* is still unknown). We are then left with n linear homogeneous equations in the n unknowns $c_1, \ldots, c_n$, with R^* appearing as a parameter

$$\sum_{i=1}^{n} K_{mi}c_i - R^* \sum_{i=1}^{n} \alpha_{mi}c_i = 0, \qquad m = 1, 2, \ldots, n. \tag{3.54}$$

These equations will have a nontrivial solution for the vector $(c_1, c_2, \ldots, c_n)$ if and only if the determinant

$$\begin{vmatrix} K_{11} - R^*\alpha_{11} & K_{12} - R^*\alpha_{12} \cdots K_{1n} - R^*\alpha_{1n} \\ \vdots & \vdots \qquad\qquad \vdots \\ K_{n1} - R^*\alpha_{n1} & K_{n2} - R^*\alpha_{n2} \cdots K_{nn} - R^*\alpha_{nn} \end{vmatrix} = 0. \tag{3.55}$$

Expanding this determinant, we obtain an nth degree polynomial in R^*. There are n roots which can be shown to be real, nonnegative, but not necessarily distinct. These roots are labeled $R_1^*, R_2^*, \ldots, R_n^*$, in decreasing order. R_1^* is the maximal value of $R(c_1, \ldots, c_n)$, and $R_1^* \leq \mu_1$. It can also be shown with the use of the Courant minimax principle that $R_k^* \leq \mu_k$; $k = 1, 2, \ldots, n$. For each of the n possible values of R^*, we obtain from (3.54) a set of coefficients $c_1, \ldots, c_n$. Let the values of the coefficients corresponding to R_k^* be labeled $c_1^{(k)}, \ldots, c_n^{(k)}$. These coefficients yield an approximation to $\varphi_k(x)$, namely $\sum\limits_{i=1}^{n} c_i^{(k)}v_i(x)$.

REMARKS. 1. With a limited set of trial functions $v_1(x), \ldots, v_n(x)$, we cannot expect to obtain a very good approximation to the eigenfunction $\varphi_1(x)$, but we *can* expect a good approximation to μ_1. In the next few pages and in the exercises, we shall find other ways of obtaining approximations to $\varphi_1(x)$; these approximations are about as good as the one obtained from the variational principle. The important thing to keep in mind is that, regardless of its origin, the approximation to φ_1 should be substituted in the *stationary* expression (3.53) to yield a good approximation to μ_1.

2. The approximations R_k^* to μ_k, and $\sum_{i=1}^{n} c_i^{(k)} v_i$ to φ_k, usually become progressively worse as k is taken larger.

3. If the set of trial functions $v_1(x), \ldots, v_n(x)$ is extended to include additional elements $v_{n+1}(x), \ldots$, all the approximations improve.

4. The set $v_1(x), \ldots, v_n(x)$ is at our disposal. The trial functions should be chosen to make the computations relatively simple (see 5). On the basis of geometric or physical insight, we are often able to predict some of the qualitative properties of the eigenfunctions. The set $\{v_i(x)\}$ should be chosen so as to have as many of these properties as possible.

5. The computations are considerably simplified if the set $\{v_j\}$ is an orthonormal set of functions over the interval (a, b). In this case,

$$\alpha_{ik} = \begin{cases} 0, & i \neq k; \\ 1, & i = k, \end{cases}$$

and the equations (3.54) reduce to

$$\sum_{i=1}^{n} K_{mi} c_i - R^* c_m = 0; \qquad m = 1, 2, \ldots, n. \qquad (3.56)$$

The determinantal equation (3.55) becomes

$$\begin{vmatrix} K_{11} - R^* & K_{12} & \cdots K_{1n} \\ K_{21} & K_{22} - R^* & K_{2n} \\ \vdots & \vdots & \vdots \\ K_{n1} & K_{n2} & K_{nn} - R^* \end{vmatrix} = 0. \qquad (3.57)$$

The parameter R^* appears only along the diagonal, and the roots $R_1^*, \ldots, R_n^*$ are more easily determined.

6. In theory we could use a *complete* orthonormal set of trial functions $v_1(x), \ldots, v_n(x), \ldots$. System (3.56) then becomes the infinite system

$$\sum_{i=1}^{\infty} K_{mi} c_i - R^* c_m = 0; \qquad m = 1, 2, \ldots. \qquad (3.58)$$

These are the same equations that are obtained by expanding in $\{v_i(x)\}$ both sides of the original integral equation $Ku = \mu u$. Let $u = \sum c_i v_i$; then $K \sum c_i v_i = \mu \sum c_i v_i$. Taking the scalar product with $v_m(x)$,

$$\sum_{i=1}^{\infty} K_{mi} c_i = \mu c_m; \qquad m = 1, 2, \ldots.$$

This system coincides with the one derived from the variational principle. We thus obtain the *exact* expansion of the eigenfunctions of K in terms of the complete set $\{v_i(x)\}$. The roots R^* of the infinite determinant corresponding to (3.58) will be the *exact* eigenvalues of K.

EXAMPLE

Let

$$k(x, \xi) = \begin{cases} x(1 - \xi), & 0 \le x < \xi; \\ \xi(1 - x), & \xi < x \le 1. \end{cases}$$

The homogeneous integral equation is

$$\int_0^1 k(x, \xi)u(\xi)d\xi = \mu u(x).$$

The exact values of μ_1 and μ_2 are respectively $1/\pi^2$ and $1/4\pi^2$ (see Example 5, Section 3.1).

(a) We take a single trial function $v_1(x) = 1$. Equation (3.54) becomes

$$c_1 K_{11} - R^* c_1 \alpha_{11} = 0;$$

$$\alpha_{11} = \int_0^1 v_1^2(x)dx = 1;$$

$$K_{11} = \int_0^1 \int_0^1 k(x, \xi)dx \, d\xi = \int_0^1 \tfrac{1}{2}\xi(1 - \xi)d\xi = \tfrac{1}{12}.$$

This yields $R^* = \tfrac{1}{12}$ as a first approximation to μ_1.

(b) We take the trial function $v(x) = A + Bx + Cx^2$. A somewhat tedious calculation is simplified by noting that the lowest eigenfunction is even about $x = \tfrac{1}{2}$; therefore we use $v(x) = A + Bx(1 - x)$. We find $R_1^* = 1/9.875$ and $R_2^* = 1/170$. The value of R_1^* is within 0.11 percent of its correct value $1/\pi^2$. On the other hand, R_2^* is a very bad approximation to μ_2, whose eigenfunction is odd about $x = \tfrac{1}{2}$. R_2^* may be considered as an approximation to μ_3 (whose eigenfunction is again even about $x = \tfrac{1}{2}$).

The Schwarz Iteration Procedure (Also Known As the Variation-Iteration Procedure)

Let K be a real, nonnegative, symmetric H.-S. operator. The nonzero eigenvalues are $\{\mu_k\}$, and the corresponding normalized eigenfunctions are $\{\varphi_k\}$. Let $f_0(x)$ be an arbitrary function, not identically zero. If K is positive, $Kf_0 \ne 0$. If K is merely nonnegative, there will exist functions $f_0(x)$, with $Kf_0 = 0$. We *exclude* such functions from the outset. Next, we define the iterations:

$$f_1(x) = Kf_0, \dots, f_n(x) = Kf_{n-1}(x) = K^n f_0, \dots. \qquad (3.59)$$

If at any stage in these successive definitions we have $f_n(x) = cf_{n-1}(x)$, then $f_{n-1}(x)$ is an eigenfunction of K, and the procedure is terminated. In general this will not happen, but the ratio $f_n(x)/f_{n-1}(x)$ will become more nearly constant as n is taken larger.

Each of the functions $f_1, \ldots, f_n$, being in the range of K, can be expanded in terms of the set $\{\varphi_k\}$. Thus, setting $c_i = \langle f_0, \varphi_i \rangle$, we obtain

$$f_1 = Kf_0 = \sum \langle Kf_0, \varphi_i \rangle \varphi_i = \sum \langle f_0, K\varphi_i \rangle \varphi_i = \sum c_i \mu_i \varphi_i;$$
$$\vdots$$
$$f_n = Kf_{n-1} = K^n f_0 = \sum \langle K^n f_0, \varphi_i \rangle \varphi_i = \sum \langle f_0, K^n \varphi_i \rangle \varphi_i = \sum c_i \mu_i^n \varphi_i.$$

We note that, since $Kf_0 \neq 0$, not every c_i can vanish in the above formulas.

At this stage it is convenient to introduce the *Schwarz constants*

$$a_k = \langle f_i, f_{k-i} \rangle = \int_a^b f_i(x) f_{k-i}(x) dx.$$

As the nomenclature suggests, the definition is independent of the index i; indeed $f_i = K^i f_0$ and $f_{k-i} = K^{k-i} f_0$, so that

$$a_k = \langle f_i, f_{k-i} \rangle = \langle K^i f_0, K^{k-i} f_0 \rangle = \langle f_0, K^k f_0 \rangle.$$

Next we show that the Schwarz constants are *positive*. For a_0 this follows from the original assumption that $\langle f_0, f_0 \rangle$ is positive. Moreover, for $n \geq 1$,

$$a_n = \langle f_0, f_n \rangle = \langle f_0, K^n f_0 \rangle = \langle f_0, \sum c_i \mu_i^n \varphi_i \rangle = \sum c_i^2 \mu_i^n,$$

which is positive, since each μ_i is positive and not every c_i vanishes.

DEFINITION. The ratios $a_{k+1}/a_k = \theta_{k+1}$ are known as the *Schwarz quotients*.

Theorem. $\{\theta_k\}$ *is a monotonically increasing sequence, bounded above by* μ_1; *therefore* θ_k *has a limit* θ, *with* $\theta \leq \mu_1$.

Proof. (a) Let $u = a_{2k-1} f_k - a_{2k} f_{k-1}$. An easy calculation yields $\langle u, Ku \rangle = a_{2k-1}(a_{2k-1} a_{2k+1} - a_{2k}^2)$. Since $\langle u, Ku \rangle \geq 0$ and $a_{2k-1} > 0$, we have

$$\frac{a_{2k+1}}{a_{2k}} \geq \frac{a_{2k}}{a_{2k-1}} \qquad \text{or} \qquad \theta_{2k+1} \geq \theta_{2k}.$$

Also, $\langle u, u \rangle = a_{2k}(a_{2k} a_{2k-2} - a_{2k-1}^2)$, so that

$$\frac{a_{2k}}{a_{2k-1}} \geq \frac{a_{2k-1}}{a_{2k-2}} \qquad \text{or} \qquad \theta_{2k} \geq \theta_{2k-1}.$$

Thus, for all k, $\theta_{k+1} \geq \theta_k$.

(b) $$\theta_{2k+1} = \frac{\langle f_k, f_{k+1} \rangle}{\langle f_k, f_k \rangle} = \frac{\langle f_k, Kf_k \rangle}{\langle f_k, f_k \rangle} = R(f_k) \leq \mu_1,$$

by the extremal principle for μ_1. From (a) it follows that $\theta_k \leq \mu_1$, for all k, and our theorem is proved.†

We now calculate $\lim_{k \to \infty} \theta_k$.

Theorem. (a) *If* $c_1 \neq 0$, *then* $\lim_{k \to \infty} \theta_k = \mu_1$. (b) *If* $c_1 = \cdots = c_{m-1} = 0$, *and* $c_m \neq 0$, *then* $\lim_{k \to \infty} \theta_k = \mu_m$.

Proof. (a) From the definition of the Schwarz quotients, we have for $k \geq 1$,

$$\theta_{k+1} = \frac{a_{k+1}}{a_k} = \frac{\sum_i c_i^2 \mu_i^{k+1}}{\sum_i c_i^2 \mu_i^k}$$

$$= \mu_1 \frac{[c_1^2 + c_2^2(\mu_2/\mu_1)^{k+1} + c_3^2(\mu_3/\mu_1)^{k+1} + \cdots]}{[c_1^2 + c_2^2(\mu_2/\mu_1)^k + c_3^2(\mu_3/\mu_1)^k + \cdots]}.$$

Let us assume that μ_1 is not degenerate; then $\mu_i/\mu_1 < 1$ for $i > 1$, so that

$$c_2^2(\mu_2/\mu_1)^k + c_3^2(\mu_3/\mu_1)^k + \cdots \leq (\mu_2/\mu_1)^k(c_2^2 + c_3^2 + \cdots).$$

Since $\lim_{k \to \infty} (\mu_2/\mu_1)^k = 0$ and $\sum c_i^2$ converges, $\lim_{k \to \infty} [c_1^2 + c_2^2(\mu_2/\mu_1)^k + \cdots] = c_1^2$. Similarly $\lim_{k \to \infty} [c_1^2 + c_2^2(\mu_2/\mu_1)^{k+1} + \cdots] = c_1^2$, hence $\lim_{k \to \infty} \theta_{k+1} = \mu_1$, as required. The reader can easily supply the modifications needed if μ_1 is degenerate.

(b) We are now starting with a function $f_0(x)$ which is orthogonal to $\varphi_1(x)$. The iteration procedure which yields successive Schwarz quotients has no way of introducing a component along $\varphi_1(x)$, and we can *no longer* expect $\lim_{k \to \infty} \theta_k = \mu_1$. In fact, we have for $k \geq 1$

$$\theta_{k+1} = \frac{\sum_{i \geq m} c_i^2 \mu_i^{k+1}}{\sum_{i \geq m} c_i^2 \mu_i^k}$$

$$= \mu_m \frac{[c_m^2 + c_{m+1}^2(\mu_{m+1}/\mu_m)^{k+1} + c_{m+2}^2(\mu_{m+2}/\mu_m)^{k+1} + \cdots]}{[c_m^2 + c_{m+1}^2(\mu_{m+1}/\mu_m)^k + c_{m+2}^2(\mu_{m+2}/\mu_m)^k + \cdots]}.$$

† It is of interest to note that the quotient θ_{2k} is also related to an extremal principle not mentioned so far. We have

$$\theta_{2k} = \frac{a_{2k}}{a_{2k-1}} = \frac{\langle f_k, f_k \rangle}{\langle f_k, f_{k-1} \rangle} = \frac{\langle Kf_{k-1}, Kf_{k-1} \rangle}{\langle Kf_{k-1}, f_{k-1} \rangle},$$

and it is not surprising (and can be proved) that $\max \langle Ku, Ku \rangle / \langle Ku, u \rangle = \mu_1$ (see Exercise 3.17).

If μ_m is not degenerate, the numerator and denominator both approach c_m^2 as $k \to \infty$, so that

$$\lim_{k \to \infty} \theta_{k+1} = \mu_m.$$

REMARKS. For practical considerations, the iteration scheme is not useful to compute $\mu_2, \mu_3, \dots$. We can never be sure that we have started with a function $f_0(x)$ which has no component along $\varphi_1(x)$. Even if we were sure that $f_0(x)$ had no component along $\varphi_1(x)$, computational errors and roundoffs would introduce a component along $\varphi_1(x)$ at the first step, and pretty soon that component would build up and $\theta_k \to \mu_1$.

The iteration scheme does enable us to compute μ_1 and its corresponding eigenfunction $\varphi_1(x)$. In fact, at the nth iteration we have

$$f_n(x) = K^n f_0 = \sum c_i \mu_i^n \varphi_i(x) = \mu_1^n \sum c_i (\mu_i/\mu_1)^n \varphi_i(x).$$

Since $(\mu_i/\mu_1)^n << 1$ for n large and $i > 1$, $\varphi_1(x)$ is nearly proportional to $f_n(x)$ when n is large. Moreover, $\int_a^b \varphi_1^2(x)dx = 1$, so that

$$\varphi_1(x) \cong \pm \frac{f_n(x)}{\left[\int_a^b f_n^2(x)dx\right]^{1/2}}.$$

If so desired, the iteration scheme can be used to compute $\varphi_1(x)$ approximately without attempting to evaluate μ_1.

Upper Bounds to Eigenvalues

In (3.51) we exhibited a maximum principle which can be used with the Ritz-Rayleigh method or the Schwarz iteration procedure to obtain lower bounds for the eigenvalues.

We would like to have an inequality in the opposite direction so as to enclose a particular eigenvalue in an interval, thereby achieving a definite estimate on the error. A few preliminary remarks may guide us in finding enclosure intervals. In what sense is a trial function $v(x)$ an approximate eigenfunction of K? The equation $Kv = \mu v$ will not usually be satisfied for any value of μ; for what value of μ does v come as close as possible to satisfying the equation? Assuming that v has been normalized, $\langle v, v \rangle = 1$, we want to choose μ so that $\|Kv - \mu v\|^2$ is a minimum. Differentiating with respect to μ and setting the derivative equal to zero, we obtain $\mu = \langle Kv, v \rangle$. The quantity $\|Kv - \langle Kv, v \rangle v\|^2 = \|Kv\|^2 - \langle Kv, v \rangle^2$ is therefore a measure of how close v is to an eigenfunction of K. It is clear that v is an eigenfunction of K if and only if $\|Kv - \langle Kv, v \rangle v\|^2 = 0$, in which case the corresponding eigenvalue is $\langle Kv, v \rangle$. We hope these remarks will give some insight in the following theorem.

Theorem (*Weinstein, Block and Fuchs, Swanson*). *Let K be a real, symmetric operator with a complete orthonormal set of eigenfunctions $\varphi_1(x), \ldots, \varphi_n(x), \ldots$, and let $v(x)$ be an arbitrary function of unit norm. Then, there exists an eigenvalue of K in the interval on the real axis*:

$$\sigma - \alpha < \mu < \sigma + \alpha,$$

where $\sigma = \langle Kv, v \rangle$ and $\alpha = [\|Kv\|^2 - \langle Kv, v \rangle^2]^{1/2}$.

Proof. Let $v = \sum v_i \varphi_i(x)$ and $K\varphi_i = \mu_i \varphi_i$. We have

$$\alpha^2 = \|Kv - \langle Kv, v \rangle v\|^2 = \sum (\mu_i - \langle Kv, v \rangle)^2 v_i^2 \geq (\mu_m - \sigma)^2,$$

where μ_m is the eigenvalue closest to σ. Therefore,

$$-\alpha + \sigma < \mu_m < \alpha + \sigma, \tag{3.60}$$

which is the desired enclosure theorem.

If we wish to use (3.60) to estimate μ_1, we must know that the interval contains only the eigenvalue μ_1. To achieve this, suppose a crude upper bound to μ_2 (say l_2 with $l_2 < \mu_1$) is known from other considerations. The Schwarz iteration process enables us to find a function v of unit norm such that $\langle Kv, v \rangle \leq \mu_1$, and $\langle Kv, v \rangle > l_2$. As the iteration proceeds, $\langle Kv, v \rangle$ gets closer and closer to μ_1, and α^2 approaches 0. Therefore, we can choose v such that $\langle Kv, v \rangle - \alpha > l_2$. The interval $(\langle Kv, v \rangle - \alpha, \langle Kv, v \rangle + \alpha)$, which must contain an eigenvalue, can only contain the eigenvalue μ_1, and therefore

$$\mu_1 < \langle Kv, v \rangle + \alpha. \tag{3.61}$$

Figure 3.2 illustrates the enclosure theorem for μ_1.

The method of Kohn and Kato [Exercise 3.16(b)] yields the upper bound

$$\mu_1 < \langle Kv, v \rangle + \frac{\alpha^2}{\langle Kv, v \rangle - l_2}. \tag{3.62}$$

This bound is not as good as (3.61), since $\alpha / \langle Kv, v \rangle - l_2 > 1$ whenever v is a reasonable approximation to φ_1. On the other hand, the Kohn-Kato method has the advantage that v need only satisfy $(Kv, v) > l_2$.

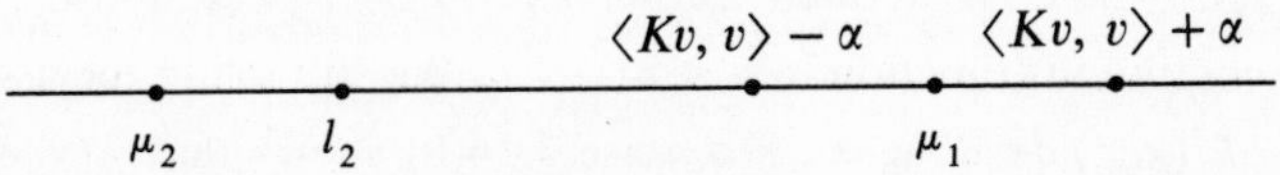

FIGURE 3.2

EXERCISES

3.16 **(a)** Show that if μ_1 is the largest eigenvalue of K and $\|v\| = 1$, $\langle Kv, v \rangle > \mu_2$, then

$$\mu_1 < \langle Kv, v \rangle + \frac{\|Kv\|^2 - \langle Kv, v \rangle^2}{\langle Kv, v \rangle - \mu_2}$$

(HINT: We must show that $\mu_1 < (\|Kv\|^2 - \mu_2 \langle Kv, v \rangle)/(\langle Kv, v \rangle - \mu_2)$; expand v in the form $\sum v_i \varphi_i(x)$ and the result follows.)

(b) If l_2 is a lower bound to μ_2 and $\langle Kv, v \rangle > l_2$, **(a)** reduces to the inequality (3.62).

(c) Let $\mu_{k-1} > \mu_k > \mu_{k+1}$ be three successive eigenvalues and let $\mu_{k+1} < \langle Kv, v \rangle < \mu_{k-1}$. Show that

$$\langle Kv, v \rangle - \frac{\|Kv\|^2 - \langle Kv, v \rangle^2}{\mu_{k-1} - \langle Kv, v \rangle} < \mu_k < \langle Kv, v \rangle + \frac{\|Kv\|^2 - \langle Kv, v \rangle^2}{\langle Kv, v \rangle - \mu_{k-1}}.$$

If we only know an upper bound l_{k+1} to μ_{k+1} and a lower bound l_{k-1} to μ_{k-1} (with $l_{k+1} < \langle Kv, v \rangle < l_{k-1}$), then the above inequality for μ_k is changed to

$$\langle Kv, v \rangle - \frac{\|Kv\|^2 - \langle Kv, v \rangle^2}{l_{k-1} - \langle Kv, v \rangle} < \mu_k < \langle Kv, v \rangle + \frac{\|Kv\|^2 - \langle Kv, v \rangle^2}{\langle Kv, v \rangle - l_{k+1}}.$$

3.17 **(a)** Prove that max $\langle Ku, Ku \rangle / \langle Ku, u \rangle = \mu_1$.

(b) Develop a maximum principle for μ_1 which involves $K^2 u$.

3.7   QUESTIONS RELATING TO CONTINUITY AND UNIFORM CONVERGENCE—THE BILINEAR SERIES FOR THE KERNEL AND THE ITERATED KERNELS

In some applications it is important to know whether or not the eigenfunctions are continuous, and whether or not the various eigenfunction expansions are valid in the sense of uniform convergence rather than merely in the sense of convergence in the mean. If a and b are finite, and $k(x, \xi)$ is continuous over the square $a \leq x, \xi \leq b$, these questions are relatively easy to answer. Unfortunately, many interesting physical problems give rise to kernels which are not bounded as functions of x and ξ. Exercise 3.14 is an example of such a kernel.

In this section we introduce an additional assumption on the symmetric kernel $k(x, \xi)$—that its iterated kernel $k_2(x, \xi) = \int_a^b k(x, u)k(u, \xi)du$ is a bounded, continuous function in $a \leq x, \xi \leq b$. We still retain the assumption that $\int_a^b \int_a^b |k^2(x, \xi)|dx\, d\xi < \infty$. [Exercise 3.14(b) shows that $k(x, \xi)$ can be unbounded, whereas $k_2(x, \xi)$ is bounded and continuous.]

Theorem 1.   *The eigenfunctions corresponding to nonzero eigenvalues are* continuous.

Proof.   For any eigenfunction $\varphi(x)$ and its corresponding eigenvalue μ, we have

$$\mu\varphi(x) = \int_a^b k(x, \xi)\varphi(\xi)d\xi;$$

$$|\varphi(x + \Delta x) - \varphi(x)| = \frac{1}{|\mu|}\left|\int_a^b [k(x + \Delta x, \xi) - k(x, \xi)]\varphi(\xi)d\xi\right|.$$

By the Schwarz inequality,

$$|\varphi(x + \Delta x) - \varphi(x)|$$

$$\leq \frac{1}{|\mu|}\left[\int_a^b |k(x + \Delta x, \xi) - k(x, \xi)|^2 \, d\xi\right]^{1/2} \left[\int_a^b |\varphi(\xi)|^2 \, d\xi\right]^{1/2}.$$

We also have

$$\int_a^b |k(x + \Delta x, \xi) - k(x, \xi)|^2 \, d\xi$$
$$= k_2(x + \Delta x, x + \Delta x) - k_2(x + \Delta x, x) - k_2(x, x + \Delta x) + k_2(x, x).$$

Recalling the assumption that $k_2(x, \xi)$ is continuous,

$$\lim_{\Delta x \to 0} \int_a^b |k(x + \Delta x, \xi) - k(x, \xi)|^2 \, d\xi = 0;$$

since $\int_a^b |\varphi|^2(x)dx < \infty$, it follows that $\lim_{\Delta x \to 0} |\varphi(x + \Delta x) - \varphi(x)| = 0$, so that $\varphi(x)$ is continuous.

Theorem 2.   *The expansion theorem (4 of Section 3.3) holds in the sense of* *uniform convergence.*

Proof.   Let f be an arbitrary function. Then, according to (3.40), we have, in the sense of convergence in the mean,

$$f = h + \sum \langle f, \varphi_i \rangle \varphi_i, \qquad \text{where } h \text{ satisfies } Kh = 0.$$

Therefore,

$$\left|Kf - K\left[\sum_{i=1}^n \langle f, \varphi_i \rangle \varphi_i\right]\right|^2 = \left|Kf - K\left[h + \sum_{i=1}^n \langle f, \varphi_i \rangle \varphi_i\right]\right|^2$$

$$= \left|\int_a^b k(x, \xi)\left\{f(\xi) - h(\xi) - \sum_{i=1}^n \langle f, \varphi_i \rangle \varphi_i(\xi)\right\}d\xi\right|^2$$

$$\leq \int_a^b |k^2(x, \xi)|d\xi \left\|f - h - \sum_{i=1}^n \langle f, \varphi_i \rangle \varphi_i\right\|^2. \quad (3.63)$$

By assumption, $\int_a^b |k^2(x, \xi)|d\xi \leq M$. From the definition of convergence in the mean, $\lim\limits_{n \to \infty} \|f - h - \sum\limits_{i=1}^{n} \langle f, \varphi_i \rangle \varphi_i\|^2 = 0$. Hence, by taking n large enough, the right side of the inequality (3.63) can be made arbitrarily small, independent of x. It follows that

$$Kf = \lim \sum_{i=1}^{n} \langle f, \varphi_i \rangle K\varphi_i, \qquad \text{uniformly in } a \leq x \leq b,$$

or

$$Kf = \sum_i \mu_i \langle f, \varphi_i \rangle \varphi_i = \sum_i \langle Kf, \varphi_i \rangle \varphi_i, \qquad \text{uniformly in } a \leq x \leq b.$$

COROLLARY. *The series solution of the inhomogeneous integral equation* (3.43), *which is given by* (3.45) *as*

$$u(x) + \frac{f(x)}{\mu} = \sum_k \frac{\mu_k \langle f, \varphi_k \rangle}{\mu(\mu_k - \mu)} \varphi_k(x),$$

converges uniformly on $a \leq x \leq b$.

We now apply Theorem 2 to self-adjoint differential systems of the second order. The nomenclature will be the same as the one following Theorem 5A near the end of Section 3.3. Consider again the systems (3.41), (3.42), (3.42a), and (3.42b), all of which (by Theorem 6) have the same complete orthonormal set of eigenfunctions $\{y_k(x)\}$. We have

Theorem 3. *If $w(x)$ is any twice-differentiable function whose second derivative is piecewise continuous, and if w satisfies the conditions $B_1(w) = 0$ and $B_2(w) = 0$, then the Fourier expansion of w in terms of $\{y_k\}$ converges uniformly to w on $a \leq x \leq b$.*

Proof. The assumptions on w imply that Mw exists and is a piecewise continuous function which we designate by $f(x)$. Since w can be considered as the unique solution of

$$Mw = f; \qquad B_1(w) = 0, \quad B_2(w) = 0,$$

it follows that $w = \int_a^b g(x, \xi)f(\xi)d\xi$, and w is in the range of the integral operator G. The Green's function $g(x, \xi)$ is a continuous function on the finite square $a \leq x, \xi \leq b$, so that Theorem 2 can be applied and Theorem 3 is proved.

Bilinear Expansions

Consider the iterated kernel $k_2(x, \xi) = \int_a^b k(x, u)k(u, \xi)du$. For each fixed value of ξ, $k_2(x, \xi)$ is of the form $Kf = \int_a^b k(x, u)f(u)du$ with $f(u) = k(u, \xi)$.

By Theorem 2, for each ξ, we have

$$k_2(x, \xi) = \sum_i \mu_i \langle k, \varphi_i \rangle \varphi_i = \sum_i \mu_i \varphi_i(x) \int_a^b k(u, \xi) \bar{\varphi}_i(u) du$$

$$= \sum_i \mu_i \varphi_i(x) \int_a^b \bar{k}(\xi, u) \bar{\varphi}_i(u) du = \sum_i \mu_i^2 \varphi_i(x) \bar{\varphi}_i(\xi),$$

where in the last step we used the fact that μ_i is real. The convergence of the series is uniform in x for each ξ, and uniform in ξ for each x. A more delicate analysis shows that the convergence is uniform in both variables, that is, over the square $a \leq x$, $\xi \leq b$. Similar bilinear expansions for the higher iterated kernels are easily obtained:

Theorem 4. *The nth iterated kernel has the bilinear expansion*

$$k_n(x, \xi) = \sum_i \mu_i^n \varphi_i(x) \bar{\varphi}_i(\xi), \qquad n \geq 2, \tag{3.64}$$

and the convergence is uniform in $a \leq x$, $\xi \leq b$.

It follows from (3.64) that, for $n \geq 2$,

$$\int_a^b k_n(x, x) dx = \sum_i \mu_i^n. \tag{3.65}$$

If $k(x, \xi)$ generates a nonnegative operator, we obtain from (3.65) an estimate for μ_1,

$$\mu_1 \leq \left[\int_a^b k_n(x, x) dx \right]^{1/n}. \tag{3.66}$$

Note that (3.66) is an upper bound to μ_1, whereas the variational principle (3.53) yields a lower bound.

One can surmise from the expansion (3.64) that $k_n(x, \xi)$ has nonzero eigenvalues $\{\mu_i^n\}$ and eigenfunctions $\{\varphi_i(x)\}$. This statement is easily proved. Indeed,

$$K^n \varphi_i = K^{n-1} K \varphi_i = \mu_i K^{n-1} \varphi_i = \cdots = \mu_i^n \varphi_i ;$$

hence every eigenfunction of K corresponding to μ_i is an eigenfunction of K^n with eigenvalue μ_i^n. Further, no eigenfunction of K^n is left out; suppose φ is a normalized eigenfunction of K^n corresponding to the eigenvalue $\mu \neq 0$, and φ is not listed among the $\{\varphi_i\}$; then $\langle \varphi, \varphi_i \rangle = 0$, and by the expansion theorem

$$K^n \varphi = \sum_i \langle K^n \varphi, \varphi_i \rangle \varphi_i = \sum_i \langle \varphi, K^n \varphi_i \rangle \varphi_i = \sum_i \mu_i^n \langle \varphi, \varphi_i \rangle \varphi_i = 0.$$

This is a contradiction, and therefore the integral operator K^n has nonzero eigenvalues $\{\mu_i^n\}$ and eigenfunctions $\{\varphi_i(x)\}$.

It is interesting to speculate as to the validity of the bilinear expansion for the case $n = 1$. It can be proved that the series $\sum \mu_i \varphi_i(x) \bar{\varphi}_i(\xi)$ always converges in the *mean* to $k(x, \xi)$, but, unfortunately, the equality in the sense of uniform or pointwise convergence cannot be guaranteed in general, even if $k(x, \xi)$ is continuous! The following theorem, whose proof we omit, covers many important cases.

Theorem 5 (Mercer's Theorem).   *If $k(x, \xi)$ is quasi-definite (that is, all but a finite number of eigenvalues are of one sign) and continuous, then*

$$k(x, \xi) = \sum_i \mu_i \varphi_i(x) \bar{\varphi}_i(\xi), \qquad \text{uniformly on } a \leq x, \xi \leq b. \qquad (3.67)$$

It follows that

$$\sum_i \mu_i = \int_a^b k(x, x)dx. \qquad (3.68)$$

If k generates a nonnegative integral operator, we can add the bound similar to (3.66),

$$\mu_1 \leq \int_a^b k(x, x)dx.$$

EXERCISES

3.18 Show that the real symmetric kernels of Exercises 3.3 and 3.4 are positive definite. Using the bilinear expansions, calculate $\sum_{k=1}^{\infty} \mu_k$ and $\sum_{k=1}^{\infty} \mu_k^2$ for both problems.

3.19 The kernel of Exercise 3.5(b) is symmetric, indefinite, and discontinuous. The bilinear expansion formally becomes

$$g(x \mid \xi; \theta) = \sum_{n=-\infty}^{\infty} \frac{e^{i2n\pi(x-\xi)}}{2\pi n - \theta} = \frac{ie^{-i\theta\xi}}{1 - e^{i\theta}} \begin{cases} e^{i\theta x}, & \xi < x \leq 1, \\ e^{i\theta}e^{i\theta x}, & 0 \leq x < \xi. \end{cases}$$

The series is the trigonometric Fourier expansion of the discontinuous function appearing on the right. From the elementary theory of such expansions, the series at $x = \xi$ should converge to the average of $g(\xi + |\xi; \theta)$ and $g(\xi - |\xi; \theta)$; that is,

$$\frac{i}{1 - e^{i\theta}} \left(\frac{1 + e^{i\theta}}{2} \right) = -\frac{1}{2} \cot \frac{\theta}{2}.$$

This leads us to the formula

$$-\frac{1}{2} \cot \frac{\theta}{2} = \sum_{n=-\infty}^{\infty} \frac{1}{2\pi n - \theta}.$$

Show that this is equivalent to the expansion

$$\cot z = \frac{1}{z} + \sum_{n=1}^{\infty} \frac{2z}{z^2 - \pi^2 n^2}$$

which is an old friend of complex analysts. A variant of this identity occurred in Exercise 1.28. Compute the iterated kernel $k_2(x, \xi) = \int_0^1 g(x|t; \theta)g(t|\xi; \theta)dt$. Show explicitly that k_2 is continuous and that $k_2(x, x) = -e^{i\theta}/(1 - e^{i\theta})^2$. Integrating the bilinear expansion for $k_2(x, x)$, show that

$$\frac{1}{2(1 - \cos \theta)} = \sum_{n=-\infty}^{\infty} \frac{1}{(2n\pi - \theta)^2}.$$

By taking an appropriate limit as $\theta \to 0$, show that

$$\sum_{n=1}^{\infty} \frac{1}{n^2} = \frac{\pi^2}{6}.$$

3.20 Let $f(x)$ be an even real function of period 2π with $\int_0^{2\pi} f^2(x)dx < \infty$. The function $f(x)$ may be expanded formally in a cosine series: $\frac{1}{2}a_0 + \sum_{n=1}^{\infty} a_n \cos nx$. Let $k(x, \xi) = f(x - \xi)$, $0 \leq x, \xi \leq 2\pi$, and consider $\int_0^{2\pi} k(x, \xi)u(\xi)d\xi = \mu u(x)$. Show that the eigenvalues are $a_n\pi$, with corresponding eigenfunctions $A \sin nx + B \cos nx$. Verify formally the bilinear formula for $k(x, \xi)$. Apply the results to the kernels of Exercises 3.12 and 3.13.

3.21 $f(x)$ has the same properties as in Exercise 3.20, but $k(x, \xi)$ is $f(x + \xi)$. Derive the corresponding results.

3.22 Let $f(x)$ be an odd real function of period 2π, with $\int_0^{2\pi} f^2(x)dx < \infty$. The function $f(x)$ may be expanded formally in the sine series

$$\sum_{n=1}^{\infty} b_n \sin nx.$$

Let $k(x, \xi) = f(x + \xi)$, $0 \leq x, \xi \leq 2\pi$, and consider

$$\int_0^{2\pi} k(x, \xi)u(\xi)d\xi = \mu u(x).$$

Show that the eigenvalues are $\pm b_n\pi$ with corresponding eigenfunctions $A(\sin nx \pm \cos nx)$, and that 0 is also an eigenvalue with a constant eigenfunction. Verify formally the bilinear formula for $k(x, \xi)$.

3.8 APPROXIMATE METHODS FOR THE SOLUTION OF INTEGRAL EQUATIONS

We consider various approximation methods for the solution of the inhomogeneous equation

$$\int_a^b k(x, \xi)u(\xi)d\xi - \mu u(x) = f(x), \qquad Ku - \mu u = f. \qquad (3.69)$$

We assume that $k(x, \xi)$ is a real, symmetric, H.-S. kernel, and that μ is not an eigenvalue of K. The approximation methods may still be effective when these conditions are not met, but problems of this kind should be treated on an individual basis. Variants of these techniques can also be applied to the eigenvalue problem $Ku = \mu u$; occasionally we shall present the corresponding results. In general, error estimates will not be given; the interested reader is referred to Kantorovich and Krylov[†] for a careful discussion of these questions.

Approximate Integration

Divide the interval $a \leq x \leq b$ into n equal parts. The center points of the subintervals are labeled $x_1, \ldots, x_n$, in increasing order. The integral $\int_a^b k(x, \xi)u(\xi)d\xi$ is replaced by the sum $\sum_{i=1}^{n} k(x, x_i)u(x_i)[(b - a)/n]$. We attempt to satisfy the integral equation (3.69) only at the points $x_1, \ldots, x_n$. Introducing the notation $f(x_i) = f_i$, $u(x_i) = u_i$, $k(x_i, x_j) = k_{ij}$, we obtain

$$\sum_{i=1}^{n} k_{ji}u_i \frac{b - a}{n} = \mu u_j + f_j, \qquad j = 1, \ldots, n. \tag{3.70}$$

These are n linear, inhomogeneous, algebraic equations for the unknowns $u_1, \ldots, u_n$. After obtaining the solution of these equations, a functional representation for $u(x)$ can be found either by interpolation or else, in closed form, by returning to the integral equation; that is,

$$u(x) = -\frac{f(x)}{\mu} + \frac{1}{\mu} \sum_{i=1}^{n} k(x, x_i)u_i \frac{b - a}{n}.$$

Equations (3.70) are the result of dividing the interval (a, b) in n equal parts and weighting the subintervals equally. More accurate formulas for approximate integration, such as Simpson's rule or the trapezoidal rule, will yield algebraic systems different from (3.70) and may be preferable in practice.

In his original development of the theory of integral equations, Fredholm obtained the solution of (3.69) as the limiting case (as $n \to \infty$) of the solution of (3.70). This approach has lost all but historical interest since the H.-S. theory, described in the previous sections, is both simpler and more powerful.

Approximation of the Kernel by a Separable Kernel

We replace $k(x, \xi)$ by the finite sum $\sum_{i=1}^{n} p_i(x)q_i(\xi)$. One way of obtaining such an approximation is by expanding k in an arbitrary real orthonormal

[†] L. V. Kantorovich and V. I. Krylov, *Approximate Methods of Analysis*, Interscience, New York, 1958.

set $q_1(\xi), \ldots, q_n(\xi)$ for the interval (a, b). The associated Fourier sum is $\sum_{i=1}^{n} p_i(x)q_i(\xi)$, where $p_i(x) = \int_a^b k(x, \xi)q_i(\xi)d\xi$. Regardless of how the separable approximation $\sum_{i=1}^{n} p_i(x)q_i(\xi)$ is obtained, the resulting integral equation [which takes the place of (3.69)] is

$$\sum_{i=1}^{n} p_i(x) \int_a^b q_i(\xi)u(\xi)d\xi - \mu u(x) = f(x). \qquad (3.71)$$

Thus $\mu u(x)$ must be of the form $\sum_{i=1}^{n} c_i p_i(x) - f(x)$. Substituting in (3.71) yields

$$\sum_{i=1}^{n} c_i p_i(x) = \sum_{i=1}^{n} \frac{p_i(x)}{\mu} \int_a^b q_i(\xi)\left[\sum_{j=1}^{n} c_j p_j(\xi) - f(\xi)\right]d\xi.$$

If the $\{p_i(x)\}$ are independent,

$$c_i = \frac{1}{\mu}\left[\sum_{j=1}^{n} c_j \int_a^b q_i(\xi)p_j(\xi)d\xi - \int_a^b q_i(\xi)f(\xi)d\xi\right], \qquad i = 1, \ldots, n.$$

These n linear, inhomogeneous, algebraic equations are solved for $c_1, \ldots, c_n$. This gives the exact solution $(1/\mu) \sum_{i=1}^{n} c_i p_i(x) - (1/\mu)f(x)$ of (3.71), and hence the approximate solution of (3.69).

Approximation of $u(x)$ in Terms of an Independent Set $v_1(x), \ldots, v_n(x)$

We have at our disposal an independent set of real functions $v_1(x), \ldots, v_n(x)$, in terms of which we wish to approximate $u(x)$, the solution of (3.69). Substituting the linear combination $\sum_{i=1}^{n} c_i v_i(x)$ in (3.69), we obtain

$$\int_a^b k(x, \xi) \sum_{i=1}^{n} c_i v_i(\xi)d\xi - \mu \sum_{i=1}^{n} c_i v_i(x) \cong f(x) \qquad (3.72)$$

or

$$\sum_{i=1}^{n} c_i g_i(x) \cong f(x), \qquad (3.73)$$

where $g_i(x) = \int_a^b k(x, \xi)v_i(\xi)d\xi - \mu v_i(x)$. Whatever the choice of $c_1, \ldots, c_n$ we cannot expect the two sides of (3.73) to be equal [unless, accidentally, the exact solution of (3.69) is of the form $\sum_{i=1}^{n} c_i v_i(x)$]. One is therefore led to a number of different ways of satisfying (3.73) approximately. The idea is to choose $c_1, \ldots, c_n$ so that the two sides of (3.73) are "as nearly equal as possible." There are various criteria for "nearly equal." We might require, for instance, that the two sides be equal at n suitably chosen points $a \leq x \leq b$. The most natural criterion is to demand that the square deviation [that is, the $\mathscr{L}_2(a, b)$ norm] of the difference be as small as possible.

1. *Least-Squares Approximation.* We wish to minimize $\left\| \sum_{i=1}^{n} c_i g_i(x) - f(x) \right\|$ or, what is equivalent, to minimize $\left\| \sum_{i=1}^{n} c_i g_i(x) - f(x) \right\|^2$. Differentiate with respect to $c_1, \ldots, c_n$ and set the derivatives equal to zero to obtain

$$\sum_{i=1}^{n} c_i \int_a^b g_m(x) g_i(x) dx - \int_a^b f(x) g_m(x) dx = 0, \qquad m = 1, 2, \ldots, n. \quad (3.74)$$

The set of equations (3.74) is a special (but optimal) case of the Galerkin equations below.

2. *Galerkin's Method.* We make the two sides of (3.73) " nearly equal " in the sense which follows. Let $w_1(x), \ldots, w_n(x)$ be a set of n independent real "weighting" functions, which may or may not coincide with the "approximating" set $v_1(x), \ldots, v_n(x)$. Take the inner product of (3.73) with respect to $w_j(x)$; we require that for $j = 1, \ldots, n$,

$$\left\langle w_j(x), \sum_{i=1}^{n} c_i g_i(x) \right\rangle = \langle f(x), w_j(x) \rangle. \quad (3.75)$$

In geometric terms we have demanded that both sides of (3.73) have the same projection on the n-dimensional subspace spanned by the functions $w_1(x), \ldots, w_n(x)$. The equations (3.75) are the so-called *Galerkin equations*,

$$\sum_{i=1}^{n} c_i \int_a^b g_i(x) w_j(x) dx = \int_a^b f(x) w_j(x) dx, \qquad j = 1, \ldots, n. \quad (3.76)$$

The least-square equations (3.74) are obtained from (3.76) by using the weighting functions $w_j(x) = g_j(x) = \int_a^b k(x, \xi) v_j(\xi) d\xi - \mu v_j(x)$. If, on the other hand, we take the weighting functions $\{w_j(x)\}$ to be the same as the approximating functions $\{v_k(x)\}$, the equations (3.76) become

$$\sum_{i=1}^{n} c_i \int_a^b g_i(x) v_j(x) dx = \int_a^b f(x) v_j(x) dx, \qquad j = 1, \ldots, n, \quad (3.77)$$

or

$$\sum_{i=1}^{n} c_i K_{ij} - \mu \sum_{i=1}^{n} c_i \alpha_{ij} = f_j, \qquad j = 1, \ldots, n, \quad (3.78)$$

where

$$f_j = \int_a^b f(x) v_j(x) dx, \qquad \alpha_{ij} = \int_a^b v_i(x) v_j(x) dx;$$

$$K_{ij} = \int_a^b \int_a^b v_j(x) k(x, \xi) v_i(\xi) dx \, d\xi.$$

For the eigenvalue problem $Ku = \mu u$, the equations (3.78) take the form

$$\sum_{i=1}^{n} c_i K_{ij} = \mu \sum_{i=1}^{n} c_i \alpha_{ij}, \qquad j = 1, \ldots, n.$$

This system is seen to be the same as system (3.54) obtained by the Ritz-Rayleigh procedure (noting that $K_{ij} = K_{ji}$, $\alpha_{ij} = \alpha_{ji}$), but no differentiation or minimization is needed with the Galerkin derivation. We construct below a variational principle for the inhomogeneous integral equation; when the Ritz-Rayleigh procedure is used in conjunction with this principle, the Galerkin equations (3.78) ensue. The Galerkin method can also be used when no variational principle is available, for instance, when the kernel is indefinite or when the integral equation is nonlinear.

Variational Principle for the Inhomogeneous Equation

The solution of the integral equation (3.69) can equally be well characterized as the function which maximizes a certain associated functional. Such variational principles in fact apply to a fairly large class of operators in Hilbert space.

Let A be a real symmetric positive operator defined on a Hilbert space $\mathscr{A}$ [which for simplicity we take as the space of all real-valued functions $u(x)$ for which $\int_{a}^{b} u^2 \, dx$ is finite]. We shall be interested in the inhomogeneous equation

$$Au = f, \tag{3.79}$$

where f is a given element in $\mathscr{A}$ and we are searching for the solution u. The solution, if it exists, must be unique. Indeed, if u_1 and u_2 are solutions of (3.79), their difference w satisfies $Aw = 0$, so that $\langle Aw, w \rangle = 0$. Since A is a positive operator, this implies $w = 0$ and $u_1 = u_2$.

Consider the nonlinear functional

$$I(v) = 2\langle f, v \rangle - \langle Av, v \rangle, \tag{3.80}$$

which is defined for all elements v in $\mathscr{A}$.

Theorem. (a) *If* (3.79) *has a solution* u, *then* $I(v)$ *attains its maximum value for* $v = u$.

(b) *If* $I(v)$ *attains its maximum value for some function* u, *then* u *is the solution of* (3.79).

Proof. (a) Let u be the solution of (3.79) and let v be an arbitrary element in $\mathscr{A}$. Then

$$\begin{aligned}
I(u) - I(v) &= 2\langle f, u \rangle - \langle Au, u \rangle - 2\langle f, v \rangle + \langle Av, v \rangle \\
&= 2\langle Au, u \rangle - \langle Au, u \rangle - 2\langle Au, v \rangle + \langle Av, v \rangle \\
&= \langle A(u - v), u - v \rangle.
\end{aligned}$$

Since A is a positive operator $\langle A(u - v), u - v \rangle > 0$ unless $u = v$. Therefore $I(u) > I(v)$ for all $v \neq u$, which proves part (a) of the theorem.

(b) Let u be a function which maximizes I. Then with η an arbitrary element in $\mathscr{A}$ and ε an arbitrary real number, we have

$$I(u + \varepsilon\eta) \leq I(u).$$

The left side is a differentiable function of ε defined for all real ε and whose maximum value occurs at $\varepsilon = 0$. Therefore,

$$\left. \frac{dI(u + \varepsilon\eta)}{d\varepsilon} \right|_{\varepsilon = 0} = 0.$$

Since

$$I(u + \varepsilon\eta) = 2\langle f, u \rangle + 2\varepsilon\langle f, \eta \rangle - \langle Au, u \rangle - \varepsilon^2 \langle A\eta, \eta \rangle - 2\varepsilon\langle Au, \eta \rangle,$$

it follows that

$$\langle f, \eta \rangle = \langle Au, \eta \rangle$$

or

$$\langle f - Au, \eta \rangle = 0.$$

This last equation is valid for all η in $\mathscr{A}$; therefore

$$Au = f,$$

and part (b) has been proved.

REMARKS. 1. Part (b) of the theorem can be used to prove the existence of solutions to (3.79) [this will entail showing that $I(v)$ actually attains a maximum]. If, on the other hand, we can prove by other means that (3.79) has a solution, part (a) of the theorem will enable us to construct approximate solutions to (3.79) by the Ritz-Rayleigh procedure outlined below.

2. We can substitute the word "minimum" for "maximum" in the theorem if we merely change the sign of the functional, that is, if we consider $-I(v)$ instead of $I(v)$. In this form the theorem often can be interpreted physically as a minimum-energy principle. This point of view will be discussed in Volume II.

3. Some simplification and additional insight can be obtained by introducing a new inner product $[w, z]$ defined by

$$[w, z] = \langle Aw, z \rangle = \langle w, Az \rangle = [z, w]. \qquad (3.81a)$$

The corresponding norm of an element w is denoted by $|w|$. Then

$$|w| = \langle w, Aw \rangle, \qquad (3.81b)$$

and $|w|$ is positive, except for $w = 0$. It is therefore clear that we have defined an acceptable inner product, that is, one which satisfies the conditions (2.6).

If (3.79) has a solution, we can rewrite (3.80) in terms of the new inner product as

$$I(v) = 2[u, v] - [v, v].$$

Then $I(u) - I(v) = [u, u] - 2[u, v] + [v, v] = [u - v, u - v]$. It is therefor obvious that the maximum of I occurs for $v = u$.

Appealing to the Schwarz inequality

$$|[u, v]|^2 \le [u, u] [v, v],$$

we obtain, for $v \ne 0$,

$$[u, u] \ge \frac{|[u, v]|^2}{[v, v]},$$

the equality being possible only if $v = cu$. Since $[v, v] = \langle Av, v \rangle$, $[u, v] = \langle Au, v \rangle = \langle f, v \rangle$, and $[u, u] = \langle Au, u \rangle = \langle f, u \rangle$, we have

$$\langle f, u \rangle = \langle Au, u \rangle \ge \frac{|\langle f, v \rangle|^2}{\langle Av, v \rangle}. \tag{3.82}$$

Setting

$$J(v) = \frac{|\langle f, v \rangle|^2}{\langle Av, v \rangle}, \tag{3.82a}$$

and observing that $J(cv) = J(v)$, we see that the maximum of $J(v)$ is attained for $v = cu$, where u is the solution of (3.79) and c is an arbitrary constant. Thus if we have found a function u_0 which maximizes $J(v)$, then $u_0 = cu$ and $Au_0 = cAu = cf$, so that $c = 1/\|f\|^2 \langle Au_0, f \rangle$ and $u = (\|f\|^2/\langle Au_0, f \rangle) u_0$. One can therefore use the maximum principle based on (3.82a) [instead of (3.80)] to characterize the solution of (3.79). These ideas may be applied to the integral equation (3.69). Here $A = K - \mu I$; if $\mu < 0$, the integral equation has a unique solution u with the property

$$\langle f, u \rangle = \int_a^b fu\, dx = \max_v \left\{ 2 \int_a^b fv\, dx - \int_a^b \int_a^b v(x)k(x, \xi)v(\xi)dx\, d\xi + \mu \int_a^b v^2\, dx \right\}$$

or

$$\langle f, u \rangle = \max_v \frac{\left\{ \int_a^b fv\, dx \right\}^2}{\int_a^b \int_a^b v(x)k(x, \xi)v(\xi)dx\, d\xi - \mu \int_a^b v^2\, dx}.$$

In the first characterization the maximum occurs for $v = u$, whereas in the second the maximum occurs for any function proportional to u. If u_0 is any such function, we have $u = \|f\|^2 u_0/(\langle Ku_0, f \rangle - \mu \langle u_0, f \rangle)$. In the many applications where the quantity $\langle f, u \rangle$ is itself of great physical interest, the second principle may prove itself more useful, for it requires guessing only the "shape" of the solution, not its "size".

The Rayleigh-Ritz Equations

To obtain an approximate solution of (3.79), we substitute the "trial" function $v = \sum_{i=1}^{n} c_i v_i(x)$ in (3.79) and adjust the constants $c_1, \ldots, c_n$ so as to maximize I. This is accomplished by setting $\partial I/\partial c_1, \ldots, \partial I/\partial c_n$ equal to zero; since $I(\sum_i c_i v_i) = 2\sum_i c_i \langle f, v_i \rangle - \sum_{i,j} c_i c_j \langle Av_i, v_j \rangle$, we obtain the *Rayleigh-Ritz equations*

$$\langle f, v_i \rangle = \sum_{j=1}^{n} \langle Av_i, v_j \rangle c_j; \qquad i = 1, 2, \ldots, n.$$

These equations are recognized as the Galerkin equations (3.78) (when $A = K - \mu I$). The only advantage of the variational method is that one obtains at the same time bounds for the quantity $\langle f, u \rangle$.

If the independent functions $v_1, \ldots, v_n$ are chosen to be orthonormal *in the inner product* (3.81a), the results simplify considerably. We then have

$$[v_i, v_j] = \langle Av_i, v_j \rangle = \begin{cases} 0, & i \neq j; \\ 1, & i = j, \end{cases}$$

and the Rayleigh-Ritz equations become

$$c_i = \langle f, v_i \rangle; \qquad i = 1, 2, \ldots, n.$$

The corresponding approximate solution of (3.79) is $\sum_{i=1}^{n} c_i v_i = \sum_{i=1}^{n} \langle f, v_i \rangle v_i$. This suggests that the Rayleigh-Ritz equations are merely an approximation of n terms to the exact solution $\sum_{i=1}^{\infty} \langle f, v_i \rangle v_i$. This is in fact true if the set $\{v_i\}$ is complete in the inner product (3.81a). For we can then expand the solution of (3.79) in a series in the $\{v_i\}$,

$$u = \sum_i [u, v_i] v_i,$$

and since

$$[u, v_i] = \langle Au, v_i \rangle = \langle f, v_i \rangle,$$

we have

$$u = \sum_{i=1}^{\infty} \langle f, v_i \rangle v_i.$$

EXERCISES

3.23 Consider the "extended" eigenvalue problem

$$Nu = \lambda Mu, \tag{3.83}$$

where N is a symmetric H.-S. operator and M is a bounded, symmetric, positive, real operator. (M is not necessarily an H.-S. operator; in fact, the most interesting cases occur when M is not completely continuous.)

(a) Show that the eigenvalues are real.

(b) Show that the eigenfunctions corresponding to different eigenvalues are orthogonal with weight M; that is,

$$\langle u, Mv \rangle = 0.$$

Show that eigenfunctions corresponding to different nonzero eigenvalues are also orthogonal with weight N; that is,

$$\langle u, Nv \rangle = 0.$$

(c) Introduce a new inner product

$$\langle u, v \rangle^* = \langle u, Mv \rangle,$$

which is permissible because M is positive. The eigenfunctions of (3.83) corresponding to nonzero eigenvalues can be chosen to form an orthonormal set in this star inner product. If M^{-1} is bounded, it can be shown that the eigenfunctions of (3.83) form a complete set. Thus each vector f can be decomposed as the sum

$$f = f_0 + \sum \langle f, \varphi_i \rangle^* \varphi_i,$$

where f_0 is in the null space of N and $\{\varphi_i\}$ are the eigenfunctions corresponding to nonzero eigenvalues. Use this result to prove that

$$\max \frac{|\langle Nu, u \rangle|}{\langle Mu, u \rangle} = |\lambda_1|, \tag{3.84}$$

where λ_1 is the eigenvalue of largest modulus of (3.83).

3.24 *Translation of inhomogeneous problem into an extended eigenvalue problem.* Consider the inhomogeneous equation

$$Mv = f, \tag{3.85}$$

where M satisfies the conditions of (3.83), and M^{-1} is bounded. The unique solution of (3.85) is denoted by v. Let us assume that f is a unit vector [this is no restriction, since we can always consider the problem $Mw = f/\|f\|$ and then $v = \|f\|w$]. We introduce the projection operator P_f with the property

$$P_f u = \langle u, f \rangle f. \tag{3.86}$$

Let us look at the extended eigenvalue problem

$$P_f u = \lambda M u. \tag{3.87}$$

Since the left side is proportional to f (unless $\langle u, f \rangle = 0$), Mu is proportional to f and u is therefore proportional to v. Substituting $u = cv$ in (3.87), we find

$$\lambda = \langle v, f \rangle.$$

Thus the only nonzero eigenvalue of (3.87) is $\lambda = \langle v, f \rangle$, and the corresponding eigenfunction is $u = cv$, where v is the solution of (3.85).

Applying (3.84), we find

$$|\langle v, f \rangle| = \max_z \frac{|\langle P_f z, z \rangle|}{\langle Mz, z \rangle} = \max_z \frac{|\langle z, f \rangle|^2}{\langle Mz, z \rangle},$$

which is just (3.82a) in a slightly more general form.

3.25 Let K be a symmetric H.-S. operator. We have called K nonnnegative if $\langle Ku, u \rangle \geq 0$ for all u. Show that K can be nonnegative even if the kernel $k(x, \xi)$ which generates K is a function which takes on negative values. [HINT Consider a kernel of the form $f(x)f(\xi)$.] Show that if $k(x, \xi) \geq 0$ and $\|K\| \neq 0$, then K has a least one positive eigenvalue.

3.26 Consider (3.79) for f complex and A a symmetric positive operator (not necessarily real). Show that if the functional in (3.80) is changed to

$$I(v) = \langle f, v \rangle + \langle v, f \rangle - \langle Av, v \rangle,$$

then the theorem following (3.80) still holds.

3.9 NONSYMMETRIC HILBERT-SCHMIDT OPERATORS

If K is a symmetric H.-S. operator, the solution of $Ku - \mu u = f$ can be obtained in the form of an expansion in the eigenfunctions of K (see Section 3.4). If K is not symmetric, the eigenfunctions of K may no longer be useful in the solution of the inhomogeneous equation. In fact, the nonsymmetric kernel

$$k(x, \xi) = \begin{cases} 0, & 0 \leq x < \xi; \\ 1, & \xi < x \leq 1. \end{cases}$$

has no eigenvalues, yet the equation $Ku - \mu u = f$ has a unique solution for $\mu \neq 0$ and each f [this solution was calculated by ad hoc considerations in (2.62)]; even in the case $\mu = 0$, the solution is unique and exists for a large class of functions f. Remarkably enough, some aspects of eigenfunction theory can be salvaged for unsymmetric operators by using the eigenfunctions of the related integral operators

$$\begin{aligned} K_R &= KK^*; \\ K_L &= K^*K. \end{aligned} \tag{3.88}$$

If K is symmetric, $K_R = K_L = K^2$; if K is not symmetric, $K_R \neq K_L$, but, as will be seen below, both K_R and K_L are symmetric.

The operator $K_L = K^*K$ has the property

$$K_L f = K^*Kf = \int_a^b \bar{k}(t, x)dt \int_a^b k(t, \xi)f(\xi)d\xi = \int_a^b k_L(x, \xi)f(\xi)d\xi,$$

where

$$k_L(x, \xi) = \int_a^b \bar{k}(t, x)k(t, \xi)dt.$$

Thus K_L is generated by the symmetric kernel $k_L(x, \xi)$, known as the *left iterate* of $k(x, \xi)$. Similarly,

$$K_R f = \int_a^b k_R(x, \xi)f(\xi)d\xi,$$

where

$$k_R(x, \xi) = \int_a^b k(x, t)\bar{k}(\xi, t)dt,$$

so that K_R is generated by the symmetric kernel $k_R(x, \xi)$, which is known as the *right iterate* of $k(x, \xi)$.

From the relations

$$\langle K_L u, u \rangle = \langle K^*Ku, u \rangle = \langle Ku, Ku \rangle = \|Ku\|^2;$$

$$\langle K_R u, u \rangle = \langle KK^*u, u \rangle = \langle K^*u, K^*u \rangle = \|K^*u\|^2,$$

we see that K_L and K_R are nonnegative operators and must therefore have real nonnegative eigenvalues. One easily verifies that K_L and K_R are H.-S. operators. We show next that K_L and K_R have the same nonzero eigenvalues, although their eigenfunctions may be different. Suppose that v is an eigenfunction of K_L belonging to the positive eigenvalue μ^2; that is,

$$K_L v = K^*Kv = \mu^2 v; \tag{3.89}$$

then the function

$$u = Kv$$

is a normalized eigenfunction of K_R belonging to the eigenvalue μ^2. Indeed,

$$K_R u = K_R Kv = KK^*Kv = KK_L v = \mu^2 Kv = \mu^2 u.$$

Similarly, if u is an eigenfunction of K_R corresponding to some positive eigenvalue μ^2; that is,

$$K_R u = KK^*u = \mu^2 u, \tag{3.90}$$

then

$$v = K^*u$$

is easily seen to be an eigenfunction of K_L corresponding to μ^2. Thus (3.89) and (3.90) have the same eigenvalues, and one can verify that the multiplicity of an eigenvalue is the same whether regarded as an eigenvalue of K_L or as one of K_R. The nonzero eigenvalues of the symmetric H.-S. operator K_R, as defined from (3.90), are denoted by $\{\mu_n^2\}$. As usual, these eigenvalues are indexed (with proper regard to multiplicity) in order of decreasing value. The corresponding orthonormal set of eigenfunctions is labeled $\{u_n\}$. We now define

$$v_n = \frac{1}{\mu_n} K^* u_n, \tag{3.91}$$

and claim that the set $\{v_n\}$ is an orthonormal set of eigenfunctions of K_L. From the previous discussion we know that $\{v_n\}$ is indeed a set of eigenfunctions of K_L; moreover,

$$\langle v_m, v_n \rangle = \frac{1}{\mu_m \mu_n} \langle K^* u_m, K^* u_n \rangle = \frac{1}{\mu_m \mu_n} \langle u_m, K K^* u_n \rangle$$

$$= \frac{\mu_n}{\mu_m} \langle u_m, u_n \rangle = \begin{cases} 0, & m \neq n; \\ 1, & m = n. \end{cases}$$

From the fact that K_L and K_R have the same nonzero eigenvalues with the same multiplicity, it is clear that all eigenfunctions of K_L belonging to nonzero eigenvalues are listed in (3.91). More precisely, if v is an eigenfunction of K_L corresponding to a simple nonzero eigenvalue, some multiple of v is listed in (3.91); if v is an eigenfunction of K_L corresponding to a nonzero eigenvalue of multiplicity k, then v is a linear combination of k listed orthonormal eigenfunctions belonging to this eigenvalue.

Conversely, if we start with the orthonormal set of all eigenfunctions $\{v_n\}$ of K_L [defined from (3.89)], then the set

$$\left\{ u_n = \frac{1}{\mu_n} K v_n \right\}$$

is an orthonormal set of eigenfunctions of K_R which includes all the eigenfunctions of K_R. Before proceeding to the solution of the inhomogeneous equation of the first kind, we need some preliminary expansion theorems.

Theorem 1. *The necessary and sufficient condition for y to be a solution of $Ky = 0$ (that is, for y to belong to the null space N_K of K) is that $\langle y, v_n \rangle = 0$ for all n.*

Proof. If $Ky = 0$, $0 = \langle Ky, u_n \rangle = \langle y, K^* u_n \rangle = \mu_n \langle y, v_n \rangle$, so that $\langle y, v_n \rangle = 0$ for all n.

If $\langle y, v_n \rangle = 0$ for all n, we have

$$0 = \langle y, K^* K v_n \rangle = \langle K^* K y, v_n \rangle, \qquad \text{for all } n,$$

which, by the theory of symmetric H.-S. operators, implies

$$K^* K y = 0.$$

Hence $0 = \langle K^* K y, y \rangle = \langle Ky, Ky \rangle = \|Ky\|^2$, from which we infer that $Ky = 0$.

COROLLARY 1.   *The orthonormal set $\{v_n\}$ is a basis for the linear manifold $(N_K)^\perp$ (that is, for the linear manifold consisting of all vectors which are orthogonal to the null space of K).*

Proof. $(N_K)^\perp$ is a closed linear manifold, hence a Hilbert space. To show that $\{v_n\}$ is a basis for $(N_K)^\perp$, it is enough to show that each vector x, for which $\langle x, v_n \rangle = 0$ for all n, is the 0 vector. By Theorem 1 any such vector x belongs to N_K, which has only the 0 vector in common with $(N_K)^\perp$, so that the desir⟨ result follows.

COROLLARY 2.   *Each vector f in $\mathscr{L}_2$ can be uniquely decomposed as*

$$f = f_0 + \sum \langle f, v_n \rangle v_n,$$

where f_0 satisfies $Kf_0 = 0$.

Theorem 2.   *If g is in the range of K (that is, if g is of the form Kf for some f in $\mathscr{L}_2$), then*

$$g = \sum_n \langle g, u_n \rangle u_n = \sum_n \langle f, v_n \rangle \mu_n u_n.$$

Proof.   From Corollary 2 we have

$$g = Kf = Kf_0 + \sum \langle f, v_n \rangle K v_n = 0 + \sum \langle f, v_n \rangle \mu_n u_n.$$

Hence g can be expanded in the set $\{u_n\}$ and by the general property of orthonormal sets we also have

$$g = \sum_n \langle g, u_n \rangle u_n.$$

The reader should have no difficulty in proving similar theorems for K^*. We list these results below.

Theorem 1A.   *The necessary and sufficient condition for y to be a solution of $K^*y = 0$ (that is, for y to belong to N_{K^*}) is that $\langle y, u_n \rangle = 0$ for all n.*

COROLLARY 1A.   *The orthonormal set $\{u_n\}$ is a basis for the linear manifold $(N_{K^*})^\perp$.*

COROLLARY 2A.   *Each vector f in $\mathscr{L}_2$ can be uniquely decomposed as*

$$f = f_0^1 + \sum \langle f, u_n \rangle u_n,$$

where f_0^1 satisfies $K^*f_0^1 = 0$.

Theorem 2A.   *If g is in the range of K^*, that is, $g = K^*f$, then*

$$g = \sum_n \langle g, v_n \rangle v_n = \sum_n \langle f, u_n \rangle \mu_n v_n.$$

Consider next the inhomogeneous equation

$$Ky = h, \tag{3.93}$$

where h is a given function in $\mathscr{L}_2$. For this equation to have a solution, h must satisfy the consistency condition

$$\langle h, z \rangle = 0, \tag{3.94}$$

for each z which is a solution of the adjoint homogeneous equation $K^*z = 0$. This requirement follows from (3.93): $\langle h, z \rangle = \langle Ky, z \rangle = \langle y, K^*z \rangle = 0$. The consistency condition is not sufficient to ensure that h is in the range of K (this difficulty occurs because the range of K is not closed, so that the alternative theorem of Chapter 2 is not applicable). We can easily determine the additional requirement that h must satisfy. If y and h are related by (3.93), we must have, for all n,

$$\langle h, u_n \rangle = \langle Ky, u_n \rangle = \langle y, K^*u_n \rangle = \mu_n \langle y, v_n \rangle.$$

By Corollary 2, this means that

$$y = y_0 + \sum \langle y, v_n \rangle v_n = y_0 + \sum \frac{\langle h, u_n \rangle}{\mu_n} v_n,$$

where y_0 satisfies $Ky_0 = 0$. By Bessel's inequality applied to y and the orthonormal set $\{v_n\}$, $\sum |\langle y, v_n \rangle|^2 < \infty$ or

$$\sum \frac{1}{\mu_n^2} |\langle h, u_n \rangle|^2 < \infty. \tag{3.95}$$

No solution of (3.93) is possible unless h satisfies the conditions (3.94) and (3.95). [Note that if the set $\{u_n\}$ is infinite, the condition (3.95) is not vacuous; in fact, in this case, $\mu_n \to 0$ and the known convergence of $\sum |\langle h, u_n \rangle|^2$ does not imply the convergence of $\sum (1/\mu_n^2) |\langle h, u_n \rangle|^2$.] We now show that conditions (3.94) and (3.95) are also sufficient for the existence of a solution to (3.93).

Theorem. *If h satisfies the conditions* (3.94) *and* (3.95), *the general solution of* (3.93) *is given by*

$$y = y_0 + \sum \frac{\langle h, u_n \rangle}{\mu_n} v_n, \tag{3.96}$$

where y_0 is the general solution of $Ky_0 = 0$.

Proof. By the assumption (3.95) the series on the right converges. Since K is continuous,

$$Ky = Ky_0 + \sum \frac{\langle h, u_n \rangle}{\mu_n} Kv_n = 0 + \sum \langle h, u_n \rangle u_n.$$

It suffices therefore to show that $\sum \langle h, u_n \rangle u_n = h$. From Corollary 2A, h can be decomposed as $h_0^1 + \sum \langle h, u_n \rangle u_n$, where h_0^1 is in N_{K^*} and the remaining sum is in $(N_{K^*})^{\perp}$. By the assumption (3.94), h satisfies $\langle h, z \rangle = 0$ for each z in N_{K^*}, so that $h_0^1 = 0$. This completes the proof.

EXAMPLE

Consider the operator K defined by

$$Ky = \int_0^x y(\xi)d\xi, \qquad 0 \le x \le 1.$$

It is easily seen that K has no eigenvalues. To apply the theory of the preceding pages, we introduce the kernel

$$k(x, \xi) = \begin{cases} 0, & 0 \le x < \xi \le 1; \\ 1, & 0 \le \xi < x \le 1, \end{cases}$$

in terms of which we can rewrite

$$Ky = \int_0^1 k(x, \xi)y(\xi)d\xi.$$

The operator K_L is generated by the kernel

$$k_L(x, \xi) = \int_0^1 \overline{k}(t, x)k(t, \xi)dt = \int_{\max(x, \xi)}^1 dt = \begin{cases} 1 - \xi, & 0 \le x < \xi; \\ 1 - x, & \xi < x \le 1. \end{cases}$$

The eigenvalue problem for K_L is

$$\mu^2 v(x) = K_L v = \int_0^x (1 - x)v(\xi)d\xi + \int_x^1 (1 - \xi)v(\xi)d\xi.$$

Differentiating twice with respect to x, we find that v satisfies the differential equation

$$\frac{d^2 v}{dx^2} + \frac{1}{\mu^2} v = 0,$$

with the boundary conditions

$$v'(0) = 0, \qquad v(1) = 0.$$

Thus, the nonzero eigenvalues of K_L are

$$\mu_n^2 = \frac{4}{(2n + 1)^2 \pi^2}; \qquad n = 0, 1, 2, \ldots,$$

and the eigenfunctions are

$$v_n(x) = \sqrt{2} \cos (2n + 1)\frac{\pi}{2}x.$$

In a similar way one finds that K_R has the same eigenvalues as K_L but the eigenfunctions are now given by

$$u_n(x) = \sqrt{2} \sin (2n + 1)\frac{\pi}{2}x.$$

Consider now the inhomogeneous equation

$$Ky = h \qquad \text{or} \qquad \int_0^x y(\xi)d\xi = h(x). \tag{3.97}$$

For a solution to exist, h must satisfy the conditions (3.94) and (3.95). Since the equations $Ky = 0$ and $K^*z = 0$ have only the trivial solution, condition (3.94) is automatically satisfied. Condition (3.95) becomes

$$\sum_{n=0}^{\infty} \frac{(2n+1)^2 \pi^2}{4} \left[\int_0^1 h(x)\sqrt{2} \sin (2n+1) \frac{\pi}{2} x \, dx \right]^2 < \infty. \tag{3.98}$$

If this condition is satisfied, the unique solution of the inhomogeneous equation can be obtained from (3.96),

$$y = \sum_{n=0}^{\infty} (2n+1)\pi \left[\int_0^1 h(x) \sin (2n+1) \frac{\pi}{2} x \, dx \right] \cos (2n+1) \frac{\pi}{2} x. \tag{3.99}$$

Direct inspection of (3.97) shows that if $h(0) = 0$ and $h(x)$ is differentiable, the unique solution is given by

$$y(x) = h'(x).$$

If we expand h in the complete orthonormal set $\{u_n\}$, we find

$$h = \sum_{n=0}^{\infty} 2 \left[\int_0^1 h(x) \sin (2n+1) \frac{\pi}{2} x \, dx \right] \sin (2n+1) \frac{\pi}{2} x.$$

Comparing with (3.99), we see that $y = h'$ if term-by-term differentiation is permitted. One can show in the theory of Fourier trigonometric series that this is possible if and only if (3.98) is satisfied, and that this in turn implies that $h(x)$ is differentiable and $h(0) = 0$.

EXERCISES

3.27 Let K be a H.-S. operator (not necessarily symmetric). By applying the expansion theorem (2), show that $\|K\| = |\mu_1|$.

3.28 Let K be a nonsymmetric H.-S. operator and consider the inhomogeneous equation

$$Ky - \lambda y = f; \qquad \lambda \text{ fixed}, \qquad \lambda \neq 0. \tag{3.100}$$

One could attempt to solve this equation by considering the eigenfunctions and eigenvalues of K_R and K_L. Since $f + \lambda y$ must be in the range of K, we must have, by Theorem 2,

$$\lambda y + f = \sum_n \langle \lambda y + f, u_n \rangle u_n = \sum_n \langle y, v_n \rangle \mu_n u_n.$$

Unfortunately these equations do not enable us to solve for $\langle y, v_n \rangle$ or $\langle y, u_n \rangle$. It is only when $\lambda = 0$ that the eigenfunctions of K_R and K_L are useful to solve the inhomogeneous equation. To remedy this situation we must introduce the left and right iterates, not of K, but of $K - \lambda I$. Our procedure will work if we use the eigenfunctions of

$$A_R = (K - \lambda I)(K - \lambda I)^* = KK^* - \lambda K^* - \bar{\lambda} K + |\lambda|^2 I$$

and

$$A_L = (K - \lambda I)^*(K - \lambda I) = K^*K - \lambda K^* - \bar{\lambda} K + |\lambda|^2 I.$$

The difficulty with this approach is that the operators A_R and A_L are complicated and it becomes too onerous to find their eigenvalues and eigenfunctions; moreover, A_R and A_L are not completely continuous.

3.29 Another method for solving equation (3.100) is based on biorthogonal expansions. If K is a H.-S. operator, then K is completely continuous; hence if $\mu \neq 0$ is an eigenvalue of K, $\bar{\mu}$ is an eigenvalue of K^* [see Exercise 2.49(c)]. Let $\{\mu_n\}$ be the set of nonzero eigenvalues of K and let $\{\varphi_n\}$ be the corresponding eigenfunctions. The nonzero eigenvalues of K^* are given by $\{\bar{\mu}_n\}$, and the corresponding eigenfunctions will be denoted by $\{\psi_n\}$. Now let $\mu_n \neq \mu_m$ and consider

$$K\varphi_n = \mu_n\varphi_n;$$
$$K^*\psi_m = \bar{\mu}_m\psi_m.$$

From these equations we obtain

$$\langle K\varphi_n, \psi_m \rangle = \mu_n \langle \varphi_n, \psi_m \rangle;$$
$$\langle \varphi_n, K^*\psi_m \rangle = \mu_m \langle \varphi_n, \psi_m \rangle.$$

Since $\langle K\varphi_n, \psi_m \rangle = \langle \varphi_n, K^*\psi_m \rangle$, we have

$$(\mu_n - \mu_m)\langle \varphi_n, \psi_m \rangle = 0.$$

Thus if $\mu_n \neq \mu_m, \langle \varphi_n, \psi_m \rangle = 0$. If $\mu_n = \mu_m$, we can choose the eigenfunctions so that $\langle \varphi_n, \psi_n \rangle = 1$. The set $\{\varphi_n, \psi_m\}$ is said to be a *biorthogonal* (or more precisely biorthonormal) set, because it satisfies

$$\langle \varphi_n, \psi_m \rangle = \begin{cases} 0, & n \neq m; \\ 1, & n = m. \end{cases}$$

Now consider (3.100) and take the inner product with respect to ψ_n to obtain

$$\langle f, \psi_n \rangle = \langle Ky, \psi_n \rangle - \lambda \langle y, \psi_n \rangle = \langle y, K^*\psi_n \rangle - \lambda \langle y, \psi_n \rangle$$
$$= \langle y, \bar{\mu}_n\psi_n \rangle - \lambda \langle y, \psi_n \rangle = (\mu_n - \lambda)\langle y, \psi_n \rangle.$$

If $\lambda \neq \mu_n$, we have

$$\langle y, \psi_n \rangle = \frac{\langle f, \psi_n \rangle}{\mu_n - \lambda}.$$

Now suppose that the set $\{\varphi_n\}$ is a basis (that is, each function in $\mathcal{L}_2$ has a unique expansion in $\{\varphi_n\}$). We can then set

$$y = \sum_n c_n \varphi_n,$$

and taking the inner product with respect to ψ_k, we find

$$\langle y, \psi_k \rangle = \sum_n c_n \langle \varphi_n, \psi_k \rangle = c_k,$$

so that

$$y = \sum_k \frac{\langle f, \psi_k \rangle}{\mu_k - \lambda} \varphi_k. \tag{3.101}$$

The solution (3.101) is predicated on the fact that the set $\{\varphi_k\}$ forms a basis. Unfortunately the simple example preceding these exercises shows that this is not necessarily the case (in fact the set may be empty!).

SUGGESTED READINGS FOR CHAPTER 3

The letters E, I, and A indicate elementary, intermediate, and advanced books, respectively.

Integral Equations

(I)   Mikhlin, S. G., *Integral Equations*, Pergamon, Oxford, 1957.
(I)   Riesz, F., and B. Sz-Nagy, *Functional Analysis*, Ungar, New York, 1955
(I)   Smithies, F., *Integral Equations*, Cambridge University Press, Cambridge, 1958.
(I)   Tricomi, F. G., *Integral Equations*, Interscience, New York, 1957.

Approximation Methods

(I)   Kantorovich, L. V., and V. I. Krylov, *Approximate Methods of Analysis*, Interscience, New York, 1958.
(I)   Mikhlin, S. G., *Variational Methods in Mathematical Physics*, Pergamon, Oxford, 1964.

Chapter 4

SPECTRAL THEORY OF SECOND-ORDER DIFFERENTIAL OPERATORS

4.1 INTRODUCTION

The main purpose of this chapter is the study of the two principal methods for solving boundary value problems for ordinary differential equations. These methods are based on the Green's function and on an expansion in eigenfunctions. We first deal with operators whose spectrum is discrete; in this case the eigenfunction expansion is a series expansion and we show how the Green's function can be expressed in a series of eigenfunctions and how, conversely, the eigenfunctions can be generated from a knowledge of the Green's function. If the spectrum is continuous, an integral expansion over a continuous parameter plays the role of the eigenfunction expansion, but our results carry over with appropriate modifications.

EXAMPLE

Consider the inhomogeneous system

$$-\frac{d^2u}{dx^2} - \lambda u = f(x), \qquad 0 < x < l; \qquad u(0) = 0, \quad u(l) = 0, \qquad (4.1)$$

where λ is a given complex number and $f(x)$ is a given complex-valued function such that $\int_0^l |f|^2 \, dx < \infty$. The related eigenvalue problem is

$$-\frac{d^2\varphi}{dx^2} = \lambda\varphi, \qquad 0 < x < l; \qquad \varphi(0) = 0, \quad \varphi(l) = 0. \qquad (4.2)$$

259

Nontrivial solutions of (4.2) can be obtained if and only if λ is one of the eigenvalues

$$\lambda_n = \frac{n^2\pi^2}{l^2}; \qquad n = 1, 2, 3, \ldots.$$

The corresponding normalized eigenfunctions are

$$\varphi_n(x) = \sqrt{\frac{2}{l}} \sin \frac{n\pi x}{l}.$$

As was shown both in Chapter 2 and in Chapter 3 (Theorem 5, Section 3.3), these eigenfunctions form a complete orthonormal set. This set is particularly suitable for solving system (4.1). Since the set $\{\varphi_n\}$ is complete, we may write

$$f(x) = \sum_{n=1}^{\infty} f_n\varphi_n(x); \qquad f_n = \langle f, \varphi_n \rangle = \sqrt{\frac{2}{l}} \int_0^l f(x) \sin \frac{n\pi x}{l}\, dx$$

and

$$u(x) = \sum_{n=1}^{\infty} u_n\varphi_n(x); \qquad u_n = \langle u, \varphi_n \rangle = \sqrt{\frac{2}{l}} \int_0^l u(x) \sin \frac{n\pi x}{l}\, dx.$$

A priori, all we know is that these series converge in the mean-square sense; that is,

$$\lim_{n \to \infty} \left\| f - \sum_{k=1}^{n} f_k\varphi_k \right\| = \lim_{n \to \infty} \left[\int_0^l \left| f(x) - \sum_{k=1}^{n} f_k\varphi_k(x) \right|^2 dx \right]^{1/2} = 0.$$

We proceed to calculate u_n; multiply the differential equation in (4.1) by $\varphi_n(x)$ and integrate from 0 to l, so that

$$-\sqrt{\frac{2}{l}} \int_0^l u'' \sin \frac{n\pi x}{l}\, dx - \lambda u_n = f_n,$$

or, after integrating by parts and using the boundary conditions on u,

$$\left(\frac{n^2\pi^2}{l^2} - \lambda \right) u_n = f_n; \qquad n = 1, 2, \ldots. \tag{4.3}$$

If λ is not equal to an eigenvalue of (4.2), that is, if $\lambda \neq \pi^2/l^2, 4\pi^2/l^2, 9\pi^2/l^2, \ldots$,

$$u_n = \frac{f_n}{(n^2\pi^2/l^2) - \lambda}$$

and

$$u(x) = \sum_{n=1}^{\infty} \frac{f_n\varphi_n(x)}{(n^2\pi^2/l^2) - \lambda} = \sum_{n=1}^{\infty} \frac{2/l}{(n^2\pi^2/l^2) - \lambda} \sin \frac{n\pi x}{l} \left[\int_0^l f(x) \sin \frac{n\pi x}{l}\, dx \right]. \tag{4.4}$$

The expression (4.4) can be shown to represent the one and only solution of (4.1), if λ is not an eigenvalue of (4.2). Since this solution depends parametrically on the complex number λ, it is better denoted by $u(x, \lambda)$. For fixed x, $u(x, \lambda)$ is an analytic function of λ except for simple poles at $\lambda = \lambda_n$, where the corresponding residue is $-f_n\varphi_n(x)$, By Cauchy's theorem, the integral of $u(x, \lambda)$ along an infinitely large circle in the complex plane will yield $2\pi i$ multiplied by the sum of the residues; that is,

$$\frac{1}{2\pi i} \oint u(x, \lambda)d\lambda = - \sum_{n=1}^{\infty} f_n\varphi_n(x) = -f(x). \tag{4.5}$$

We now turn to the Green's function $g(x \mid \xi; \lambda)$, which satisfies the system

$$-\frac{d^2g}{dx^2} - \lambda g = \delta(x - \xi), \qquad 0 < x, \xi < l; \qquad g(0 \mid \xi; \lambda) = g(l \mid \xi; \lambda) = 0. \tag{4.6}$$

This system can be considered as a particular case of (4.1), with $f(x) = \delta(x - \xi)$. Since

$$\int_0^l \delta(x - \xi) \sin \frac{n\pi x}{l} \, dx = \sin \frac{n\pi \xi}{l},$$

we have

$$\delta(x - \xi) = \sum_{n=1}^{\infty} \frac{2}{l} \sin \frac{n\pi x}{l} \sin \frac{n\pi \xi}{l} = \sum_{n=1}^{\infty} \varphi_n(x)\varphi_n(\xi) \tag{4.7}$$

and

$$g(x \mid \xi; \lambda) = \sum_{n=1}^{\infty} \frac{(2/l) \sin (n\pi x/l) \sin (n\pi \xi/l)}{(n^2\pi^2/l^2) - \lambda} = \sum_{n=1}^{\infty} \frac{\varphi_n(x)\varphi_n(\xi)}{\lambda_n - \lambda}. \tag{4.8}$$

The expansion (4.8) is known as the *bilinear series* for the Green's function. Thus, whenever the parameter λ in (4.6) is *not* one of the eigenvalues of (4.2), we can express the Green's function $g(x \mid \xi; \lambda)$ as the series (4.8). Moreover, if we apply (4.5) to g, we find the important relation

$$\frac{1}{2\pi i} \oint g(x \mid \xi; \lambda)d\lambda = - \sum_{n=1}^{\infty} \frac{2}{l} \sin \frac{n\pi x}{l} \sin \frac{n\pi \xi}{l} = -\delta(x - \xi). \tag{4.9}$$

It is usual to regard (4.8) as a formula to calculate $g(x \mid \xi; \lambda)$ in terms of the eigenfunctions and eigenvalues of (4.2) which have somehow been previously determined.

In practice, another point of view may prove more useful. By the methods of Chapter 1, we can find a simple expression for $g(x \mid \xi; \lambda)$ directly from (4.6); it is natural to ask if the eigenfunctions and eigenvalues can be generated from this simple form for g. According to (4.9) this goal can be achieved by integrating g along a large circle in the complex λ plane, so as to ultimately enclose all the singularities of g as a function of λ.

We first construct $g(x\,|\,\xi;\lambda)$ by the methods of Chapter 1. From (4.6) we have

$$g(x\,|\,\xi;\lambda) = \begin{cases} A \sin \sqrt{\lambda}(l-x), & \xi < x < l; \\ B \sin \sqrt{\lambda}\, x, & 0 < x < \xi, \end{cases}$$

where $\sqrt{\lambda}$ could stand for either of the two square roots of the complex number λ. For definiteness we choose $\sqrt{\lambda}$ unambiguously as follows. Let $\lambda = |\lambda|e^{i\theta}$, where $0 \leq \theta < 2\pi$; then

$$\sqrt{\lambda} = |\lambda|^{1/2}e^{i\theta/2},$$

where $|\lambda|^{1/2}$ stands for the *positive* square root of the positive number $|\lambda|$ (of course, if $\lambda = 0$, $\sqrt{\lambda} = 0$). Our choice of $\sqrt{\lambda}$ guarantees that this quantity always has a nonnegative imaginary part. In fact, $\sqrt{\lambda}$ has a positive imaginary part, unless λ belongs to $[0, \infty)$;† if λ belongs to $[0, \infty)$, $\sqrt{\lambda}$ is real and nonnegative. We observe that $\sqrt{\lambda}$ is continuous and analytic in the entire λ plane *except on the positive real axis* $[0, \infty)$. In fact, directly above and on the positive real axis we have $\sqrt{\lambda} = |\lambda|^{1/2}$, whereas directly below the positive real axis (where $\theta = 2\pi -$), we have $\sqrt{\lambda} = -|\lambda|^{1/2}$. In the language of complex variables we have chosen the *branch cut* for $\sqrt{\lambda}$ along the positive real axis.

Returning to the calculation of $g(x\,|\,\xi;\lambda)$, we require that g be continuous at $x = \xi$ and that the jump condition $dg/dx|_{x=\xi+} - dg/dx|_{x=\xi-} = -1$ be satisfied. This leads to

$$g(x\,|\,\xi;\lambda) = \frac{1}{\sqrt{\lambda}\sin\sqrt{\lambda}\,l}\,[\sin\sqrt{\lambda}\,x_< \sin\sqrt{\lambda}\,(l-x_>)]; \qquad 0 < x, \xi < l,$$

$$(4.10)$$

where $x_<$ stands for the lesser of x and ξ, $x_>$ for the greater of x and ξ. In the case $\lambda = 0$, the solutions of the homogeneous equation are no longer sines and cosines, and a separate calculation is required which yields

$$g(x\,|\,\xi; 0) = \frac{1}{l}\,[x_<(l-x_>)].\qquad (4.11)$$

It is worth observing that

$$\lim_{\lambda\to 0} g(x\,|\,\xi;\lambda) = g(x\,|\,\xi; 0),$$

† The symbol $[0, \infty)$ stands for the set of real, nonnegative numbers.

so that $g(x \mid \xi; \lambda)$ is continuous at $\lambda = 0$. As a function of λ, the expression (4.10) has singularities when $\lambda = n^2\pi^2/l^2$, $n = 1, 2, 3, \ldots$. In this case our definition of the square root yields $\sqrt{\lambda} = n\pi/l$ and *not* $-n\pi/l$, so that g has simple poles at each of the points $\lambda = n^2\pi^2/l^2$. In spite of appearances, g does *not* have a branch cut on the positive real axis. In fact, directly above and on the positive real axis, we have

$$g(x \mid \xi; \lambda) = [\sin |\lambda|^{1/2}x_< \sin |\lambda|^{1/2}(l - x_>)] \frac{1}{|\lambda|^{1/2} \sin |\lambda|^{1/2}l},$$

whereas directly below the real axis

$$g(x \mid \xi; \lambda) = [\sin (-|\lambda|^{1/2}x_<) \sin (-|\lambda|^{1/2})(l - x_>)] \frac{1}{(-|\lambda|^{1/2}) \sin (-|\lambda|^{1/2}l)},$$

and since the sine is an odd function, these two expressions are identical.

Thus the only singularities of g as a function of λ occur where λ is an eigenvalue of (4.2). Of course these are just the values of λ for which we could have predicted that g could not be constructed. Our remaining task is to construct the eigenfunctions of (4.2) by integrating (4.10) along a large circle in the complex λ plane. The residue of g at $\lambda = n^2\pi^2/l^2$ is

$$\frac{\sin (n\pi/l)x_< \sin (n\pi/l)(l - x_>)}{n\pi/l} \left\{ \frac{1}{[(d/d\lambda) \sin \sqrt{\lambda} \, l]} \right\}_{\lambda = n^2\pi^2/l^2}$$

$$= \left[\sin \frac{n\pi}{l} x_< \sin \frac{n\pi}{l} (l - x_>) \right] \left[\frac{2}{l \cos n\pi} \right].$$

Now

$$\sin \frac{n\pi}{l} (l - x_>) = -\cos n\pi \sin \frac{n\pi}{l} x_> ,$$

so that

$$\frac{1}{2\pi i} \oint g(x \mid \xi; \lambda)d\lambda = -\frac{2}{l} \sum_{n=1}^{\infty} \sin \frac{n\pi}{l} x_< \sin \frac{n\pi}{l} x_> .$$

We observe that whether $x > \xi$ or $x < \xi$, $\sin (n\pi/l)x_< \sin (n\pi/l)x_>$ is always $\sin (n\pi/l)x \sin (n\pi/l)\xi$; hence

$$\frac{1}{2\pi i} \oint g(x \mid \xi; \lambda)d\lambda = -\delta(x - \xi) = -\frac{2}{l} \sum_{n=1}^{\infty} \sin \frac{n\pi x}{l} \sin \frac{n\pi \xi}{l}. \quad (4.12)$$

Thus we have *constructed* the normalized eigenfunctions $\sqrt{2/l} \sin (n\pi x/l)$ of (4.2) from the simple form (4.10) for $g(x \mid \xi; \lambda)$.

REMARKS. 1. The solution of (4.1) can also be written $u(x) = \int_0^l g(x \mid \xi; \lambda) f(\xi) d\xi$. If we then substitute (4.8) for g, we again obtain (4.4).

2. The system (4.1) can also be translated into an inhomogeneous integral equation with kernel $g(x \mid \xi; 0) = (1/l)[x_<(l - x_>)]$. Treating λu as an inhomogeneous term in (4.1), we have

$$u(x) = \lambda \int_0^l g(x \mid \xi; 0) u(\xi) d\xi + \int_0^l g(x \mid \xi; 0) f(\xi) d\xi$$

or

$$\int_0^l g(x \mid \xi; 0) u(\xi) d\xi = \mu u(x) + F(x), \qquad (4.13)$$

where $\mu = 1/\lambda$ and $F(x) = -(1/\lambda) \int_0^l g(x \mid \xi; 0) f(\xi) d\xi$.

Similarly, the eigenvalue problem (4.2) is equivalent to the eigen-value integral equation

$$\int_0^l g(x \mid \xi; 0) \varphi(\xi) d\xi = \mu \varphi(x). \qquad (4.14)$$

The eigenvalues of (4.14) are $\mu_n = 1/\lambda_n = l^2/n^2\pi^2$ and the normalized eigenfunctions are $\varphi_n(x) = \sqrt{2/l} \sin(n\pi x/l)$. Using (3.45) we can obtain the solution of (4.13) as an expansion

$$u(x) = -\frac{F}{\mu} + \sum_{k=1}^{\infty} \mu_k \frac{\langle F, \varphi_k \rangle}{\mu(\mu_k - \mu)} \varphi_k.$$

Since $\langle F, \varphi_k \rangle = -(1/\lambda) \mu_k f_k$, and since the set $\{\varphi_k\}$ is complete, we find

$$u(x) = -\sum_{k=1}^{\infty} \frac{\mu_k \mu}{\mu_k - \mu} f_k \varphi_k = \sum_{k=1}^{\infty} \frac{f_k}{\lambda_k - \lambda} \varphi_k,$$

which is just the same result as (4.4).

3. Let us now consider the inhomogeneous system (4.1) for a value of λ which coincides with an eigenvalue of (4.2), say $\lambda = \lambda_k = k^2\pi^2/l^2$, where k is a fixed positive integer. If (4.1) has a solution, this solution (just like any other function) can be expanded in the complete set $\{\varphi_n(x)\}$, so that the conditions (4.3) must again be satisfied, namely

$$\left(\frac{n^2\pi^2}{l^2} - \frac{k^2\pi^2}{l^2} \right) u_n = f_n; \qquad n = 1, 2, \ldots.$$

For $n \neq k$, we have $u_n = f_n/[(n^2\pi^2/l^2) - (k^2\pi^2/l^2)]$; on the other hand, unless $f_k = 0$, there is no solution for u_k, and if $f_k = 0$ then u_k is arbitrary.

Thus, if $\lambda = k^2\pi^2/l^2$, the system (4.1) has *no solution* unless the *consistency condition* $\int_0^l f(x) \sin(k\pi x/l)dx = 0$ is satisfied, in which case the general solution of (4.1) is

$$u(x) = A \sin\frac{k\pi x}{l} + \sum_{\substack{n=1 \\ n \ne k}}^{\infty} \frac{2/l}{(n^2\pi^2/l^2) - (k^2\pi^2/l^2)} \sin\frac{n\pi x}{l}\left[\int_0^l f(x) \sin\frac{n\pi x}{l}\,dx\right],$$

(4.15)

where A is an arbitrary constant.

4. Consider next the system with inhomogeneous boundary conditions;

$$-\frac{d^2v}{dx^2} - \lambda v = 0, \qquad 0 < x < l; \qquad v(0) = \alpha, v(l) = \beta, \qquad (4.16)$$

where λ, α, β are given complex numbers.

By inspection, we find

$$v(x) = \alpha \cos\sqrt{\lambda}x + \left[\frac{\beta - \alpha\cos\sqrt{\lambda}l}{\sin\sqrt{\lambda}l}\right] \sin\sqrt{\lambda}x. \qquad (4.17)$$

We can, also find the expansion of $v(x)$ in the form $\sum_{n=1}^{\infty} v_n\varphi_n(x)$. To this end multiply the differential equation in (4.16) by $\varphi_n(x)$ and integrate from 0 to l so that

$$-\int_0^l v''\varphi_n\,dx - \lambda\int_0^l v\varphi_n\,dx = 0.$$

Now

$$-\int_0^l v''\varphi_n\,dx = \int_0^l v'\varphi_n'\,dx - v'\varphi_n\Big]_0^l = \int_0^l v'\varphi_n'\,dx$$

$$= -\int_0^l v\varphi_n''\,dx + v\varphi_n'\Big]_0^l.$$

Since $-\varphi_n'' = (n^2\pi^2/l^2)\varphi_n$, and $\varphi_n' = (\sqrt{2/l})(n\pi/l)\cos(n\pi x/l)$, we find

$$v_n\left[\left(\frac{n^2\pi^2}{l^2}\right) - \lambda\right] = \sqrt{\frac{2}{l}}\left(\frac{n\pi}{l}\right)(\alpha - \beta\cos n\pi); \qquad n = 1, 2, \ldots.$$

If λ is not an eigenvalue of (4.2), we obtain

$$v(x) = \sum_{n=1}^{\infty} v_n\varphi_n(x) = \frac{2}{l}\sum_{n=1}^{\infty}\left(\frac{n\pi}{l}\right)\frac{(\alpha - \beta\cos n\pi)}{(n^2\pi^2/l^2) - \lambda}\sin\frac{n\pi x}{l}. \qquad (4.18)$$

The series in (4.18) is merely the expansion of (4.17) in a Fourier sine series. Consider, for instance, the simple case when $\lambda = 0$, $\alpha = 1$,

$\beta = 1$. The solution of (4.16) is the function $v(x) \equiv 1$, $0 \leq x \leq l$, whereas (4.18) reduces to

$$\sum_{n \text{ odd}} \frac{4}{n\pi} \sin \frac{n\pi x}{l},$$

which is the well-known expansion of the function 1 in a Fourier sine series.

Although the series (4.18) converges in the mean to the function $v(x)$ given by (4.17), it will converge pointwise to $v(x)$ only in the interior of the interval $(0, l)$. In fact, the series vanishes at $x = 0$ and $x = l$, whereas the solution of (4.16) assumes the values α and β, respectively. The series therefore cannot converge uniformly in $0 \leq x \leq l$, for a uniformly convergent series of continuous functions must converge to a continuous function, and our series is discontinuous at $x = 0$ and l.

A related difficulty with the series (4.18) is its slow convergence. We observe that the coefficients are of order $1/n$ for large n; series (4.4), on the other hand, has coefficients which approach 0 faster than $1/n^2$ (these coefficients are essentially f_n/n^2 with $f_n \to 0$). These remarks indicate that (4.18) is of dubious computational value.

5. The following argument is often used to obtain the eigenfunction expansion (4.4). Substitute $u = \sum_{n=1}^{\infty} u_n \varphi_n$ and $f = \sum_{n=1}^{\infty} f_n \varphi_n$ in (4.1) and differentiate term by term to obtain

$$-\sum u_n \varphi_n'' - \lambda \sum u_n \varphi_n = \sum f_n \varphi_n.$$

Now $-\varphi_n'' = \lambda_n \varphi_n$, so that by equating coefficients of φ_n, we have

$$u_n = \frac{f_n}{\lambda_n - \lambda},$$

which agrees with (4.4).

Flushed with success, we try the same argument on (4.16); this yields

$$-\sum v_n \varphi_n'' - \lambda \sum v_n \varphi_n = 0$$

or

$$\sum (\lambda_n - \lambda) v_n \varphi_n = 0,$$

and, consequently $v_n = 0$.

This last result is false, as evidenced by the correct expression (4.18). The explanation of this apparent paradox is that the series for v *cannot* be differentiated term by term (unless we take into account the discontinuous behavior at the end points, for instance, by using the theory of generalized solutions of differential equations). In solving (4.1), the term-by-term differentiation is permissible, because u satisfies the same boundary conditions as φ_n. To be safe, we shall always obtain the eigenfunction expansions by multiplying the differential equation by φ_n and integrating by parts.

EXERCISES

4.1 (a) Consider (4.16) when $\lambda = \lambda_k = k^2\pi^2/l^2$. What consistency condition must be satisfied for (4.16) to have a solution? If this condition is satisfied, find both the elementary form of the solution and the eigenfunction expansion.

(b) By superposition of (4.1) and (4.16) we can find the solution of

$$-w'' - \lambda w = f(x), \qquad 0 < x < l; \qquad w(0) = \alpha, \quad w(l) = \beta,$$

when $\lambda \neq \lambda_k$. If $\lambda = \lambda_k$, show that the consistency condition becomes

$$\frac{k\pi}{l}[\alpha - (-1)^k\beta] + \int_0^l f(x) \sin\frac{k\pi x}{l}\,dx = 0.$$

4.2 Construct the Green's function $g(x\,|\,\xi;\lambda)$ which satisfies

$$-\frac{d^2g}{dx^2} - \lambda g = \delta(x - \xi), \qquad 0 < x, \xi < l;$$

$$\frac{dg}{dx}(0\,|\,\xi;\lambda) = \frac{dg}{dx}(l\,|\,\xi;\lambda) = 0.$$

Show that g has simple poles at $\lambda = n^2\pi^2/l^2$ with $n = 0, 1, 2, \ldots$. By integrating g along a large circle in the λ plane, show that

$$\delta(x - \xi) = \frac{1}{l} + \sum_{n=1}^{\infty}\frac{2}{l}\cos\frac{n\pi x}{l}\cos\frac{n\pi \xi}{l}. \tag{4.19}$$

Obtain the solution of

$$-\frac{d^2u}{dx^2} - \lambda u = f(x), \qquad 0 < x, \xi < l; \qquad u'(0) = 0, \quad u'(l) = 0,$$

as an eigenfunction expansion. Find the consistency condition if $\lambda = \lambda_k$. What is the bilinear series for $g(x\,|\,\xi;\lambda)$? Discuss the equation with inhomogeneous boundary conditions.

4.3 Consider the eigenvalue problem

$$-\frac{d^2\varphi}{dx^2} - \lambda\varphi = 0, \qquad 0 < x < l; \qquad \varphi(0) = \varphi(l), \quad \varphi'(0) = \varphi'(l).$$

Show that the eigenvalues are

$$\lambda_n = \frac{4n^2\pi^2}{l^2}; \qquad n = 0, 1, 2, \ldots,$$

and that each eigenvalue except $\lambda = 0$ is degenerate. Show that the normalized eigenfunctions can be written either as

$$\varphi_0(x) = \sqrt{\frac{1}{l}}, \qquad \varphi_n^{(1)}(x) = \sqrt{\frac{2}{l}} \sin \frac{2n\pi x}{l}, \qquad \varphi_n^{(2)}(x) = \sqrt{\frac{2}{l}} \cos \frac{2n\pi x}{l}$$

or

$$\psi_0(x) = \sqrt{\frac{1}{l}}, \quad \psi_n^{(1)}(x) = \sqrt{\frac{1}{l}} \exp\left(\frac{i2n\pi x}{l}\right), \quad \psi_n^{(2)}(x) = \sqrt{\frac{1}{l}} \exp\left(-\frac{i2n\pi x}{l}\right).$$

Construct $g(x\,|\,\xi;\lambda)$ directly from the differential equation which it satisfies and, by integrating g along a large circle in the complex plane, obtain the alternative forms

$$\delta(x - \xi) = \frac{1}{l} + \sum_{n=1}^{\infty} \frac{2}{l}\left(\sin \frac{2n\pi x}{l} \sin \frac{2n\pi\xi}{l} + \cos \frac{2n\pi x}{l} \cos \frac{2n\pi\xi}{l}\right) \qquad (4.20a)$$

and

$$\delta(x - \xi) = \sum_{n=-\infty}^{\infty} \frac{1}{l} \exp\left(\frac{i2n\pi x}{l}\right) \exp\left(-\frac{i2n\pi\xi}{l}\right). \qquad (4.20b)$$

If we set $l = 2$ in (4.20a), we obtain (1.22a).

4.2 THE REGULAR BOUNDARY VALUE PROBLEM

Consider the second-order differential operators L and L_λ defined, respectively, by

$$L = -\frac{d}{dx}\left[p(x)\frac{d}{dx}\right] + q(x) \qquad (4.21)$$

and

$$L_\lambda = -\frac{d}{dx}\left[p(x)\frac{d}{dx}\right] + q(x) - \lambda s(x). \qquad (4.22)$$

We shall investigate the following differential equations involving L_λ:

$$L_\lambda\varphi = L\varphi - \lambda s(x)\varphi = 0 \qquad \text{or} \qquad -(p\varphi')' + q\varphi - \lambda s\varphi = 0; \qquad (4.23)$$

$$L_\lambda u = Lu - \lambda s(x)u = f(x) \qquad \text{or} \qquad -(pu')' + qu - \lambda su = f; \qquad (4.24)$$

$$L_\lambda g = Lg - \lambda s(x)g = \delta(x - \xi) \qquad \text{or} \qquad -(pg')' + qg - \lambda sg = \delta(x - \xi). \qquad (4.25)$$

The parameter λ is an arbitrary complex number; $p(x)$, $p'(x)$, $q(x)$, $s(x)$ are *real-valued* continuous functions in $a < x < b$, and $p(x)$ and $s(x)$ are *positive* in $a < x < b$.

If the interval (a, b) is finite and the conditions on p, p', q, s hold in the closed interval $a \le x \le b$, the problem is said to be *regular*; otherwise the problem is *singular*. For regular problems we shall associate certain boundary conditions with the equations (4.23) to (4.25). These will consist of two un-mixed conditions (one condition for the end point $x = a$, another for $x = b$), namely,

$$B_a y = \alpha_1 y(a) + \alpha_2 y'(a) = 0;$$
$$B_b y = \beta_1 y(b) + \beta_2 y'(b) = 0, \tag{4.26}$$

where α_1, α_2, β_1, β_2 are *real* numbers and $|\alpha_1| + |\alpha_2| \ne 0$, $|\beta_1| + |\beta_2| \ne 0$. We observe that if $y(x)$ satisfies (4.26), so does $\bar{y}(x)$. The question of boundary conditions for the singular case will be discussed in succeeding sections.

Many aspects of (4.23) to (4.25) subject to the conditions (4.26) were examined in Chapter 1 for the case when λ, f, φ, u, and g were real; we now extend these ideas to complex values of these quantities. We shall therefore employ the inner product appropriate for complex-valued functions $u(x)$, $v(x)$ over the basic interval (a, b):

$$\langle u, v \rangle = \int_a^b u \bar{v} \, dx.$$

The principal properties of this inner product are given in (2.13) to (2.16).

Before studying any differential equations, let us observe some properties of the operator L which follow directly from the definition (4.21). In the following, the complex-valued functions u and v have continuous second derivatives, so that Lu and Lv are continuous functions in $a \le x \le b$.

(a) For any u,

$$L\bar{u} = \overline{Lu}. \tag{4.27}$$

This property depends on the fact that p and q are real, so that it does not hold for L_λ unless λ is a real number.

(b) For any u and v,

$$\bar{v} Lu - u \overline{Lv} = \frac{d}{dx} [p(u\bar{v}' - \bar{v}u')]. \tag{4.28a}$$

Since $u\bar{v}' - \bar{v}u'$ is the Wronskian of u and $\bar{v}$ [see (1.46)], we may write

$$\bar{v} Lu - u \overline{Lv} = \frac{d}{dx} [p(x)W(u, \bar{v}; x)]. \tag{4.28b}$$

(c) From (4.28b), it follows that

$$\int_a^b (\bar{v} Lu - u \overline{Lv}) dx = p(b)W(u, \bar{v}; b) - p(a)W(u, \bar{v}; a) \tag{4.29a}$$

or

$$\langle Lu, v \rangle - \langle u, Lv \rangle = p(b)W(u, \bar{v}; b) - p(a)W(u, \bar{v}; a). \tag{4.29b}$$

(d) If u and v satisfy the boundary conditions (4.26), then $W(u, \bar{v}; a)$ and $W(u, \bar{v}; b)$ both vanish, so that

$$\langle Lu, v \rangle = \langle u, Lv \rangle \qquad (4.30)$$

and

$$\langle Lu, u \rangle \text{ is real.} \qquad (4.31)$$

Thus if we consider L as an operator whose domain D_L consists of functions having a continuous second derivative and satisfying (4.26), then L is symmetric.

We now investigate some of the properties of the eigenvalue problem (4.23), namely,

$$L\varphi - \lambda s\varphi = 0, \qquad a < x < b; \qquad B_a(\varphi) = 0, \quad B_b(\varphi) = 0. \qquad (4.32)$$

1. *The Eigenvalues Are Real.* From (4.32), we have

$$\langle L\varphi, \varphi \rangle = \lambda \langle s\varphi, \varphi \rangle = \lambda \int_a^b s|\varphi|^2 \, dx.$$

Since φ is an eigenfunction $\int_a^b |\varphi|^2 \, dx > 0$, so that, because s is positive, $\int_a^b s|\varphi|^2 \, dx > 0$. The quantity $\langle L\varphi, \varphi \rangle$ is real by (4.31); hence λ is real.

2. *Eigenfunctions Corresponding to Different Eigenvalues Are Orthogonal with Weight $s(x)$.* Let φ and ψ satisfy (4.32) with respective parameters λ, μ. Then

$$\langle L\varphi, \psi \rangle = \langle \lambda s\varphi, \psi \rangle = \lambda \int_a^b s\varphi\bar{\psi} \, dx$$

and

$$\langle \varphi, L\psi \rangle = \langle \varphi, \mu s\psi \rangle = \bar{\mu} \int_a^b s\varphi\bar{\psi} \, dx.$$

By (4.30), $\langle \varphi, L\psi \rangle = \langle L\varphi, \psi \rangle$; hence

$$(\lambda - \bar{\mu}) \int_a^b s\varphi\bar{\psi} \, dx = 0.$$

Since μ must be real, $\lambda \neq \mu$ implies $\lambda \neq \bar{\mu}$; hence

$$\int_a^b s\varphi\bar{\psi} \, dx = 0, \qquad (4.33)$$

so that φ and ψ are orthogonal with weight $s(x)$. We can state this another way by saying that $\sqrt{s}\varphi$ and $\sqrt{s}\psi$ are orthogonal.

3. *There Can Be at Most a Denumerable Number of Eigenvalues.* Otherwise we would have a corresponding nondenumerable set of orthogonal functions $\sqrt{s}\varphi$, which is impossible in a separable Hilbert space (see Chapter 2). Since

the set of real numbers is not denumerable, there must exist a real λ_0 which is *not* an eigenvalue. In fact, we shall be able to show much more by appealing to the theory of integral quations.

We now turn our attention to the Green's function $g(x\,|\,\xi;\lambda)$, which satisfies

$$Lg - \lambda sg = \delta(x - \xi), \quad a < x, \xi < b; \quad B_a(g) = 0, \quad B_b(g) = 0. \tag{4.34}$$

To construct g we need as building blocks two solutions of the homogeneous equation which satisfy the boundary condition at a and the boundary condition at b, respectively. Each of these solutions is determined only to a multiplicative constant; we choose the solutions so that they will be analytic functions of λ in the whole λ plane, which in turn will help us in determining the singularities of g as a function of λ.

Let $w(x, \lambda)$ be the unique solution of the homogeneous equation $Lw - \lambda sw = 0$ which satisfies the initial conditions

$$w(a, \lambda) = -\alpha_2, \qquad \frac{dw}{dx}(a, \lambda) = \alpha_1,$$

and let $z(x, \lambda)$ be the unique solution of the same equation satisfying

$$z(b, \lambda) = -\beta_2, \qquad \frac{dz}{dx}(b, \lambda) = \beta_1.$$

Both w and z are analytic functions of λ (see Exercise 4.5). Moreover,

$$B_a(w) = \alpha_1 w(a, \lambda) + \alpha_2 w'(a, \lambda) = 0$$

and

$$B_b(z) = \beta_1 z(b, \lambda) + \beta_2 z'(b, \lambda) = 0,$$

so that w satisfies the boundary condition at $x = a$, and z the one at $x = b$. We observe for further reference that w and z are real for real λ. Thus we have

$$g = Aw(x_<, \lambda)z(x_>, \lambda),$$

and A can be calculated from the jump condition

$$\left.\frac{dg}{dx}\right|_{\xi-}^{\xi+} = -\frac{1}{p(\xi)},$$

which reduces to

$$A[w(\xi, \lambda)z'(\xi, \lambda) - z(\xi, \lambda)w'(\xi, \lambda)] = -\frac{1}{p(\xi)}.$$

The quantity in brackets is the Wronskian of w and z; now, by (1.47), this Wronskian is of the form $C/p(\xi)$, where C is independent of ξ, so that C can depend only on λ. Therefore,

$$g(x\,|\,\xi;\lambda) = -\frac{w(x_<,\lambda)z(x_>,\lambda)}{C(\lambda)}, \qquad (4.35)$$

where $C(\lambda)$ is defined unambiguously from

$$W[w(x,\lambda),z(x,\lambda);x] = \frac{C(\lambda)}{p(x)}.$$

Since w and z are analytic functions of λ, so are dw/dx and dz/dx and hence W and $C(\lambda)$. Therefore the only singularities of g occur at the zeros of $C(\lambda)$. We shall take advantage of this fact later to generate the eigenfunctions of (4.32). We note that g is real when λ is real and that for all λ,

$$g(x\,|\,\xi;\lambda) = g(\xi\,|\,x;\lambda). \qquad (4.36)$$

Let us now return to the eigenvalue problem. We know there exists a real number, say θ, which is not an eigenvalue of (4.32). We can therefore translate the eigenvalue problem into

$$\varphi(x) = (\lambda - \theta)\int_a^b g(x\,|\,\xi;\theta)s(\xi)\varphi(\xi)d\xi.$$

Setting

$$\mu = \frac{1}{\lambda - \theta}, \qquad k(x,\xi) = \sqrt{s(x)}g(x\,|\,\xi;\theta)\sqrt{s(\xi)}, \qquad \psi(x) = \sqrt{s(x)}\varphi(x),$$

we find that the preceding equation becomes

$$\mu\psi = \int_a^b k(x,\xi)\psi(\xi)d\xi. \qquad (4.37)$$

The arguments used in Section 3.3, Theorem 6, show that k is a real symmetric H.-S. kernel for which $\mu = 0$ is not an eigenvalue. The set of eigenfunctions $\psi_i(x) = \sqrt{s}\,\varphi_i$ is therefore a complete orthonormal set (in different language; the set φ_i is a complete orthonormal set with weight s). From the theory of integral equations we know that $\lim_{n\to\infty}|\mu_n| = 0$, so that we must have

$$\lim_{n\to\infty}|\lambda_n| = \infty.$$

In many cases we can assert that all eigenvalues λ_n are positive; Exercise 4.7 shows that there are at most a finite number of negative eigenvalues in the general case. Thus we always have $\lim_{n\to\infty}\lambda_n = +\infty$. The inhomogeneous system

$$Lu - \lambda su = f(x); \qquad a < x < b; \qquad B_a(u) = 0, \quad B_b(u) = 0 \qquad (4.38)$$

can be solved in two different ways if λ is not an eigenvalue of (4.32). By using $g(x \,|\, \xi; \lambda)$ we have

$$u(x) = \int_a^b g(x \,|\, \xi; \lambda) f(\xi) d\xi.$$

We can also find the expansion of u in the eigenfunctions $\{\varphi_n\}$. Let

$$u = \sum_n u_n \varphi_n; \qquad (4.39)$$

then

$$\langle u, s\varphi_k \rangle = \sum_n u_n \langle \varphi_n, s\varphi_k \rangle = u_k,$$

so that

$$u_k = \langle u, s\varphi_k \rangle = \int_a^b s(x) u(x) \bar\varphi_k(x) dx. \qquad (4.40)$$

To obtain u_n we take the inner product of (4.38) with φ_n; this yields

$$\langle Lu, \varphi_n \rangle - \lambda \langle su, \varphi_n \rangle = \langle f, \varphi_n \rangle,$$

or, since $\langle Lu, \varphi_n \rangle = \langle u, L\varphi_n \rangle = \lambda_n \langle su, \varphi_n \rangle$,

$$u_n(\lambda_n - \lambda) = \langle f, \varphi_n \rangle = \int_a^b f(x) \bar\varphi_n(x) dx.$$

If $\lambda \neq \lambda_n$, we have

$$u_n = \frac{\langle f, \varphi_n \rangle}{\lambda_n - \lambda}$$

and

$$u(x) = \sum_n \frac{\langle f, \varphi_n \rangle}{\lambda_n - \lambda} \varphi_n(x), \qquad (4.41)$$

which is the one and only solution of (4.38). In the case $f(x) = \delta(x - \xi)$, $u(x)$ is $g(x \,|\, \xi; \lambda)$, so that

$$g(x \,|\, \xi; \lambda) = \sum_n \frac{\langle \delta(x - \xi), \varphi_n \rangle}{\lambda_n - \lambda} \varphi_n(x).$$

Now

$$\langle \delta(x - \xi), \varphi_n \rangle = \int_a^b \delta(x - \xi) \bar\varphi_n(x) dx = \bar\varphi_n(\xi)$$

and

$$g(x \,|\, \xi; \lambda) = \sum_n \frac{\varphi_n(x) \bar\varphi_n(\xi)}{\lambda_n - \lambda}, \qquad (4.42)$$

which is the bilinear series for $g(x \,|\, \xi; \lambda)$. From (4.39) and (4.40) we also have

$$\frac{\delta(x - \xi)}{s(x)} = \sum_n \varphi_n(x) \bar\varphi_n(\xi). \qquad (4.43)$$

By integrating (4.42) around a large circle in the complex plane, we find

$$\frac{1}{2\pi i} \oint g(x \,|\, \xi; \lambda) d\lambda = - \sum_n \varphi_n(x) \bar{\varphi}_n(\xi) = - \frac{\delta(x - \xi)}{s(x)}. \qquad (4.44)$$

We should therefore be able to generate explicit expressions for the eigenfunctions by integrating (4.35) along a large circle in the λ plane. The zeros of $C(\lambda)$ are located at isolated points $\lambda_1, \ldots, \lambda_n, \ldots$ on the real axis (see Exercise 4.6). At any such point λ_n, the Wronskian of w and z vanishes, so that $w(x, \lambda_n)$ and $z(x, \lambda_n)$ are dependent solutions. The initial conditions on w and z ensure that neither of these functions vanishes identically in x; since $w(x, \lambda_n)$ and $z(x, \lambda_n)$ are real functions, there must exist a real constant $k_n \neq 0$ such that

$$w(x, \lambda_n) = k_n z(x, \lambda_n). \qquad (4.45)$$

The function $w(x, \lambda_n)$ is therefore a nontrivial function satisfying both the boundary conditions in (4.32); it is therefore clear that the eigenvalues of (4.32) are just these numbers $\lambda_1, \ldots, \lambda_n, \ldots$ and every eigenfunction associated with λ_n is a constant multiple of the real eigenfunction $w(x, \lambda_n)$. Thus the eigenvalue λ_n is nondegenerate. (If we had considered the more general case of mixed boundary conditions, the possibility of degenerate eigenvalues arises.)

Since $w(x, \lambda)$, $z(x, \lambda)$, and $C(\lambda)$ are entire functions of λ (that is, w, z, and C have no singularities in the finite portion of the λ plane), the only singularities of g are at the zeros of $C(\lambda)$. From (4.35) we see that the residue of g at $\lambda = \lambda_n$ is

$$- \frac{w(x_<, \lambda_n) z(x_>, \lambda_n)}{C'(\lambda_n)} = - \frac{k_n}{C'(\lambda_n)} z(x, \lambda_n) z(\xi, \lambda_n) = - \frac{w(x, \lambda_n) w(\xi, \lambda_n)}{k_n C'(\lambda_n)}.$$

Hence by (4.44),

$$\frac{1}{2\pi i} \oint g(x \,|\, \xi; \lambda) d\lambda = - \frac{\delta(x - \xi)}{s(x)} = - \sum \varphi_n(x) \bar{\varphi}_n(\xi) = - \sum_{n=1}^{\infty} \frac{w(x, \lambda_n) w(\xi, \lambda_n)}{k_n C'(\lambda_n)}.$$

Thus the real *normalized* eigenfunctions (that is, such that $\int_a^b s|\varphi_n|^2 \, dx = 1$) of (4.32) are given by

$$\varphi_n(x) = \pm \frac{w(x, \lambda_n)}{[k_n C'(\lambda_n)]^{1/2}} = \pm \left[\frac{k_n}{C'(\lambda_n)} \right]^{1/2} z(x, \lambda_n). \qquad (4.46)$$

Another method of obtaining the normalized eigenfunctions is described in Exercise 4.8.

As a simple illustration, let us consider the eigenvalue problem

$$-\frac{d^2\varphi}{dx^2} - \lambda\varphi = 0, \quad 0 < x < l; \qquad \varphi'(0) = 0, \quad \varphi'(l) = 0.$$

Referring to (4.26), we have $\alpha_1 = \beta_1 = 0$ and $\alpha_2 = \beta_2 = 1$, so that $w(x, \lambda)$ is the solution of the homogeneous equation satisfying the initial condition

$$w(0, \lambda) = -1, \qquad \frac{dw}{dx}(0, \lambda) = 0.$$

Hence

$$w(x, \lambda) = -\cos\sqrt{\lambda}\,x.$$

Similarly,

$$z(x, \lambda) = -\cos\sqrt{\lambda}(l - x)$$

and

$$W(w, z; x) = \sqrt{\lambda}[\cos\sqrt{\lambda}x \sin\sqrt{\lambda}(l - x) + \sin\sqrt{\lambda}x \cos\sqrt{\lambda}(l - x)]$$

$$= \sqrt{\lambda}\sin\sqrt{\lambda}l = C(\lambda).$$

The reader should verify that, in spite of the square-root signs which appear, w, z, and W are entire functions of λ (all that is required is to show that none of these functions has a branch on the real λ axis).

The zeros of W are at $\lambda = n^2\pi^2/l^2$, $n = 0, 1, 2, \ldots$, and we therefore index the eigenvalues starting with $n = 0$. The explicit form of the Green's function is

$$g(x\,|\,\xi; \lambda) = -\frac{\cos\sqrt{\lambda}x_< \cos\sqrt{\lambda}(l - x_>)}{\sqrt{\lambda}\sin\sqrt{\lambda}l}.$$

We have

$$C'(\lambda) = \tfrac{1}{2}l \cos\sqrt{\lambda}l + \frac{1}{2\sqrt{\lambda}}\sin\sqrt{\lambda}l$$

and

$$C'(\lambda_n) = \tfrac{1}{2}l \cos n\pi; \qquad n = 1, 2, \ldots,$$

$$C'(\lambda_0) = l.$$

Also,

$$w(x, \lambda_n) = -\cos\frac{n\pi x}{l};$$

$$z(x, \lambda_n) = -\cos\frac{n\pi}{l}(l - x) = -\cos n\pi \cos\frac{n\pi x}{l} = w(x, \lambda_n) \cos n\pi;$$

$$k_n = \frac{1}{\cos n\pi}.$$

Thus the normalized eigenfunctions are

$$\varphi_n(x) = \left(\frac{2}{l}\right)^{1/2} \cos \frac{n\pi x}{l}, \qquad n = 1, 2, \ldots,$$

$$\varphi_0(x) = \left(\frac{1}{l}\right)^{1/2}$$

Equation (4.43) becomes

$$\delta(x - \xi) = \frac{1}{l} + \frac{2}{l} \sum_{n=1}^{\infty} \cos \frac{n\pi x}{l} \cos \frac{n\pi \xi}{l}; \qquad 0 < x, \xi < l,$$

which agrees with (1.22a).

Multiplying this last equation by $f(x)$ and integrating from 0 to l, we obtain the usual Fourier cosine expansion. We also observe that (4.42) becomes

$$g(x \mid \xi; \lambda) = -\frac{1}{\lambda l} + \frac{2}{l} \sum_{n=1}^{\infty} \frac{\cos (n\pi x/l) \cos (n\pi \xi/l)}{(n^2 \pi^2/l^2) - \lambda}.$$

EXERCISES

4.4 With L_λ defined as in (4.22) show that, for any u,

$$L_\lambda \bar{u} - \overline{L_\lambda u} = (\bar{\lambda} - \lambda) s \bar{u}$$

and

$$\langle L_\lambda u, v \rangle - \langle u, L_\lambda v \rangle$$
$$= p(b)W(u, \bar{v}; b) - p(a)W(u, \bar{v}; a) + (\bar{\lambda} - \lambda) \int_a^b suv \, dx.$$

Observe that, unless λ is real, L_λ is not symmetric on D_L [see following (4.31) for definition of D_L].

4.5 Let $u(x, \lambda)$ be the unique solution of the initial-value problem

$$Lu - \lambda s u = 0, \qquad a \le x \le b; \qquad u(x_0, \lambda) = 1, \qquad \frac{du}{dx}(x_0, \lambda) = 0,$$

where x_0 is a fixed arbitrary point $a \le x_0 \le b$. Show that

$$u(x, \lambda) = \lambda \int_{x_0}^x v_\xi(x) s(\xi) u(\xi, \lambda) d\xi + u(x, 0),$$

where $v_\xi(x)$ is the solution of the equation $Lv = 0$ satisfying the initial conditions $v(\xi) = 0$, $v'(\xi) = -1/p(\xi)$. [HINT: See (1.50).]

Thus $u(x, \lambda)$ satisfies a Volterra integral equation whose unique solution is, for any fixed x, an entire function of λ [this follows directly from the series (3.33), which converges uniformly in any finite region of the λ plane].

4.6 By using the result of Exercise 4.5, show that the functions $w(x, \lambda)$, $z(x, \lambda)$, $C(\lambda)$, introduced in the present section, are entire functions of λ.

Now $C(\lambda)$ cannot vanish for Im $\lambda \neq 0$, because the eigenvalues of (4.32) are real. Thus $C(\lambda)$ is an entire function of λ which is not identically zero. It follows that $C(\lambda)$ can vanish only at isolated real points $\lambda_1, \ldots,$ $\lambda_n, \ldots$ whose only limit points are $\lambda = +\infty$ and $\lambda = -\infty$.

4.7 (a) Let u be a solution of $Lu - \lambda su = 0$. Take the inner product with respect to u to show that

$$\lambda \int_a^b s|u|^2 \, dx = \langle Lu, u \rangle = \int_a^b [p|u'|^2 + q|u|^2]dx - p\bar{u}u']_a^b.$$

(b) Consider the eigenvalue problem (4.32), where, as usual, p and s are positive. Show that all eigenvalues are nonnegative if $q(x) \geq 0$, $\beta_1/\beta_2 \geq 0$, and $\alpha_1/\alpha_2 \leq 0$. The result also holds if $\alpha_2 = \beta_2 = 0$, $\alpha_2 = 0$ and $\beta_1/\beta_2 \geq 0$, or $\beta_2 = 0$ and $\alpha_1/\alpha_2 \leq 0$.

(c) A symmetric operator L for which there exists a real constant α (possibly negative) such that

$$\langle Lu, u \rangle \geq \alpha \|u\|^2, \qquad \text{for all } u$$

is said to be *bounded below*.

Show that the operator L [given by (4.21)] on the domain of functions satisfying (4.26) is bounded below.

HINT: Follow these steps:

(1) There exists x_0 such that

$$\|u\|^2 = (b - a)|u(x_0)|^2.$$

(2) $$\int_a^{x_0} \frac{d}{dx} (u\bar{u}) \, dx = |u(x_0)|^2 - |u(a)|^2.$$

(3) By the above and Schwarz's inequality,

$$|u(a)|^2 \leq \frac{\|u\|^2}{b - a} + 2\|u\| \, \|u'\|,$$

and similarly for $|u(b)|^2$.

(4) $$\langle Lu, u \rangle \geq m_1 \|u'\|^2 + m_2 \|u\|^2 + m_3 \|u\| \, \|u'\|,$$

where m_1, m_2, m_3 are real and $m_1 > 0$.

(5) $$\frac{\langle Lu, u \rangle}{\|u\|^2} \geq A; \qquad \text{therefore} \qquad \frac{\langle Lu, u \rangle}{\int_a^b s|u|^2 \, dx} \geq B.$$

It follows from (5) that every eigenvalue of (4.32) is greater than B. This implies [in conjunction with the fact that the eigenvalues of (4.32) can only have $+\infty$ or $-\infty$ as limit points] that (4.32) has only a *finite number of negative eigenvalues*.

4.8 Let $w(x, \lambda)$ be defined as in this section; then $w_n(x) = w(x, \lambda_n)$ is an eigenfunction of (4.32) corresponding to the eigenvalue λ_n, To calculate $\int_a^b sw_n^2\, dx$, obtain the preliminary formula

$$(\lambda - \lambda_n) \int_a^b sw_n(x)w(x, \lambda)dx = p(b)W(w, w_n; b).$$

By taking the limit as $\lambda \to \lambda_n$ show that

$$\int_a^b sw_n^2(x)dx = p(b)\left[w_n'(b) \frac{dw(b, \lambda)}{d\lambda}\bigg|_{\lambda = \lambda_n} - w_n(b) \frac{d}{d\lambda} w'(b, \lambda)\bigg|_{\lambda = \lambda_n}\right],$$

where the prime denotes differentiation with respect to x.

   Show that this result coincides with the normalization factor obtained earlier in this section [equation (4.46)].

4.9 Consider the eigenvalue problem

$$-(x^2\varphi')' - \lambda\varphi = 0, \qquad 1 < x < e; \qquad \varphi(1) = 0, \quad \varphi(e) = 0.$$

   (a) Show that the eigenvalues are positive.
   (b) Try solutions of the form $\varphi = x^\mu$ to show that the general solution of the differential equation is of the form

$$x^{-1/2}(Ax^{\sqrt{(1/4)-\lambda}} + Bx^{-\sqrt{(1/4)-\lambda}}), \qquad \lambda \neq \tfrac{1}{4}.$$

Find the solution for the case $\lambda = \tfrac{1}{4}$. Show that if $\lambda \leq \tfrac{1}{4}$, the boundary conditions cannot be satisfied. For $\lambda > \tfrac{1}{4}$, rewrite the general solution as

$$x^{-1/2}[C \sin (\sqrt{\lambda - (1/4)} \log x) + D \cos (\sqrt{\lambda - (1/4)} \log x)].$$

To satisfy the boundary conditions we must have $D = 0$ and $\lambda = \lambda_n = n^2\pi^2 + \tfrac{1}{4}$, $n = 1, 2, \ldots$.
   (c) Let

$$u_n(x) = x^{-1/2} \sin (n\pi \log x); \quad u(x, \lambda) = x^{-1/2} \sin (\sqrt{\lambda - (1/4)} \log x).$$

By considering the differential equations satisfied by these functions (see Exercise 4.8), prove that

$$\int_1^e u_n^2\, dx = e^2 u_n'(e) \frac{d}{d\lambda} u(e, \lambda)\bigg|_{\lambda = \lambda_n} = \tfrac{1}{2}.$$

Of course, this result can also be obtained by elementary methods (make the substitution $t = \log x$ in the integral).

4.10 *The normal form of the differential equation.* Consider

$$-\frac{d}{dx}\left[p(x)\frac{d\varphi}{dx}\right] + q(x)\varphi - \lambda s(x)\varphi = 0.$$

Make the one-to-one change of independent variable

$$t = \int_{x_0}^{x} \frac{1}{p(\xi)}\, d\xi$$

to reduce the differential equation to the *normal form*

$$-\frac{d^2\psi}{dt^2} + Q(t)\psi - \lambda S(t)\psi = 0. \tag{4.47}$$

Here

$$\psi(t) = \varphi[x(t)];$$
$$Q(t) = q[x(t)]p[x(t)];$$
$$S(t) = s[x(t)]p[x(t)].$$

Since $p(x)$ and $s(x)$ are positive, $S(t)$ is positive.

4.11 Consider the eigenvalue problem

$$-\varphi'' - \lambda\varphi = 0, \qquad 0 < x < l;$$
$$\varphi(0) = 0, \qquad \cos\beta\,\varphi(l) + \sin\beta\,\varphi'(l) = 0, \tag{4.48}$$

where β is a given real number, $0 \le \beta < \pi$. As β runs through this set of values, every possible boundary condition of the form $\beta_1\varphi(l) + \beta_2\varphi'(l) = 0$ is included. In fact $\beta = 0$ corresponds to the boundary condition $\varphi(l) = 0$; $\beta = \pi/2$ to $\varphi'(l) = 0$; $0 < \beta < \pi/2$ to $\varphi(l) + \tan\beta\,\varphi'(l) = 0$, with $\tan\beta > 0$; and $\pi/2 < \beta < \pi$ to $\varphi(l) + \tan\beta\,\varphi'(l) = 0$, with $\tan\beta < 0$. The problems with $0 \le \beta \le \pi/2$ occur in one-dimensional heat conduction in a rod of length l; the case $\beta = 0$ means that the temperature at the right end is kept at 0; the case $\beta = \pi/2$ describes a rod whose right end is insulated; the case $0 < \beta < \pi/2$ corresponds to the rod radiating heat from the right end into a surrounding atmosphere at zero temperature. On the basis of such physical considerations, one can therefore expect that the eigenvalues decrease as β increases. Show that

$$w(x, \lambda) = \frac{\sin\sqrt{\lambda}x}{\sqrt{\lambda}},$$

$$z(x, \lambda) = -\frac{\cos\beta}{\sqrt{\lambda}}\sin\sqrt{\lambda}(l - x) - \sin\beta\cos\sqrt{\lambda}(l - x);$$

$$W(w, z; x) = \frac{\cos\beta\sin\sqrt{\lambda}l}{\sqrt{\lambda}} + \sin\beta\cos\sqrt{\lambda}l.$$

Observe that w, z, W are analytic functions of λ. The eigenvalues of (4.48) are the values of λ for which W vanishes. Since the eigenvalues must be real, we need consider only three cases, $\lambda = 0$, $\lambda < 0$, $\lambda > 0$. W vanishes for $\lambda = 0$ if and only if $l \cos \beta + \sin \beta = 0$, that is, $\beta = \hat{\beta}$, where $\hat{\beta}$ is the unambiguous number in $(\pi/2, \pi)$ for which $\tan \hat{\beta} = -l$. The corresponding eigenfunction is then proportional to x.

Consider next the case $\lambda < 0$ and set $\sqrt{\lambda} l = ir$ with $r > 0$. The equation $W = 0$ becomes

$$\tanh r = -\frac{\tan \beta}{l} r; \qquad r > 0, \quad \lambda = -\frac{r^2}{l^2}.$$

The solution of this equation will be found at the intersection of the curve $y = \tanh r$ and the straight line $-(\tan \beta/l)r$ shown in Figure 4.1. Such an intersection is possible only if $\hat{\beta} < \beta < \pi$. Letting the corresponding values of r and λ be r_0 and λ_0, the associated eigenfunction is proportional to $\sinh(r_0/l)x$. Show that

$$N_0 = \int_0^l \sinh^2 \frac{r_0 x}{l}\, dx$$

$$= -\frac{l}{2} + \frac{l \sinh 2r_0}{4r_0} = \frac{l}{2}\left[\frac{-\lambda_0 \tan^2 \beta - 1 - (1/l)\tan \beta}{1 + \lambda_0 \tan^2 \beta}\right].$$

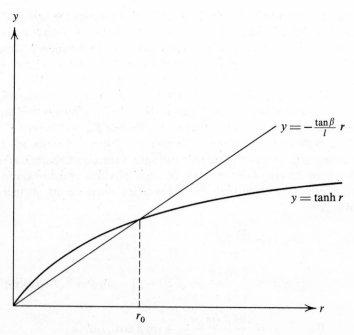

FIGURE 4.1

Next we consider $\lambda > 0$ and set $\sqrt{\lambda} l = r$, with $r > 0$. The equation $W = 0$ becomes

$$\tan r = -\frac{\tan \beta}{l} r; \qquad r > 0, \quad \lambda = \frac{r^2}{l^2}.$$

This equation always has an infinite number of solutions, as shown in Figure 4.2. The straight lines (1) to (6) represent increasing values of β between 0 and π. It is quite clear that the eigenvalues decrease from case (1) through case (4); for (5) (which is tangent to $\tan r$ at $r = 0$), $\beta = \hat{\beta}$ and 0 is an eigenvalue as was shown previously; for (6), $\beta > \hat{\beta}$ and there is a negative eigenvalue $-r_0^2$ previously considered in Figure 4.1. Thus as β increases from 0 to π, the smallest eigenvalue decreases (and the same is true for the kth eigenvalue, taking into account the fact that when $\beta \geq \hat{\beta}$ there is an extra nonpositive eigenvalue which does not appear in Figure 4.2).

Let r_n, $n = 1, 2, \dots$ represent the intersections in Figure 4.2 for some specific β. The eigenvalues are $\lambda_n = r_n^2/l^2$, and the corresponding eigenfunctions are proportional to $\sin (r_n/l) x$.

Show [by (4.46), by Exercise 4.8, or by elementary integration] that

$$N_n = \int_0^l \sin^2 \frac{r_n}{l} x \, dx = \frac{l}{2}\left(1 - \frac{\sin 2r_n}{2r_n}\right) = \frac{l}{2}\left[\frac{1 + \lambda_n \tan^2 \beta + (1/l) \tan \beta}{1 + \lambda_n \tan^2 \beta}\right].$$

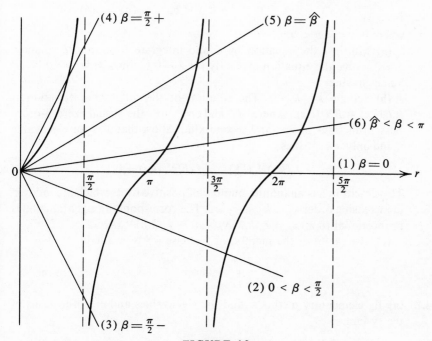

FIGURE 4.2

Derive the expansions

$$\delta(x - \xi) = \sum_{n=1}^{\infty} \frac{1}{N_n} \sin \frac{r_n}{l} x \sin \frac{r_n}{l} \xi, \qquad\qquad \text{if } 0 \le \beta < \hat{\beta};$$

$$\delta(x - \xi) = \frac{3}{l^3} x \xi + \sum_{n=1}^{\infty} \frac{1}{N_n} \sin \frac{r_n}{l} x \sin \frac{r_n}{l} \xi, \qquad\qquad \text{if } \beta = \hat{\beta};$$

$$\delta(x - \xi) = \frac{1}{N_0} \sinh \frac{r_0}{l} x \sinh \frac{r_0}{l} \xi + \sum_{n=1}^{\infty} \frac{1}{N_n} \sin \frac{r_n}{l} x \sin \frac{r_n}{l} \xi, \text{ if } \hat{\beta} < \beta < \pi.$$

Here, of course, N_0, r_0, r_n, N_n all depend on β. Show that for large n and $\beta \ne 0$, $\beta < \hat{\beta}$,

$$r_n = (n - \tfrac{1}{2})\pi + \frac{l}{\pi n \tan \beta} + o\left(\frac{1}{n}\right)$$

and

$$N_n = \frac{l}{2} + \frac{l^2}{2\pi^2 n^2 \tan \beta} + o\left(\frac{1}{n^2}\right).$$

Modify these formulas for $\beta > \hat{\beta}$.

4.12 Consider the eigenvalue problem

$$-(x\varphi')' - \lambda x \varphi = 0, \qquad a < x < b, \qquad \varphi(a) = \varphi(b) = 0,$$

where $0 < a < b < \infty$.

(a) Multiply the equation by $\bar{\varphi}$ and integrate from a to b to show $\lambda \ge 0$. Solve the equation explicitly for $\lambda = 0$ to show that $\lambda = 0$ is *not* an eigenvalue.

(b) Set $\lambda = k^2$, $k > 0$. The solution of the differential equation is $A J_0(kx) + B N_0(kx)$, where J_0 and N_0 are the usual zeroth-order Bessel functions of first and second kind. Show that λ is an eigenvalue if and only if k satisfies

$$J_0(ka)N_0(kb) - J_0(kb)N_0(ka) = 0.$$

This equation has an infinite number of positive roots which are indexed in increasing order $k_1 < k_2 < k_3 \ldots$. The corresponding eigenfunction is proportional to $u_n(x) = J_0(k_n x)N_0(k_n a) - J_0(k_n a)N_0(k_n x)$.

(c) Use (4.46) or the method of Exercise 4.8 to evaluate

$$\int_a^b x u_n^2(x) dx.$$

4.13 (a) By elementary methods, find the eigenvalues and eigenfunctions of the system

$$-\varphi'' - 2\varphi' - \varphi - \lambda \varphi = 0, \qquad 0 < x < 1; \qquad \varphi(0) = \varphi(1) = 0.$$

(b) Multiply by a suitable function $s(x)$ to write the above differential equation in the form (4.23). Check that the eigenfunctions are orthogonal with weight $s(x)$, as predicted by the theory.

4.3 INTRODUCTORY EXAMPLES OF SINGULAR PROBLEMS

We shall consider the operator $-(d^2/dx^2) - \lambda$ over the intervals $0 < x < \infty$ and $-\infty < x < \infty$. Before attacking any boundary value problems, let us make some simple observations about the solutions of the homogeneous equation

$$-\frac{d^2\varphi}{dx^2} - \lambda\varphi = 0.$$

With $\lambda = |\lambda|e^{i\theta}$, $0 \le \theta < 2\pi$, we define (as usual) $\sqrt{\lambda} = |\lambda|^{1/2}e^{i\theta/2} = \alpha + i\beta$, where $\beta \ge 0$. The general solution of the differential equation for $\lambda \ne 0$ may be written

$$A \sin \sqrt{\lambda}x + B \cos \sqrt{\lambda}x$$

or

$$C \exp (i\sqrt{\lambda}x) + D \exp (-i\sqrt{\lambda}x),$$

while for $\lambda = 0$ the general solution is

$$A + Bx.$$

1. *There is no nontrivial solution in* $\mathscr{L}_2^{(c)}(-\infty, \infty)$ *for any* λ. In fact, we have

$$|\exp (i\sqrt{\lambda}x)|^2 = e^{-2\beta x}, \qquad |\exp (-i\sqrt{\lambda}x)|^2 = e^{2\beta x}.$$

Clearly for any β (including $\beta = 0$),

$$\int_{-\infty}^{\infty} |\exp (i\sqrt{\lambda}x)|^2 \, dx = +\infty, \qquad \int_{-\infty}^{\infty} |\exp (-i\sqrt{\lambda}x)|^2 \, dx = +\infty.$$

2. If $\operatorname{Im} \sqrt{\lambda} > 0$ [which corresponds to λ not in $[0, \infty)$], there is one solution $[C \exp (i\sqrt{\lambda}\,x)]$ in $\mathscr{L}_2^{(c)}(0, \infty)$ and one solution $[C \exp (-i\sqrt{\lambda}\,x)]$ in $\mathscr{L}_2^{(c)}(-\infty, 0)$.

3. If $\operatorname{Im} \sqrt{\lambda} = 0$ [which corresponds to λ in $[0, \infty)$], there is no solution in $\mathscr{L}_2^{(c)}(0, \infty)$ or in $\mathscr{L}_2^{(c)}(-\infty, 0)$.

Let us now consider differential equations associated with the operator $-(d^2/dx^2) - \lambda$ on the interval $0 < x < \infty$. These problems are singular by the definition introduced in Section 4.2, because the right end of the interval is at infinity. To obtain a unique solution of the inhomogeneous equation $-u'' - \lambda u = f$, we expect to have to impose a boundary condition at $x = 0$ (say $u = 0$) but we do not know what to do at $x = +\infty$. Since we wish to take advantage of the great simplifications which occur in a Hilbert space we shall require that both the inhomogeneous term $f(x)$ and the solution $u(x)$ belong to $\mathscr{L}_2^{(c)}(0, \infty)$. It will then turn out that for our particular problem no boundary condition has to be imposed at $x = +\infty$. Thus we examine the problem

$$-u'' - \lambda u = f(x), \qquad 0 < x < \infty; \qquad u(0) = 0, \tag{4.49}$$

with $\int_0^\infty |f|^2 \, dx < \infty$. We look for solutions $u(x)$ with the property

$$\int_0^\infty |u|^2 \, dx < \infty.$$

There are three principal questions related to the system:

(a) Is there one and only one solution for each f? (The answer is yes for λ not in $[0, \infty)$; if λ is in $[0, \infty)$, the solution is unique but does not exist for each f.)

(b) Can the solution be obtained by a Green's function method? The answer is affirmative.

(c) Is there an eigenfunction expansion? The answer is a qualified yes—we shall need to generalize the notion of eigenfunctions. The difficulty can be seen immediately from the fact that the homogeneous system

$$-\varphi'' - \lambda\varphi = 0, \quad 0 < x < \infty; \qquad \varphi(0) = 0 \tag{4.50}$$

has no eigenvalues. Indeed the only solution which is square-integrable in $(0, \infty)$ is $C \exp(i\sqrt{\lambda}\,x)$, and this does not satisfy the boundary condition at $x = 0$ for any λ.

Our approach to (4.49) will principally be via the Green's function $g(x\,|\,\xi;\,\lambda)$, which satisfies

$$-\frac{d^2g}{dx^2} - \lambda g = \delta(x - \xi), \quad 0 < x, \xi < \infty; \qquad g(0\,|\,\xi;\,\lambda) = 0. \tag{4.51}$$

We shall require that

$$\int_0^\infty |g|^2 \, dx < \infty, \tag{4.52}$$

and this requirement will play the role of a boundary condition at $x = +\infty$. If λ does not belong to $[0, \infty)$, $\exp(i\sqrt{\lambda}x)$ is a solution of the homogeneous equation satisfying the condition at ∞, and $\sin\sqrt{\lambda}x$ satisfies the boundary condition at $x = 0$. Since g is continuous at $x = \xi$, we have

$$g(x\,|\,\xi;\,\lambda) = A \sin\sqrt{\lambda}x_< \exp(i\sqrt{\lambda}x_>).$$

The jump in dg/dx at $x = \xi$ must be -1, so that A is determined from

$$Ai\sqrt{\lambda} \exp(i\sqrt{\lambda}\xi) \sin\sqrt{\lambda}\xi - A\exp(i\sqrt{\lambda}\xi)\sqrt{\lambda}\cos\sqrt{\lambda}\xi = -1$$

or

$$A = \frac{1}{\sqrt{\lambda}}.$$

Thus

$$g(x \mid \xi; \lambda) = \frac{1}{\sqrt{\lambda}} \sin\sqrt{\lambda}x_< \exp(i\sqrt{\lambda}x_>), \qquad \lambda \text{ not in } [0, \infty). \quad (4.53)$$

If we examine g as a function of λ, we detect a striking contrast to the regular case; in the regular case g has only poles and no branches, whereas in our case g has no poles (not even at $\lambda = 0$) but has a branch along the positive real λ axis. Directly above and on the positive real axis, we have

$$g_+ = \frac{1}{|\lambda|^{1/2}} \sin |\lambda|^{1/2}x_< \exp(i|\lambda|^{1/2}x_>),$$

and directly below the positive real axis

$$g_- = \frac{1}{-|\lambda|^{1/2}} \sin(-|\lambda|^{1/2}x_<) \exp(-i|\lambda|^{1/2}x_>)'$$

$$= \frac{1}{|\lambda|^{1/2}} \sin |\lambda|^{1/2}x_< \exp(-i|\lambda|^{1/2}x_>).$$

Thus the jump $[g]$ as we cross the positive real λ axis is

$$[g] = g_+ - g_- = \frac{1}{|\lambda|^{1/2}} (\sin |\lambda|^{1/2}x_<)(2i\sin |\lambda|^{1/2}x_>)$$

$$= \frac{2i}{|\lambda|^{1/2}} (\sin |\lambda|^{1/2}x)(\sin |\lambda|^{1/2}\xi). \quad (4.54)$$

If we assume that (4.44) is still valid in the form

$$\frac{1}{2\pi i} \oint g(x \mid \xi; \lambda)d\lambda = -\delta(x - \xi), \quad (4.55)$$

then by integrating g along a large circle in the complex λ plane we should be able to generate the equivalent to the sum $-\sum_n \varphi_n(x)\bar{\varphi}_n(\xi)$. In our case we shall see that the branch cut in g causes the sum to become an integral over the positive real λ axis.

Since g is analytic except on the positive real λ axis, we have

$$\int_c g \, d\lambda = 0, \quad (4.56)$$

where C consists of the large circle and C_+ and C_- (see Figure 4.3). On the other hand,

$$\int_C g \, d\lambda = \oint g \, d\lambda + \int_{C_+} g \, d\lambda + \int_{C_-} g \, d\lambda.$$

Since on C_-, λ ranges from $+\infty$ to 0, we have

$$\int_C g \, d\lambda = \oint g \, d\lambda + \int_0^\infty [g] \, d\lambda,$$

where $[g]$ is given by (4.54).

Using (4.55) and (4.56), we obtain

$$\delta(x - \xi) = \frac{1}{2\pi i} \int_0^\infty [g] \, d\lambda. \tag{4.57}$$

Substituting (4.54), we find

$$\delta(x - \xi) = \frac{1}{\pi} \int_0^\infty \frac{\sin |\lambda|^{1/2} x \sin |\lambda|^{1/2} \xi}{|\lambda|^{1/2}} \, d\lambda, \tag{4.58}$$

or, letting $|\lambda| = v^2$, $0 < v < \infty$,

$$\delta(x - \xi) = \frac{2}{\pi} \int_0^\infty \sin vx \sin v\xi \, dv. \tag{4.58a}$$

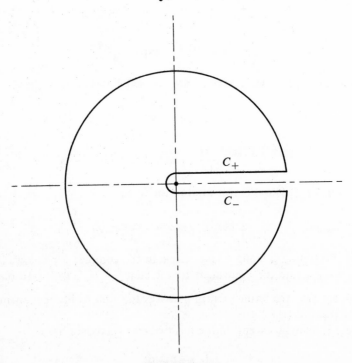

FIGURE 4.3

Comparing this with (4.43) we are tempted to think of $(2/\pi)^{1/2} \sin vx$ as normalized "eigenfunctions" corresponding to the continuous parameter v. Honesty compels us to recognize that $(2/\pi)^{1/2} \sin vx$ is not square-integrable in $(0, \infty)$, so that it is not a legitimate eigenfunction. Exercise 4.20 shows that every value of λ in $[0, \infty)$ is in the continuous spectrum. Equation (4.58) holds rigorously in the theory of distributions, but we are content to regard it as a formal expansion. From (4.58a) we may obtain the familiar formulas for Fourier sine transforms. Multiplying by $f(x)$ and integrating from 0 to ∞, we have

$$f(\xi) = \frac{2}{\pi} \int_0^\infty f(x)dx \int_0^\infty \sin vx \sin v\xi \, dv. \tag{4.59}$$

Thus if we define

$$F_s(v) = \left(\frac{2}{\pi}\right)^{1/2} \int_0^\infty f(x) \sin vx \, dx, \tag{4.60}$$

(4.60) yields the inversion formula

$$f(\xi) = \left(\frac{2}{\pi}\right)^{1/2} \int_0^\infty F_s(v) \sin v\xi \, dv,$$

or, by renaming the variable ξ,

$$f(x) = \left(\frac{2}{\pi}\right)^{1/2} \int_0^\infty F_s(v) \sin vx \, dv. \tag{4.61}$$

We may regard (4.61) as an expansion (over a continuous parameter v) in the functions $(2/\pi)^{1/2} \sin vx$ with "coefficients" $F_s(v)$ given by (4.60). $F_s(v)$ is known as the *Fourier sine transform* of $f(x)$.

The pair of formulas (4.60) and (4.61) holds for all functions $f(x)$ in $\mathscr{L}_2(0, \infty)$ if we interpret (4.61) in the sense of convergence in the mean; that is,

$$\lim_{R \to \infty} \int_0^\infty |f(x) - \left(\frac{2}{\pi}\right)^{1/2} \int_0^R F_s(v) \sin vx \, dv|^2 \, dx = 0.$$

It is worthwhile to justify our results by a different approach based on considering the eigenvalue problem (4.50) on a finite interval (with $\varphi = 0$ at $x = l$) and then letting $l \to \infty$. The eigenvalues and eigenfunctions for the finite-interval problem are

$$\lambda_n(l) = \frac{n^2\pi^2}{l^2}, \qquad n = 1, 2, \ldots,$$

$$\varphi_n(x, l) = \left(\frac{2}{l}\right)^{1/2} \sin \frac{n\pi x}{l}.$$

It is clear that as l increases, the eigenvalues become more and more dense, until in the limit as $l \to \infty$ they fill the real positive λ axis. The eigenfunctions do not appear to have any limit as $l \to \infty$. Consider now the expansion of an arbitrary function $f(x)$ defined in $0 < x < l$ in terms of $\varphi_n(x, l)$. We have

$$f(x) = \sum_{n=1}^{\infty} \frac{2}{l} \sin \frac{n\pi x}{l} \int_0^l \sin \frac{n\pi \xi}{l} f(\xi)d\xi = \sum_{n=1}^{\infty} \frac{2}{\pi} \Delta v \, g(v_n, x), \quad (4.62)$$

where

$$g(v, x) = \int_0^l \sin vx \sin v\xi \, f(\xi)d\xi;$$

$$v_n = \frac{n\pi}{l}, \qquad \Delta v = \frac{\pi}{l}.$$

It is clear that for large l and fixed x, Δv is small and $g(v, x)$ is to be evaluated at points Δv apart, where v ranges from 0 to ∞. Hence in the limit as $l \to \infty$, we expect (4.62) to become

$$f(x) = \int_0^{\infty} \frac{2}{\pi} \, dv \, g(v, x),$$

where

$$g(v, x) = \int_0^{\infty} \sin vx \sin v\xi \, f(\xi)d\xi.$$

These formulas are clearly equivalent to (4.60) and (4.61). We also recall Parseval's equality for the finite sine expansion,

$$\int_0^l |f(x)|^2 \, dx = \sum_{n=1}^{\infty} \frac{2}{l} \left| \int_0^l \sin \frac{n\pi \xi}{l} f(\xi)d\xi \right|^2 = \sum_{n=1}^{\infty} \frac{2}{\pi} \Delta v \, h(v_n),$$

where

$$h(v) = \left| \int_0^l \sin v\xi \, f(\xi)d\xi \right|^2.$$

As $l \to \infty$, we are led to

$$\int_0^{\infty} |f(x)|^2 \, dx = \frac{2}{\pi} \int_0^{\infty} dv \left| \int_0^{\infty} \sin v\xi \, f(\xi)d\xi \right|^2,$$

or, using (4.60),

$$\int_0^{\infty} |f(x)|^2 \, dx = \int_0^{\infty} |F_s(v)|^2 \, dv. \quad (4.63)$$

The Green's function for the finite interval problem [see (4.10)] is

$$g_l(x\,|\,\xi;\lambda) = \frac{1}{\sqrt{\lambda}\,\sin\sqrt{\lambda}l}\,[\sin\sqrt{\lambda}x_< \sin\sqrt{\lambda}(l-x_>)]; \qquad 0 < x, \xi < l.$$

Now

$$\sin\sqrt{\lambda}(l-x_>) = \sin\sqrt{\lambda}l\cos\sqrt{\lambda}x_> - \sin\sqrt{\lambda}x_>\cos\sqrt{\lambda}l;$$

setting $\sqrt{\lambda} = \alpha + i\beta$ with $\beta \ge 0$, we have

$$g_l(x\,|\,\xi;\lambda) = \frac{\sin\sqrt{\lambda}x_< \cos\sqrt{\lambda}x_>}{\sqrt{\lambda}}$$
$$- \frac{i}{\sqrt{\lambda}}[\sin\sqrt{\lambda}x_< \sin\sqrt{\lambda}x_>]\left(\frac{e^{i\alpha l-\beta l} + e^{-i\alpha l+\beta l}}{e^{i\alpha l-\beta l} - e^{-i\alpha l+\beta l}}\right).$$

As $l \to \infty$, the term in parentheses yields -1 if $\beta > 0$, whereas no limit exists if $\beta = 0$. Therefore, if λ is not in $[0, \infty)$, we have

$$\lim_{l\to\infty} g_l(x\,|\,\xi;\lambda) = \frac{\sin\sqrt{\lambda}x_< \exp(i\sqrt{\lambda}x_>)}{\sqrt{\lambda}},$$

which is just (4.53). This limiting process illustrates the manner by which the isolated poles of g_l coalesce into the branch cut for (4.53).

Let us now consider the inhomogeneous system (4.49), repeated below for convenience,

$$-\frac{d^2u}{dx^2} - \lambda u = f(x); \qquad 0 < x < \infty; \qquad u(0) = 0. \tag{4.64}$$

We assume that f is in $\mathscr{L}_2^{(c)}(0, \infty)$, and we are looking for solutions u which are in $\mathscr{L}_2^{(c)}(0, \infty)$.

Theorem 1. *If λ is not in $[0, \infty)$, and f is piecewise continuous, there exists one and only one $\mathscr{L}_2$ solution of (4.64),*

$$u(x) = \int_0^\infty g(x\,|\,\xi;\lambda)f(\xi)\,d\xi, \tag{4.65}$$

where g is given by (4.53).

Proof. Let $u(x)$ be given by (4.65). Then the boundary condition at $x = 0$ is obviously satisfied. Let x be a point at which f is continuous; since g is continuous, we have

$$u'(x) = \int_0^\infty \frac{\partial g}{\partial x}f(\xi)d\xi = \int_0^{x-} \frac{\partial g}{\partial x}f(\xi)d\xi + \int_{x+}^\infty \frac{\partial g}{\partial x}f(\xi)d\xi$$

and

$$u''(x) = \int_0^{x-} \frac{\partial^2 g}{\partial x^2}f(\xi)d\xi + f(x)\frac{\partial g}{\partial x}\Big|_{\xi=x-} + \int_{x+}^\infty \frac{\partial^2 g}{\partial x^2}f(\xi)d\xi - f(x)\frac{\partial g}{\partial x}\Big|_{\xi=x+}.$$

In each of the intervals $(0, x-)$ and $(x+, \infty)$, we have $\partial^2 g/\partial x^2 = -\lambda g$; moreover,

$$\frac{\partial g}{\partial x}\bigg|_{\xi=x-} - \frac{\partial g}{\partial x}\bigg|_{\xi=x+} = -1,$$

so that

$$u'' + \lambda u = -f(x).$$

It remains to show that u is in $\mathscr{L}_2^{(c)}(0, \infty)$. This is the subject of Exercises 4.14 and 4.15. These exercises also imply that the result can be extended to the case where f is not piecewise continuous [but of course in $\mathscr{L}_2^{(c)}(0, \infty)$].

Theorem 2. *If λ is not in $[0, \infty)$, the solution $u(x)$ of (4.64) can be written as the Fourier sine integral* (4.66).

Proof. Multiply (4.64) by $(2/\pi)^{1/2} \sin vx$ and integrate from 0 to ∞. Since u and u' vanish at ∞ and u and $\sin vx$ vanish at 0, we obtain, after integrating the first term by parts twice,

$$v^2 U_s(v) - \lambda U_s(v) = F_s(v),$$

where U_s and F_s are the respective Fourier sine transforms of $u(x)$ and $f(x)$. Thus, by (4.61),

$$\begin{aligned} u(x) &= \left(\frac{2}{\pi}\right)^{1/2} \int_0^\infty \frac{F_s(v)}{v^2 - \lambda} \sin vx \, dv \\ &= \left(\frac{2}{\pi}\right) \int_0^\infty \frac{\sin vx}{v^2 - \lambda} \left[\int_0^\infty f(x) \sin vx \, dx\right] dv. \end{aligned} \tag{4.66}$$

The reader is invited to compare these formulas with the finite-interval expansion (4.4).

In the particular case where $f(x) = \delta(x - \xi)$, we proceed formally to obtain

$$F_s(v) = \left(\frac{2}{\pi}\right)^{1/2} \int_0^\infty \delta(x - \xi) \sin vx \, dx = \left(\frac{2}{\pi}\right)^{1/2} \sin v\xi$$

and

$$g(x \mid \xi; \lambda) = \frac{2}{\pi} \int_0^\infty \frac{\sin vx \sin v\xi}{v^2 - \lambda} \, dv, \qquad \lambda \text{ not in } [0, \infty). \tag{4.67}$$

This is the *bilinear expansion* which is formally similar to the bilinear series (4.8).

EXERCISES

4.14 Consider the integral operator K defined from

$$u(x) = Kf = \int_a^b k(x, \xi) f(\xi) d\xi,$$

where f is in $\mathscr{L}_2^{(c)}(a, b)$ and the interval (a, b) may be infinite. In Chapter 2 we showed that if $\int_a^b \int_a^b |k|^2 \, dx \, d\xi < \infty$, the operator K is not only bounded but completely continuous. We now look for milder conditions on $k(x, \xi)$ which will ensure the boundedness (but not complete continuity) of K. We have

$$|u(x)|^2 \leq \int_a^b \int_a^b |k(x, \xi)| \, |k(x, \eta)| \, |f(\xi)| \, |f(\eta)| d\xi \, d\eta.$$

Since $|f(\xi)| \, |f(\eta)| \leq \frac{1}{2}(|f(\xi)|^2 + |f(\eta)|^2)$,

$$|u|^2 \leq \int_a^b \int_a^b |k(x, \xi)| \, |k(x, \eta)| \, |f(\xi)|^2 d\xi \, d\eta.$$

Now *assume* that

$$\int_a^b |k(x, \xi)| d\xi \leq l, \qquad \int_a^b |k(x, \xi)| dx \leq l, \qquad (4.68)$$

where l is a constant independent of x and ξ. Then

$$\|u\|^2 = \int_a^b |u|^2 \, dx \leq l^2 \int_a^b |f|^2 \, d\xi = l^2 \|f\|^2.$$

Thus, if conditions (4.68) are satisfied, K is a bounded integral operator and $\|K\| \leq l$.

4.15 Consider, for fixed λ not in $[0, \infty)$, the kernel $g(x \mid \xi; \lambda)$ given by (4.53). Show that

$$\int_0^\infty |g(x \mid \xi; \lambda)| d\xi = \int_0^\infty |g(x \mid \xi; \lambda)| dx \leq l,$$

where l is independent of x and ξ.

Hence by Exercise 4.14, the integral operator G_λ corresponding to this kernel is a bounded operator defined on the whole of $\mathscr{L}_2^{(c)}(0, \infty)$. Note that G_λ is not Hilbert-Schmidt, since

$$\int_0^\infty \int_0^\infty |g|^2 \, dx \, d\xi = \infty.$$

4.16 Consider the system

$$-u'' - \lambda u = f(x), \quad 0 < x < \infty, \qquad u(0) = 0,$$

where λ is a given real positive number, $f \equiv 0$ for $x > l$, $\int_0^l |f|^2 \, dx < \infty$.

Show that the system has an $\mathscr{L}_2^{(c)}(0, \infty)$ solution if and only if $\int_0^l \sin \sqrt{\lambda} x f(x) dx = 0$. Show that if $\lambda = 0$, the condition is replaced by

$$\int_0^l x f(x) dx = 0.$$

4.17 Show that the general solution of

$$-u'' - \lambda u = e^{-x}, \quad 0 < x < \infty, \qquad u(0) = 0$$

is

$$u(x) = A \sin \sqrt{\lambda} x + \frac{\cos \sqrt{\lambda} x - e^{-x}}{1 + \lambda}.$$

Hence the system does not have any solution in $\mathscr{L}_2^{(c)}(0, \infty)$ for real positive λ. Show that this conclusion is also valid if $\lambda = 0$. Find the unique $\mathscr{L}_2$ solution if λ is not in $[0, \infty)$.

4.18 Let $r(x)$ be a function which is square-integrable over every finite interval but not necessarily in $\mathscr{L}_2^{(c)}(0, \infty)$. Consider the subset M of $\mathscr{L}_2^{(c)}(0, \infty)$ consisting of functions $u(x)$ which vanish for sufficiently large x and such that $\int_0^\infty r(x)u(x)dx = 0$. Show that M is dense in $\mathscr{L}_2^{(c)}(0, \infty)$ if and only if $\int_0^\infty |r^2|dx = \infty$.

4.19 (a) It is obvious that there exists a twice-differentiable function $F(x)$ defined over $0 \le x \le 1$, such that $F(0) = 0, F'(0) = 1, F(1) = 0, F'(1) = 0$. Construct such a function explicitly.

    (b) Let $f_n(x)$ be defined as

$$f_n(x) = \begin{cases} \dfrac{1}{\sqrt{\lambda}} \sin \sqrt{\lambda} x, & 0 \le x < l_n; \\ F(x - l_n), & l_n \le x < l_n + 1; \\ 0, & l_n + 1 \le x. \end{cases}$$

Here $\sqrt{\lambda}$ is a fixed positive number, $l_n = 2n\pi/\sqrt{\lambda}$, and F is the function of part (a). The function $f_n(x)$ is continuous, has a continuous first derivative, and a piecewise continuous second derivative.

    (c) Show that

$$-f_n'' - \lambda f_n = \begin{cases} 0, & 0 \le x \le l_n; \\ s_n(x), & l_n \le x < l_n + 1; \\ 0, & l_n + 1 \le x, \end{cases}$$

where $\int_{l_n}^{l_n+1} s_n^2(x)dx$ is a finite number independent of n.

    (d) Show that

$$\|f_n\|^2 \ge \frac{n\pi}{\lambda^{3/2}};$$

hence

$$\lim_{n \to \infty} \frac{\|f_n\|}{\|s_n\|} = \infty.$$

4.20 Consider the differential operators $L = - d^2/dx^2$ and $L_\lambda = -(d^2/dx^2) - \lambda$ on the linear manifold D of $\mathscr{L}_2^{(c)}(0, \infty)$ consisting of functions u such that u and u' are absolutely continuous, and u and u'' are in $\mathscr{L}_2^{(c)}(0, \infty)$ and $u(0) = 0$.

Then every value of λ not in $[0, \infty)$ is a regular value for L; that is, L_λ^{-1} is defined for each f in $\mathscr{L}_2^{(c)}(0, \infty)$ and L_λ^{-1} is a bounded operator. This merely restates the result of Exercise 4.15 ($L_\lambda^{-1} = G_\lambda$) in Hilbert-space terminology. Every value of λ in $[0, \infty)$ is in the continuous spectrum. We must show that L_λ^{-1} exists for a dense subset of $\mathscr{L}_2^{(c)}(0, \infty)$ and that L_λ^{-1} is unbounded. The first part follows from Exercises 4.16 and 4.18 and the second part from Exercise 4.19.

4.21 Over the interval $0 < x < \infty$, consider the three systems

$$-\varphi'' - \lambda\varphi = 0, \qquad\qquad \varphi'(0) = 0; \qquad\qquad (4.69a)$$

$$-u'' - \lambda u = f(x), \qquad\qquad u'(0) = 0; \qquad\qquad (4.69b)$$

$$-\frac{d^2 g}{dx^2} - \lambda g = \delta(x - \xi), \qquad \left.\frac{dg}{dx}\right|_{x=0} = 0. \qquad (4.69c)$$

Show that (4.69a) has no eigenvalues. Show that if λ is not in $[0, \infty)$, $g = (i/\sqrt{\lambda}) \cos \sqrt{\lambda}x_< \exp (i\sqrt{\lambda}x_>)$. Use (4.44) to show that

$$\delta(x - \xi) = \frac{2}{\pi} \int_0^\infty \cos vx \cos v\xi \, dv, \qquad (4.70)$$

and hence obtain the usual cosine transform formulas

$$F_c(v) = \left(\frac{2}{\pi}\right)^{1/2} \int_0^\infty f(x)\cos vx \, dx;$$

$$f(x) = \left(\frac{2}{\pi}\right)^{1/2} \int_0^\infty F_c(v)\cos vx \, dv. \qquad (4.71)$$

Show that if λ is not in $[0, \infty)$, the system (4.69b) has a unique solution for each f in $\mathscr{L}_2^{(c)}(0, \infty)$. Express this solution as a Fourier cosine integral and find the bilinear expansion for g.

4.22 Over the interval $-\infty < x < \infty$, consider the three systems

$$-\varphi'' - \lambda\varphi = 0; \qquad\qquad (4.72a)$$

$$-u'' - \lambda u = f(x); \qquad\qquad (4.72b)$$

$$-\frac{d^2 g}{dx^2} - \lambda g = \delta(x - \xi). \qquad\qquad (4.72c)$$

We are looking for solutions in $\mathcal{L}_2^{(c)}(-\infty, \infty)$ and assume that f is in $\mathcal{L}_2^{(c)}(-\infty, \infty)$. Show that (4.72a) has no eigenvalues. Show that if λ is not in $[0, \infty)$,

$$g(x \mid \xi; \lambda) = \frac{i}{2\sqrt{\lambda}} \exp(i\sqrt{\lambda}x_>) \exp(-i\sqrt{\lambda}x_<) = \frac{i}{2\sqrt{\lambda}} \exp(i\sqrt{\lambda}|x - \xi|).$$

Using (4.44), obtain the expansion

$$\delta(x - \xi) = \frac{1}{\pi} \int_0^\infty [\cos vx \cos v\xi + \sin vx \sin v\xi]dv, \qquad (4.73)$$

from which one deduces the trigonometric form of the Fourier integral theorem

$$f(\xi) = \frac{1}{\pi} \int_0^\infty \cos v\xi \left[\int_{-\infty}^\infty f(x) \cos vx \, dx \right] dv$$

$$+ \frac{1}{\pi} \int_0^\infty \sin v\xi \left[\int_{-\infty}^\infty f(x) \sin vx \, dx \right] dv. \qquad (4.74)$$

Show that (4.73) can be rewritten

$$\delta(x - \xi) = \frac{1}{2\pi} \int_{-\infty}^\infty e^{iv(x-\xi)} \, dv, \qquad (4.75)$$

from which the exponential form of the Fourier integral theorem devolves:

$$f(\xi) = \frac{1}{2\pi} \int_{-\infty}^\infty e^{-iv\xi} \left[\int_{-\infty}^\infty f(x)e^{ivx} \, dx \right] dv. \qquad (4.76)$$

Show that if λ is not in $[0, \infty)$, system (4.72b) has a unique $\mathcal{L}_2^{(c)}(-\infty, \infty)$ solution

$$u(x) = \int_{-\infty}^\infty g(x \mid \xi; \lambda)f(\xi)d\xi.$$

Express $u(x)$ as a Fourier integral (exponential form) and obtain the bilinear expansion for g.

4.23 Discuss the solution of

$$-w'' - \lambda w = f(x), \quad 0 < x < \infty; \qquad u(0) = A,$$

where A is a given complex number and f is in $\mathcal{L}_2^{(c)}(0, \infty)$.

4.24 Consider the problem over the interval $0 < x < \infty$,

$$-\frac{d^2\varphi}{dx^2} - \lambda\varphi = 0, \qquad \varphi'(0) + h\varphi(0) = 0,$$

where h is a given real number. The case $h < 0$ corresponds to the physical problem of heat conduction in a rod whose left end radiates into a surrounding atmosphere at zero temperature. Here we consider all possible real values of h.

(a) Show by elementary methods that the system has an eigenvalue if and only if $h > 0$, the single eigenvalue being $\lambda = -h$ and the corresponding normalized eigenfunction $\sqrt{2h}\, e^{-2hx}$.

(b) Show that the Green's function is given by

$$g(x \mid \xi; \lambda) = \frac{h}{\lambda^{1/2}(h + i\lambda^{1/2})} \exp (i\sqrt{\lambda} x_>)\left[\sin \lambda^{1/2} x_< - \frac{\lambda^{1/2}}{h} \cos \lambda^{1/2} x_< \right].$$

Using (4.44), find the expansion (for $h < 0$)

$$\delta(x - \xi) = \frac{2h^2}{\pi} \int_0^\infty \frac{1}{h^2 + v^2}\, u_v(x)u_v(\xi)dv,$$

where $u_v(x) = \sin vx - (v/h) \cos vx$. Note that for $h = 0$ this expansion becomes (4.70). If $h > 0$, g also has a pole at $\sqrt{\lambda} = ih$, that is, at $\lambda = -h^2$. Show that the corresponding expansion is

$$\delta(x - \xi) = \frac{2h^2}{\pi} \int_0^\infty \frac{1}{h^2 + v^2}\, u_v(x)u_v(\xi)dv + 2he^{-hx}e^{-h\xi}.$$

4.4   THE GENERAL SINGULAR PROBLEM

Consider the homogeneous equation

$$L\varphi = \lambda s\varphi, \qquad a < x < b, \tag{4.77}$$

where

$$L\varphi = -(p\varphi')' + q\varphi,$$

and the points a and b may be singular points [for instance, b would be singular if either $b = +\infty$ or $p(b) = 0$].

We divide (4.77) by $s(x)$ to put in the standard form of an operator which, acting on φ, yields a constant multiple of φ; thus

$$A\varphi = \lambda\varphi, \qquad a < x < b, \tag{4.77a}$$

where

$$A\varphi = -\frac{1}{s}(p\varphi')' + \frac{1}{s}q\varphi.$$

It is convenient at this stage to introduce the space of all complex valued functions $u(x)$ such that

$$\int_a^b s|u|^2\, dx < \infty. \tag{4.78}$$

Suppose that u and v both satisfy the condition (4.78); then the Schwarz inequality implies the existence of $\int_a^b su\bar{v}\, dx$ and

$$\left| \int_a^b su\bar{v}\, dx \right| \leq \left[\int_a^b s|u|^2\, dx \right]^{1/2} \left[\int_a^b s|v|^2\, dx \right]^{1/2}.$$

The space of functions satisfying (4.78) is a Hilbert space with inner product

$$\langle u, v \rangle_s = \int_a^b su\bar{v}\, dx,$$

and norm

$$\|u\|_s = \langle u, u \rangle_s^{1/2} = \left[\int_a^b s|u|^2\, dx \right]^{1/2}.$$

A function satisfying (4.78) will be said to be of *finite s norm over* (a, b).

From the definition of A, we have for any twice-differentiable functions u and v,

$$\bar{v}Au - uA\bar{v} = \frac{1}{s}\frac{d}{dx}\left[p(u\bar{v}' - u'\bar{v}) \right], \qquad a < x < b.$$

For any a_0, b_0 such that $a < a_0 < b_0 < b$,

$$\int_{a_0}^{b_0} s(\bar{v}Au - uA\bar{v})dx = \int_{a_0}^{b_0} (\bar{v}Lu - uL\bar{v})dx$$

$$= p(b_0)W(u, \bar{v}; b_0) - p(a_0)W(u, \bar{v}; a_0), \qquad (4.79)$$

where $W(u, \bar{v}; x) = (u\bar{v}' - u'\bar{v})$ is the Wronskian of u and $\bar{v}$. To extend this formula to the interval (a, b), we must require that terms like $\int_a^b s\bar{v}Au\, dx$ have finite values. Consider therefore the set D of all functions $u(x)$ such that u and u' are absolutely continuous and such that both u and Au are of finite s norm over (a, b). Such functions clearly comprise a linear manifold in the Hilbert space of functions with finite s norm over (a, b).

Now let u and v belong to D; then since $\langle Au, v \rangle_s$ and $\langle u, Av \rangle_s$ exist, we have, from (4.79),

$$\langle Au, v \rangle_s - \langle u, Av \rangle_s = \lim_{\substack{a_0 \to a \\ b_0 \to b}} \left[p(b_0)W(u, \bar{v}; b_0) - p(a_0)W(u, \bar{v}, a_0) \right]. \quad (4.79a)$$

Since the two limits may be taken separately, we infer that both

$$\lim_{a_0 \to a} p(a_0)W(u, \bar{v}; a_0) \qquad \text{and} \qquad \lim_{b_0 \to b} p(b_0)W(u, \bar{v}; b_0)$$

exist. These limits will be denoted by $p(a)W(u, \bar{v}; a)$ and $p(b)W(u, \bar{v}; b)$, respectively.

Let λ be a complex number and let $\varphi(x)$ be a solution of $L\varphi = \lambda s\varphi$; then since the coefficients in L are real, we also have $L\bar\varphi = \bar\lambda s\bar\varphi$, so that

$$(\lambda - \bar\lambda)s|\varphi|^2 = \bar\varphi L\varphi - \varphi L\bar\varphi = \frac{d}{dx}\left[p(x)W(\varphi, \bar\varphi; x)\right]$$

and

$$2i(\text{Im }\lambda)\int_{a_0}^{b_0} s|\varphi|^2\,dx = p(b_0)W(\varphi, \bar\varphi; b_0) - p(a_0)W(\varphi, \bar\varphi; a_0). \quad (4.80)$$

If φ is also in D, we have

$$2i(\text{Im }\lambda)\int_a^b s|\varphi|^2\,dx = p(b)W(\varphi, \bar\varphi; b) - p(a)W(\varphi, \bar\varphi; a). \quad (4.80a)$$

Next we investigate whether (4.77) has any solutions of finite s norm. The following theorem of H. Weyl is fundamental.

Weyl's Theorem. *Let a be a regular point and b a singular point, and consider the equation*

$$-(pu')' + qu - \lambda su = 0, \quad a < x < b. \quad (4.81)$$

1. If for some particular value of λ every solution of (4.81) is of finite s norm over (a, b), then for any other value of λ, every solution is again of finite s norm over (a, b).

2. For every λ with $\text{Im }\lambda \neq 0$, there exists at least one solution of finite s norm over (a, b).

According to the theorem we can classify the behavior at the singular point b as follows: Either all solutions are of finite s norm over (a, b) for all λ (the so-called *limit-circle* case at b), or for $\text{Im }\lambda \neq 0$ there is exactly one solution (up to a multiplicative constant) of finite s norm over (a, b) (we then say that we have the *limit-point* case at b).

If a is a singular point but b is not, the same kind of classification can be used at a. If both a and b are singular, we introduce a point l such that $a < l < b$ and classify b according to the behavior of solutions over (l, b) and classify a according to the behavior of solutions in (a, l).

Proof of Weyl's theorem. Part 1. Let u_1 and u_2 be two independent solutions of (4.81). By assumption u_1 and u_2 have finite s norms over (a, b). For each fixed ξ, the function $\varphi_\xi(x) = u_1(\xi)u_2(x) - u_1(x)u_2(\xi)$ satisfies (4.81) and the conditions $\varphi_\xi(\xi) = 0$, $(d\varphi_\xi/dx)(\xi) = C/p(\xi)$, where C is independent of ξ.

Now let v be a solution of

$$-(pv')' + qv - \mu sv = 0$$

or

$$-(pv')' + qv - \lambda sv = (\mu - \lambda)sv.$$

From (1.50), with $a_0(x) = -p(x)$, we have

$$v(x) = \psi(x) + (\mu - \lambda) \int_a^x -\frac{\varphi_\xi(x)}{C} s(\xi) v(\xi) d\xi,$$

where $\psi(x)$ is some linear combination of u_1 and u_2. This integral equation can be used to estimate $\|v\|_s$. First we note that $(\alpha + \beta)^2/2 \le \alpha^2 + \beta^2$ for any real numbers α and β, so that

$$\frac{|v|^2}{2} \le |\psi|^2 + \frac{2|\mu - \lambda|^2}{|C|^2}\left[|u_1(x)|^2 \left|\int_a^x u_2 s v \, d\xi\right|^2 + |u_2(x)|^2 \left|\int_a^x u_1 s v \, d\xi\right|^2\right].$$

Using the Schwarz inequality,

$$\frac{|v|^2}{2} \le |\psi|^2 + \frac{2|\mu - \lambda|^2}{|C|^2}\bigg[|u_1(x)|^2 \int_a^x s|u_2|^2 \, d\xi$$

$$+ |u_2(x)|^2 \int_a^x s|u_1|^2 \, d\xi\bigg]\bigg[\int_a^x s|v|^2 \, d\xi\bigg]$$

or

$$\frac{|v|^2}{2} \le |\psi|^2 + \frac{2|\mu - \lambda|^2}{|C|^2}\left[|u_1(x)|^2\|u_2\|_s^2 + |u_2(x)|^2\|u_1\|_s^2\right]\left[\int_a^x s|v|^2 \, d\xi\right].$$

Since u_1 and u_2 are of finite s norm over (a, b), there exists a constant M such that

$$\frac{|v|^2}{2} \le |\psi|^2 + M(|u_1(x)|^2 + |u_2(x)|^2) \int_a^x s|v|^2 \, d\xi.$$

With $a < a_0 < b_0 < b$, we have

$$\frac{1}{2}\int_{a_0}^{b_0} s|v|^2 \, dx \le \int_{a_0}^{b_0} s|\psi|^2 \, dx + M\left[\int_{a_0}^{b_0}(s|u_1|^2 + s|u_2|^2)dx\right]\left[\int_a^{b_0} s|v|^2 \, d\xi\right].$$

Because u_1 and u_2 are of finite s norms, we can choose a_0 sufficiently near b so that $M\left[\int_{a_0}^{b_0}(s|u_1|^2 + s|u_2|^2)dx\right] < \frac{1}{4}$. Then

$$\frac{1}{4}\int_{a_0}^{b_0} s|v|^2 \, dx \le \int_{a_0}^{b_0} s|\psi|^2 \, dx + \frac{1}{4}\int_a^{a_0} s|v|^2 \, d\xi.$$

Now let $b_0 \to b$; since ψ is of finite s norm over (a, b), we find that $\int_{a_0}^b s|v|^2 \, dx$ is finite, and therefore $\int_a^b s|v|^2 \, dx$ is finite, which completes the proof.

Part 2. Let $\varphi(x, \lambda)$ and $\psi(x, \lambda)$ be the two independent solutions of (4.81) satisfying, respectively, the initial conditions at the regular point a:

$$\varphi(a, \lambda) = -\alpha_2, \qquad \varphi'(a, \lambda) = \frac{\alpha_1}{p(a)};$$

$$\psi(a, \lambda) = \alpha_1, \qquad \psi'(a, \lambda) = \frac{\alpha_2}{p(a)},$$

where α_1 and α_2 are real and not both 0. We observe that φ and ψ are independent, since $p(a)W(\varphi, \psi; a) = -\alpha_1^2 - \alpha_2^2 \neq 0$. Moreover, $\varphi(x, \lambda)$ satisfies the boundary condition at $x = a$:

$$\alpha_1 \varphi(a, \lambda) + \alpha_2 p(a)\varphi'(a, \lambda) = 0,$$

whereas $\psi(x, \lambda)$ satisfies the boundary condition

$$\alpha_2 \psi(a, \lambda) - \alpha_1 p(a)\psi'(a, \lambda) = 0.$$

Every solution of (4.81), except multiples of ψ, can be written as a constant multiple of

$$u = \varphi + m\psi,$$

where m is a complex number.

We shall consider a regular boundary condition at a point $b_0 < b$, which we write in the form

$$\beta_1 u(b_0, \lambda) + \beta_2 p(b_0)u'(b_0, \lambda) = 0, \tag{4.82}$$

where β_1 and β_2 are arbitrary real numbers, not both 0. We are interested in investigating the limit as $b_0 \to b$ [The boundary condition (4.82) cannot be imposed directly at the point b, because there is no guarantee that u or u' is finite at the singular point b.] A function u satisfies the condition (4.82) for some real β_1, β_2 if and only if

$$p(b_0)W(u, \bar{u}; b_0) = 0. \tag{4.82a}$$

One should observe that ψ cannot satisfy the boundary condition at $x = b_0$ for Im $\lambda \neq 0$. Otherwise by (4.80a) we would have $\int_a^{b_0} s|\psi|^2 \, dx = 0$, which is impossible. Now $u = \varphi + m\psi$ will satisfy (4.82) if and only if

$$m = -\frac{h\varphi(b_0, \lambda) + p(b_0)\varphi'(b_0, \lambda)}{h\psi(b_0, \lambda) + p(b_0)\psi'(b_0, \lambda)}, \quad \text{with } h = \frac{\beta_1}{\beta_2}. \tag{4.83}$$

The admissible numbers m are equally well characterized by condition (4.82a); that is,

$$p(b_0)[W(\varphi, \bar{\varphi}; b_0) + m\bar{m}W(\psi, \bar{\psi}; b_0) + mW(\psi, \bar{\varphi}; b_0) + \bar{m}W(\varphi, \bar{\psi}; \beta_0)] = 0. \tag{4.83a}$$

Now let h run through all real numbers. Then, if Im $\lambda \neq 0$, m describes a circle in the complex plane; on the other hand, if Im $\lambda = 0$, then φ, φ', ψ, ψ' are real, and therefore m describes the real axis. The center of the circle and its radius are easily calculated from (4.83a), which may be rewritten as $[m - A][\bar{m} - \bar{A}] = r^2$, where

$$A = -\frac{W(\varphi, \bar{\psi}; b_0)}{W(\psi, \bar{\psi}; b_0)}$$

is the center of the circle and

$$r^2 = \frac{W(\psi, \bar{\varphi}; b_0)W(\varphi, \bar{\psi}; b_0) - W(\varphi, \bar{\varphi}; b_0)W(\psi, \bar{\psi}; b_0)}{W^2(\psi, \bar{\psi}; b_0)}$$

determines the radius r.

From (4.80) we have

$$p(b_0)W(\psi, \bar{\psi}; b_0) = 2i(\operatorname{Im} \lambda) \int_a^{b_0} s|\psi|^2 \, dx;$$

$$p(b_0)W(\varphi, \bar{\varphi}; b_0) = 2i(\operatorname{Im} \lambda) \int_a^{b_0} s|\varphi|^2 \, dx.$$

One can also show that

$$W(\varphi, \bar{\varphi}; b_0)W(\psi, \bar{\psi}; b_0) - W(\psi, \bar{\varphi}; b_0)W(\varphi, \bar{\psi}; b_0) = |W(\varphi, \psi; b_0)|^2.$$

Since $p(b_0)W(\varphi, \psi; b_0) = p(a)W(\varphi, \psi; a) = -\alpha_1^2 - \alpha_2^2$, we have

$$r^2 = \frac{\alpha_1^2 + \alpha_2^2}{4(\operatorname{Im} \lambda)^2 \left[\int_a^{b_0} s|\psi|^2 \, dx \right]^2}; \qquad r = \frac{(\alpha_1^2 + \alpha_2^2)^{1/2}}{2|\operatorname{Im} \lambda| \left[\int_a^{b_0} s|\psi|^2 \, dx \right]}. \qquad (4.84)$$

Our circle can be described in still another way. We have

$$W(u, \bar{u}; a) = W(\varphi + m\psi, \bar{\varphi} + \bar{m}\bar{\psi}; a) = mW(\psi, \bar{\varphi}; a) + \bar{m}W(\varphi, \bar{\psi}; a)$$

$$= (m - \bar{m})\left[\frac{\alpha_1^2 + \alpha_2^2}{p(a)} \right].$$

By (4.80) we find

$$p(b_0)W(u, \bar{u}; b_0) = 2i(\operatorname{Im} m)(\alpha_1^2 + \alpha_2^2) + 2i(\operatorname{Im} \lambda) \int_a^{b_0} s|u|^2 \, dx. \quad (4.85)$$

Thus the circle $W(u, \bar{u}; b_0) = 0$ consists of those values of m for which

$$\int_a^{b_0} s|u|^2 \, dx = -\frac{(\operatorname{Im} m)}{(\operatorname{Im} \lambda)}(\alpha_1^2 + \alpha_2^2).$$

One can easily verify that the interior of the circle consists of those values of m for which

$$\int_a^{b_0} s|u|^2 \, dx < -\frac{(\operatorname{Im} m)}{(\operatorname{Im} \lambda)}(\alpha_1^2 + \alpha_2^2).$$

It is quite clear from (4.84) that, as b_0 increases (with λ fixed, $\operatorname{Im} \lambda \neq 0$), the radius r decreases. Moreover, it can be shown that each circle is contained in those for smaller values of b_0. Therefore, as $b_0 \to b$, either the circles approach a *limit circle* $C_b(\lambda)$ or a *limit point* $m_b(\lambda)$. If m is any point on the limit circle or if m is the limit point, m is interior to all circles and, therefore,

$$\int_a^{b_0} s|u|^2 \, dx < -\frac{(\text{Im } m)}{(\text{Im } \lambda)}(\alpha_1^2 + \alpha_2^2)$$

and

$$\int_a^b s|u|^2 \, dx \le -\frac{(\text{Im } m)}{(\text{Im } \lambda)}(\alpha_1^2 + \alpha_2^2).$$

Hence if $\text{Im } \lambda \ne 0$ and m is either the limit point or any point on the limit circle, the solution $u = \varphi + m\psi$ is of finite s norm over (a, b). In the limit-circle case we have from (4.84) that $\int_a^b s|\psi|^2 \, dx < \infty$, so that the independent solutions ψ and $\varphi + m\psi$ are of finite s norm and therefore every solution of (4.81) is of finite s norm. Although this has been proved only for $\text{Im } \lambda \ne 0$, it follows from part 1 that all solutions are of finite s norm for all λ.

In the limit-point case, we have from (4.84) that ψ is of infinite s norm over (a, b) if $\text{Im } \lambda \ne 0$. Therefore, there is exactly one solution of finite s norm in this case—$u = \varphi(x, \lambda) + m_b(\lambda)\psi(x, \lambda)$.

We also observe that if m is the limit point or any point on the limit circle, then with $u = \varphi + m\psi$,

$$\lim_{b_0 \to b} p(b_0)W(u, \bar{u}; b_0) = 0. \tag{4.86}$$

EXAMPLES

Example 1. **(a)** $-u'' - \lambda u = 0$, $0 < x < \infty$; $s(x) = 1$, $p(x) = 1$. Then 0 is a regular point but ∞ is a singular point. If $\lambda = 0$, the general solution is $Ax + B$. Since no nontrivial solution is in $\mathscr{L}_2^{(s)}(0, \infty)$, we must be in the *limit-point case at* ∞. Indeed, whenever $\text{Im } \lambda \ne 0$, the solution $\exp(i\sqrt{\lambda}x)$ is the only one of finite norm. (If $\text{Im } \lambda = 0$ and $\text{Re } \lambda \ge 0$, no solution is of finite norm, whereas for $\text{Im } \lambda = 0$ and $\text{Re } \lambda < 0$, exactly one solution is of finite norm.)

(b) $-u'' - \lambda u = 0$, $-\infty < x < \infty$; $s(x) = 1$, $p(x) = 1$. Both the points $+\infty$ and $-\infty$ are in the *limit-point* case.

Example 2. *Bessel's equation of order 0, with parameter λ.* **(a)** Consider

$$-(xu')' - \lambda xu = 0, \qquad 0 < x < b; \qquad s(x) = x, \quad p(x) = x, \tag{4.87}$$

where b is a *finite* positive number. Since $p(0) = 0$, the point $x = 0$ is a singular point. If $\lambda = 0$, the functions $u_1(x) = 1$ and $u_2(x) = \log x$ are independent solutions of the equation. Since $\int_0^b xu_1^2 \, dx$ and $\int_0^b xu_2^2 \, dx$ are both finite, we have the *limit-circle case at* $x = 0$. This agrees with the fact that the general solution $[AJ_0(\sqrt{\lambda} \, x) + BN_0(\sqrt{\lambda} \, x)]$ for arbitrary λ is of finite s norm.

(b) Consider the same equation as in **(a)** over the interval $a < x < \infty$, where a is positive. The point at ∞ is singular, and since $\int_a^\infty x u_1^2 \, dx$ and $\int_a^\infty x u_2^2 \, dx$ are both infinite, we have the *limit-point case at* ∞ (this conclusion would follow even if only one of the integrals diverged). Observe that for λ not in $[0, \infty)$ the solution $H_0^{(1)}(\sqrt{\lambda}\, x)$ is the only one which is of finite s norm. If λ is in $[0, \infty)$, there is no solution of finite s norm.

Example 3. *The Hermite equation.* Consider the Hermite differential equation

$$-u'' + x^2 u - \lambda u = 0, \qquad -\infty < x < \infty; \qquad s(x) = 1, \quad p(x) = 1. \qquad (4.88)$$

Let $u = z \exp(x^2/2)$, then the equation for z becomes

$$-z'' - 2xz' - z = \lambda z. \qquad (4.88a)$$

If $\lambda = -1$, the functions $z_1 = 1$ and $z_2 = \int_0^x \exp(-t^2)dt$ are independent solutions, so that for this value of λ two independent solutions of the original equation are

$$u_1(x) = \exp(x^2/2), \qquad u_2(x) = \exp(x^2/2) \int_0^x \exp(-t^2)dt.$$

Since $u_1(x)$ is of infinite norm in $(-\infty, l)$ and in (l, ∞) for any finite l, we have the *limit-point case at both* $-\infty$ *and* $+\infty$.

Example 4. Consider

$$-(xu')' - \lambda \frac{u}{x} = 0, \qquad 0 < x < \infty; \qquad p(x) = x, \quad s(x) = \frac{1}{x}. \qquad (4.89)$$

This equation occurs as the radial equation when separation of variables is used for the two-dimensional Laplace equation. If $\lambda = 0$, two independent solutions are $u_1(x) = 1$, $u_2(x) = \log x$. Since $\int_0^l s|u_1|^2 \, dx = \int_0^l 1/x \, dx = \infty$ and $\int_0^l s|u_2|^2 \, dx = \infty$, surely we have the *limit-point case at* $x = 0$. In fact, for $\lambda \neq 0$, two independent solutions are $x^{i\sqrt{\lambda}}$ and $x^{-i\sqrt{\lambda}}$; if λ is not in $(0, \infty)$, only the second of these is of finite s norm over the finite interval $(0, l)$ whereas if λ is real positive, neither is of finite s norm. This case should be contrasted with Example 2(a), illustrating how sensitively the classification depends on $s(x)$. To analyze the point at ∞, we observe that for $\lambda = 0$ we have

$$\int_l^\infty s|u_1|^2 \, dx = \infty \qquad \text{and} \qquad \int_l^\infty s|u_2|^2 \, dx = \infty,$$

so that we are in the *limit-point case at* ∞.

Example 5. *The Legendre equation is*

$$-[(1 - x^2)u']' + \lambda u = 0, \quad -1 < x < 1; \qquad p(x) = 1 - x^2, \quad s(x) = 1. \ (4.90)$$

Since $p(1) = p(-1) = 0$, both -1 and 1 are singular points. For $\lambda = 0$, two independent solutions are $u_1(x) = 1$ and $u_2(x) = \log(1 + x) - \log(1 - x)$; clearly $\int_{-1}^{l} |u_1|^2 \, dx$ and $\int_{l}^{1} |u_1|^2 \, dx$ are finite and one can verify that $\int_{-1}^{l} |u_2|^2 \, dx$ and $\int_{l}^{1} |u_2|^2 \, dx$ are also finite. Thus we have the *limit-circle case at* $x = \pm 1$.

Inhomogeneous Equation and Green's Function

The Green's function is the solution $g(x|\xi; \lambda)$ of

$$Lg - \lambda s g = \delta(x - \xi), \qquad a < x, \xi < b, \qquad (4.91)$$

satisfying some additional boundary conditions at $x = a$ and $x = b$.† For definiteness we shall assume that a is a regular point and b is a singular point. The required modifications for the case of two singular points will be illustrated in the examples.

In line with the notation used in the proof of part 2 of Weyl's theorem, we shall take the boundary condition at $x = a$ to be of the form

$$B_a(g) = \alpha_2 g \bigg|_{x=a} - \alpha_1 p(a) \frac{dg}{dx}\bigg|_{x=a} = 0, \qquad (4.92)$$

where α_1 and α_2 are real and not both 0.

The most obvious approach for constructing g is to introduce the regular boundary condition (4.82) at a point $b_0 < b$ and then take the limit as $b_0 \to b$.

According to part 2 of the proof of Weyl's theorem, the Green's function for the regular problem over (a, b_0) is

$$\hat{g} = A\psi(x_<, \lambda) u(x_>, \lambda),$$

where $u = \varphi + m\psi$ and m is a point on the circle (4.83) (the point corresponding to the value of $h = \beta_1/\beta_2$ used in the boundary condition at b_0).

Since $\hat{g}$ satisfies (4.91) for $a < x, \xi < b_0$, we have the jump condition

$$\left(\frac{d\hat{g}}{dx}\right)_{x=\xi+} - \left(\frac{d\hat{g}}{dx}\right)_{x=\xi-} = -\frac{1}{p(\xi)} = AW(\psi, u; \xi),$$

where

$$W(\psi, u; \xi) = W(\psi, \varphi + m\psi; \xi) = W(\psi, \varphi; \xi) = \frac{\alpha_1^2 + \alpha_2^2}{p(\xi)}.$$

Hence

$$\hat{g} = -(\alpha_1^2 + \alpha_2^2)[\psi(x_<, \lambda)][\varphi(x_>, \lambda) + m\psi(x_>, \lambda)], \qquad (4.93)$$

where m is a function of h, b_0, and λ.

---

† It might appear more natural to define $\tilde{g}$ from $A\tilde{g} - \lambda\tilde{g} = \delta(x - \xi)$, but our definition turns out to be a trifle more convenient. Of course, g and $\tilde{g}$ are related by $\tilde{g} = sg$.

From our treatment of the regular case, we know that the functions φ and ψ are entire functions of λ, whereas m is a meromorphic function of λ (that is, the only singularities of m in the finite part of the λ plane are poles). We can easily investigate what happens as $b_0 \to b$ in the case where b is of the *limit-point* type and Im $\lambda \neq 0$. Indeed it then follows that regardless of h, $\lim\limits_{b \to b_0} m(b_0, h, \lambda) = m_b(\lambda)$, where $m_b(\lambda)$ is the limit point. Simultaneously, $\varphi(x, \lambda) + m\psi(x, \lambda)$ approaches the only solution which is of finite s norm. This indicates that we do not need to calculate the Green's function $\hat{g}$ but can directly focus our attention on g by requiring that the solution of the inhomogeneous equation used for $x > \xi$ be of finite s norm.

Thus we can characterize g either as

$$g(x \,|\, \xi; \lambda) = \lim_{b \to b_0} \hat{g}(x \,|\, \xi; \lambda) \tag{4.94}$$

or as the only solution of

$$Lg - \lambda s g = \delta(x - \xi), \quad a < x, \, \xi < b; \quad B_a(g) = 0, \quad \int_a^b s|g|^2 \, dx < \infty. \tag{4.94a}$$

Observe that the unambiguous construction of g is always possible for all λ such that Im $\lambda \neq 0$. As a function of λ, $m_b(\lambda)$ may be meromorphic or may also have branch cuts. If we accept the validity of (4.44), we have

$$\frac{1}{2\pi i} \oint g(x \,|\, \xi; \lambda) d\lambda = -\frac{\delta(x - \xi)}{s(x)}.$$

The integral around the large circle in the complex plane can be reduced to a sum of residues [which stem from the poles of $m_b(\lambda)$ and correspond to the point spectrum] plus an integral over a portion of the real axis [which arises from the branch cut in $m_b(\lambda)$ and corresponds to the continuous spectrum]. Thus we find

$$\frac{1}{2\pi i} \oint g(x \,|\, \xi; \lambda) d\lambda = -\sum_n \varphi_n(x)\bar{\varphi}_n(\xi) - \int \varphi_\nu(x)\bar{\varphi}_\nu(\xi) d\nu. \tag{4.95}$$

The problem studied in Section 4.3 has a continuous spectrum, $0 \leq \nu < \infty$, and no point spectrum. The same is true for Exercises 4.21 and 4.22. On the other hand, Exercise 4.24 shows the possibility of both a continuous spectrum and a point spectrum. Next we consider an example of the limit-point case which is particularly important in applications and which has a pure point spectrum. If there is a pure point spectrum, it can be shown that the *eigenfunctions form a complete orthonormal set with weight s*. Although we do not prove this theorem, we shall often give ad hoc proofs in particular examples, these proofs usually relying on the theory of integral equations.

For problems which have regular end points or singular end points in the limit-circle case, we show later that we always have a pure point spectrum, and (4.95) contains only the series term and not the integral term.

EXAMPLES

Example 1.   Consider Bessel's equation of order v with parameter λ:

$$-(x\varphi')' + \frac{v^2}{x}\varphi - \lambda x\varphi = 0; \qquad 0 < x < 1; \qquad s(x) = x, \quad p(x) = x.$$

$$(4.96)$$

Here v^2 is a given real positive number with v its positive square root.

The point $x = 0$ is singular, and with $\lambda = 0$ we find $\varphi_1(x) = x^v$ and $\varphi_2(x) = x^{-v}$ to be independent solutions of the equation. Clearly,

$$\int_0^1 s|\varphi_1|^2 \, dx < \infty;$$

$$\int_0^1 s|\varphi_2|^2 \, dx = \infty, \qquad v \geq 1;$$

$$\int_0^1 s|\varphi_2|^2 \, dx < \infty, \qquad v < 1.$$

Thus we have the limit-point case at $x = 0$ if $v \geq 1$ [otherwise we have the limit-circle case; see, for instance, equation (4.87)].

Then consider the case $v \geq 1$. We impose the boundary condition $\varphi(1) = 0$ at the regular point b. Then $g(x \mid \xi; \lambda)$ can be constructed for all λ such that Im $\lambda \neq 0$ and also for some real values of λ. For instance, for $\lambda = 0$ we have

$$g(x \mid \xi; 0) = C(x_<^v)(x_>^{-v} - x_>^v),$$

where C is to be determined from the jump condition on dg/dx at $x = \xi$. We readily find $C = 1/2v$.

The homogeneous problem

$$-(x\varphi')' + \frac{v^2}{x}\varphi - \lambda s\varphi = 0, \qquad 0 < x < 1, \quad \varphi(1) = 0, \qquad \int_0^1 x|\varphi|^2 \, dx < \infty$$

$$(4.97)$$

can be translated into the integral equation

$$\varphi(x) = \lambda \int_0^1 g(x \mid \xi; 0)s(\xi)\varphi(\xi)d\xi$$

or

$$\mu\psi(x) = \int_0^1 k(x, \xi)\psi(\xi)d\xi, \qquad (4.98)$$

where

$$\mu = \frac{1}{\lambda}, \qquad \psi(x) = \sqrt{s}\varphi(x), \qquad k(x, \xi) = \sqrt{s(x)s(\xi)}g(x \mid \xi; 0).$$

It is easily verified that $\int_0^1 \int_0^1 |k|^2 \, dx \, d\xi < \infty$. Thus the set of eigenfunctions of (4.98) forms a *complete orthonormal set* and those of (4.97) form a complete set with weight s. The eigenfunctions of (4.95) are (not normalized)

$$J_\nu(\sqrt{\lambda_i} x),$$

where $\sqrt{\lambda_i}$ is the ith root of $J_\nu(x)$. It is instructive to calculate the normalization factor by constructing $g(x \mid \xi; \lambda)$ and using (4.95). For Im $\lambda \neq 0$, $J_\nu(\sqrt{\lambda} x)$ and $Z_\nu(\sqrt{\lambda} x) = N_\nu(\sqrt{\lambda}) J_\nu(\sqrt{\lambda} x) - J_\nu(\sqrt{\lambda}) N_\nu(\sqrt{\lambda} x)$ are independent solutions of (4.97). Now $J_\nu(\sqrt{\lambda} x)$ satisfies the condition of finite s norm, whereas $Z_\nu(\sqrt{\lambda} x)$ satisfies the boundary condition at $x = 1$. Moreover,

$$\frac{dZ}{dx}(\sqrt{\lambda} x)\big|_{x=1} = \sqrt{\lambda}\,[N_\nu(\sqrt{\lambda}) J_\nu'(\sqrt{\lambda}) - J_\nu(\sqrt{\lambda}) N_\nu'(\sqrt{\lambda})] = \sqrt{\lambda}\, W(N_\nu, J_\nu; \sqrt{\lambda}).$$

It is known (see Appendix B) that

$$W(J_\nu, N_\nu; x) = \frac{2}{\pi x}, \tag{4.99}$$

so that

$$\frac{dZ}{dx}(\sqrt{\lambda} x)\bigg|_{x=1} = -\frac{2}{\pi}.$$

Since $Z_\nu(\sqrt{\lambda} x)$ satisfies initial conditions independent of λ at the regular point $x = 1$, it follows that Z is an entire function of λ. The Green's function $g(x \mid \xi; \lambda)$ is given by

$$g = A J_\nu(\sqrt{\lambda} x_<) Z_\nu(\sqrt{\lambda} x_>),$$

where

$$A \sqrt{\lambda}\, W(J_\nu, Z_\nu; \sqrt{\lambda} \xi) = -\frac{1}{\xi}.$$

Now

$$W(J_\nu, Z_\nu; x) = -J_\nu(\sqrt{\lambda}) W(J_\nu, N_\nu; x) = \frac{-2 J_\nu(\sqrt{\lambda})}{\pi x}.$$

Hence

$$A = \frac{\pi}{2 J_\nu(\sqrt{\lambda})},$$

so that

$$g(x \mid \xi; \lambda) = \frac{\pi}{2 J_\nu(\sqrt{\lambda})} J_\nu(\sqrt{\lambda} x_<) Z_\nu(\sqrt{\lambda} x_>). \tag{4.100}$$

The function $Z_\nu(\sqrt{\lambda} x_>)$ is an entire function of λ. The functions $J_\nu(\sqrt{\lambda} x_<)$ and $J_\nu(\sqrt{\lambda})$ are analytic except for a branch on the positive real λ axis. This branch disappears for the quotient $J_\nu(\sqrt{\lambda} x_<)/J_\nu(\sqrt{\lambda})$; in fact, directly above and on the real axis we have

$$\frac{J_\nu(\sqrt{\lambda} x_<)}{J_\nu(\sqrt{\lambda})} = \frac{J_\nu(|\lambda|^{1/2} x_<)}{J_\nu(|\lambda|^{1/2})},$$

whereas directly below the real axis,

$$\frac{J_\nu(\sqrt{\lambda} x_<)}{J_\nu(\sqrt{\lambda})} = \frac{J_\nu(-|\lambda|^{1/2} x_<)}{J_\nu(-|\lambda|^{1/2})} = \frac{J_\nu(|\lambda|^{1/2} x_<)}{J_\nu(|\lambda|^{1/2})},$$

where we have used $J_\nu(-u) = e^{\nu \pi i} J_\nu(u)$. Therefore the only singularities of (4.100) are simple poles at the zeros of $J_\nu(\sqrt{\lambda})$, all of which are real. Let λ_k be such a zero; then the corresponding residue of (4.100) at λ_k is

$$R(\lambda_k) = \frac{\pi(\sqrt{\lambda_k})}{J_\nu'(\sqrt{\lambda_k})} J_\nu(\sqrt{\lambda_k} x_<) Z_\nu(\sqrt{\lambda_k} x_>),$$

which, from the definition of Z_ν, becomes

$$R(\lambda_k) = \frac{\pi \sqrt{\lambda_k}}{J_\nu'(\sqrt{\lambda_k})} J_\nu(\sqrt{\lambda_k} x_<) N_\nu(\sqrt{\lambda_k}) J_\nu(\sqrt{\lambda_k} x_>)$$

$$= \frac{\pi \sqrt{\lambda_k} N_\nu(\sqrt{\lambda_k})}{J_\nu'(\sqrt{\lambda_k})} J_\nu(\sqrt{\lambda_k} x) J_\nu(\sqrt{\lambda_k} \xi).$$

From (4.99),

$$J_\nu(\sqrt{\lambda_k}) N_\nu'(\sqrt{\lambda_k}) - J_\nu'(\sqrt{\lambda_k}) N_\nu(\sqrt{\lambda_k}) = \frac{2}{\pi \sqrt{\lambda_k}};$$

hence

$$N_\nu(\sqrt{\lambda_k}) = -\frac{2}{\pi \sqrt{\lambda_k} J_\nu'(\sqrt{\lambda_k})}$$

and the residue at λ_k is

$$R(\lambda_k) = -\frac{2}{[J_\nu'(\sqrt{\lambda_k})]^2} J_\nu(\sqrt{\lambda_k} x) J_\nu(\sqrt{\lambda_k} \xi).$$

Therefore (4.95) yields

$$\frac{\delta(x - \xi)}{x} = \frac{\delta(x - \xi)}{\sqrt{x\xi}} = \sum_{k=1}^\infty \frac{2}{[J_\nu'(\sqrt{\lambda_k})]^2} J_\nu(\sqrt{\lambda_k} x) J_\nu(\sqrt{\lambda_k} \xi). \quad (4.101)$$

The normalized eigenfunctions are

$$\frac{\sqrt{2} \sqrt{x} J_\nu(\sqrt{\lambda_k} x)}{J_\nu'(\sqrt{\lambda_k})}.$$

From (4.101) we obtain the usual Fourier-Bessel expansion for an arbitrary function $f(x)$,

$$f(\xi) = 2 \sum_{k=1}^{\infty} \frac{\sqrt{\xi} J_\nu(\sqrt{\lambda_k}\xi)}{[J_\nu'(\sqrt{\lambda_k})]^2} \int_0^1 \sqrt{x} f(x) J_\nu(\sqrt{\lambda_k}x)\,dx. \qquad (4.102)$$

Although the expansion (4.102) has been proved only for $\nu \geq 1$, it actually holds for $\nu > -1$, as we shall see under the examples of the limit-circle type.

Example 2. *The Mellin transform.* As a second example we consider a problem already studied in connection with Weyl's theorem [see Example 4 and equation (4.89)]. The homogeneous equation is

$$-(xu')' - \lambda \frac{u}{x} = 0, \qquad 0 < x < \infty; \qquad p(x) = x, \quad s(x) = \frac{1}{x}.$$

As was shown previously, both the points $x = 0$ and $x = \infty$ are of the limit-point type. Two independent solutions are $u_1(x) = x^{i\sqrt{\lambda}}$ and $u_2(x) = x^{-i\sqrt{\lambda}}$. When λ is not in $[0, \infty)$, $\sqrt{\lambda} = \alpha + i\beta$, where $\beta > 0$ and $u_1(x)$ is the only solution of finite s norm in (l, ∞). Indeed we have

$$\int_l^\infty \frac{|u_1|^2}{x}\,dx = \int_l^\infty \frac{x^{-2\beta}}{x}\,dx = \int_l^\infty \frac{1}{x^{1+2\beta}}\,dx < \infty,$$

whereas

$$\int_l^\infty \frac{|u_2|^2}{x}\,dx = \int_l^\infty \frac{x^{2\beta}}{x}\,dx = \infty.$$

Similarly, $u_2(x)$ is the only solution of finite s norm in $(0, l)$ when λ is not in $[0, \infty)$. Therefore whenever λ is not in $[0, \infty)$ we can construct the Green's function $g(x|\xi; \lambda)$ which satisfies

$$-\frac{d}{dx}\left(x\frac{dg}{dx}\right) - \lambda\frac{g}{x} = \delta(x - \xi); \qquad 0 < x, \xi < \infty; \qquad \int_0^\infty \frac{|g|^2}{x}\,dx < \infty. \qquad (4.103)$$

We have

$$g = A x_<^{-i\sqrt{\lambda}} x_>^{i\sqrt{\lambda}}.$$

Using the matching condition at $x = \xi$, we find $A = i/2\sqrt{\lambda}$, so that

$$g = \frac{i}{2\sqrt{\lambda}} x_<^{-i\sqrt{\lambda}} x_>^{i\sqrt{\lambda}}. \qquad (4.104)$$

To find the spectral representation we use (4.95),

$$\frac{1}{2\pi i}\oint g\,d\lambda = -\frac{\delta(x - \xi)}{s(x)} = -x\delta(x - \xi). \qquad (4.105)$$

Now g, as given by (4.104), has no poles but has a branch on the positive real λ axis. Using the notation introduced in Section 4.3 [after (4.53)], we find

$$g_+ = \frac{i}{2|\lambda|^{1/2}} x_<^{-i|\lambda|^{1/2}} x_>^{i|\lambda|^{1/2}};$$

$$g_- = \frac{i}{-2|\lambda|^{1/2}} x_<^{i|\lambda|^{1/2}} x_>^{-i|\lambda|^{1/2}};$$

$$[g] = g_+ - g_- = \frac{i}{2|\lambda|^{1/2}} [x_<^{-i|\lambda|^{1/2}} x_>^{i|\lambda|^{1/2}} + x_<^{i|\lambda|^{1/2}} x_>^{-i|\lambda|^{1/2}}].$$

Since the right side is clearly symmetric in x, ξ, we have

$$[g] = \frac{i}{2|\lambda|^{1/2}} [x^{-i|\lambda|^{1/2}} \xi^{i|\lambda|^{1/2}} + \xi^{-i|\lambda|^{1/2}} x^{i|\lambda|^{1/2}}].$$

Now (4.105) reduces to

$$x\delta(x - \xi) = \int_0^\infty [g]d\lambda,$$

and letting $\lambda = v^2$,

$$x\delta(x - \xi) = \frac{1}{2\pi} \int_0^\infty (x^{-iv}\xi^{iv} + x^{iv}\xi^{-iv})dv; \qquad 0 < x, \xi < \infty. \quad (4.106)$$

Making the substitution $v' = -v$ in the second integral we find the alternative representation

$$x\delta(x - \xi) = \frac{1}{2\pi} \int_{-\infty}^\infty x^{-iv}\xi^{iv} \, dv; \qquad 0 < x, \xi < \infty. \quad (4.106a)$$

Equation (4.106a) is the nucleus of the Mellin transform. In fact, multiplying (4.106a) by $f(x)/x$ and integrating from 0 to ∞, we have

$$f(\xi) = \frac{1}{2\pi} \int_{-\infty}^\infty \xi^{iv} F_M(v)dv, \quad (4.107)$$

where

$$F_M(v) = \int_0^\infty \frac{f(x)}{x} x^{-iv} \, dx. \quad (4.108)$$

Formula (4.108) defines the Mellin transform F_M of f and (4.107) is the inversion formula. The reader should observe that the change of variable $y = \log x$ reduces (4.108) and (4.107) to the exponential form of the Fourier integral theorem (4.76). In fact, this same change of variable transforms $-(xu')' - (\lambda u/x) = 0$, $0 < x < \infty$, into $-y'' - \lambda y = 0$, $-\infty < y < \infty$. Thus the relation between (4.76) and (4.108) is a very natural one.

Now consider the inhomogeneous equation

$$Au - \lambda u = f \quad \text{or} \quad Lu - \lambda su = sf, \qquad a < x < b, \quad (4.109)$$

where f is of finite s norm over (a, b) and Im $\lambda \neq 0$.

We look for solutions u of finite s norm over (a, b); if either or both end points are regular, we attach boundary conditions of the form (4.92); at the end points which are singular in the *limit-point case*, no boundary condition is applied. The limit-circle case is discussed later. The one and only solution of (4.109) is given by

$$u(x) = \int_a^b g(x\,|\,\xi;\,\lambda)s(\xi)f(\xi)d\xi. \tag{4.110}$$

The only difficulty in the proof (which we omit) is to show that u is of finite s norm and that the integral operator which appears in (4.110) is bounded.

One can also write (4.110) as an expansion in terms of the functions $\varphi_n(x)$ and $\varphi_\nu(x)$ of (4.95). If we only have a point spectrum, the expansion is the usual series in eigenfunctions; in the case of a pure continuous spectrum, we have an integral expansion; and in the general case we have both a series and an integral contribution. Similar remarks apply to the bilinear expansion for the Green's function.

The Limit-Circle Case

We begin with a problem for which a is a regular point and b is a singular point of the limit-circle type. The reader will be able to supply the necessary changes when both a and b are in the limit-circle case.

The Green's function $g(x\,|\,\xi;\,\lambda)$ satisfies

$$Lg - \lambda sg = \delta(x - \xi) \quad \text{or} \quad Ag - \lambda g = \frac{\delta(x - \xi)}{s(x)}; \quad a < x, \xi < b.$$

At the point a we have a regular boundary condition of type (4.92), which determines the form of g for $x < \xi$; in fact, $g(x\,|\,\xi;\,\lambda) = C\psi(x, \lambda)$ for $x < \xi$, where $\psi(x, \lambda)$ is the nontrivial solution of the homogeneous equation which satisfies the given boundary condition $B_a(\psi) = 0$. To determine g for $x > \xi$, we must impose some kind of condition at $x = b$. The criterion of finite s norm is no longer sufficient to determine g unambiguously for $x > \xi$, since all solutions of the homogeneous equation satisfy this criterion! One possible approach is to impose a regular boundary condition $hy(b_0) + p(b_0)y'(b_0) = 0$, with h real, at a point $b_0 < b$ and then take the limit as $b_0 \to b$. The difficulty with this procedure is that to obtain all points on the limit circle at b it may be required to have h be a function of b_0. Instead we shall use an approach which deals directly with the entire interval $a < x < b$. Let λ_0 be a fixed value of λ such that Im $\lambda_0 \neq 0$. Consider a particular point $m(\lambda_0)$ on the limit circle corresponding to λ_0; the corresponding solution $u(x, \lambda_0) = \varphi(x, \lambda_0) + m\psi(x, \lambda_0)$ of $Lu - \lambda_0 su = 0$ satisfies the condition (4.86),

$$\lim_{b_0 \to b} p(b_0)W(u, \bar{u}; b_0) = 0. \tag{4.111}$$

In fact the criterion (4.111) selects exactly those solutions of $Lu - \lambda_0 su = 0$ which correspond to points on the limit circle. There are of course many such $u(x, \lambda_0)$, although u is not entirely arbitrary, since it must satisfy (4.111).

We claim that $\psi(x, \lambda_0)$ and $u(x, \lambda_0)$ are independent; otherwise u would be a constant multiple of ψ and therefore would satisfy both (4.111) and the condition at a, which can be rewritten $p(a)W(u, \bar{u} : a) = 0$. From (4.80a) it then follows that $u \equiv 0$, which is impossible.

The possibility of choosing u so as to satisfy (4.111) and be independent of ψ for real λ_0 is explored in some of the examples, but for the present we retain the assumption Im $\lambda_0 \neq 0$. Since ψ and u are independent solutions of $Lu - \lambda_0 su = 0$, we may assume

$$p(x)W(\psi, u; x) = -1, \tag{4.112}$$

so that

$$g(x \mid \xi; \lambda_0) = \psi(x_<, \lambda_0)u(x_>, \lambda_0). \tag{4.113}$$

Observe that for each choice of a function $u(x, \lambda_0)$ satisfying (4.111) we obtain a different Green's function.

Consider next the inhomogeneous system

$$Lv - \lambda_0 sv = sf \quad \text{or} \quad Av - \lambda_0 v = f; \quad a < x < b, \tag{4.114}$$

with $B_a(v) = 0$. One solution of (4.114) which satisfies the boundary condition at $x = a$ is

$$v(x, \lambda_0) = \int_a^b g(x \mid \xi; \lambda_0)s(\xi)f(\xi)d\xi$$

$$= u(x, \lambda_0)\int_a^x \psi(\xi, \lambda_0)s(\xi)f(\xi)d\xi + \psi(x, \lambda_0)\int_x^b u(\xi, \lambda_0)s(\xi)f(\xi)d\xi. \tag{4.115}$$

From (4.115) we observe that

$$v'(x, \lambda_0) = u'(x, \lambda_0)\int_a^x \psi(\xi, \lambda_0)s(\xi)f(\xi)d\xi + \psi'(x, \lambda_0)\int_x^b u(\xi, \lambda_0)s(\xi)f(\xi)d\xi,$$

and, therefore,

$$p(x)W(v, \bar{u}; x) = p(x)W(u, \bar{u}; x)\int_a^x \psi(\xi, \lambda_0)s(\xi)f(\xi)d\xi$$

$$+ p(x)W(\psi, \bar{u}; x)\int_x^b u(\xi, \lambda_0)s(\xi)f(\xi)d\xi.$$

Now let $x \to b$ and use the relation (4.111) to obtain

$$\lim_{b_0 \to b} p(b_0)W(v, \bar{u}; b_0) = 0. \tag{4.116}$$

Thus (4.116) may be regarded as a boundary condition satisfied by the particular solution (4.115) of (4.114). In fact, (4.115) is the one and only solution of the system

$$Lv - \lambda_0 sv = sf, \quad a < x < b; \quad B_a(v) = 0; \quad p(b)W(v, \bar{u}; b) = 0.$$
$$(4.117)$$

We can easily show that v is of finite s norm and even stronger results hold. From (4.115) we have

$$\|v\|_s^2 = \int_a^b s(x)\left[\left|\int_a^b g(x \mid \xi; \lambda_0)s(\xi)f(\xi)d\xi\right|^2\right]dx$$

$$\leq \left[\int_a^b\int_a^b s(x)s(\xi) \mid g(x \mid \xi; \lambda_0) \mid^2 dx\, d\xi\right]\|f\|_s^2.$$

Thus if we succeed in showing that

$$\int_a^b\int_a^b s(x)s(\xi)|g|^2 dx\, d\xi < \infty, \qquad (4.118)$$

we will have proved not only that $\|v\|_s$ is finite, but that $k(x, \xi) = \sqrt{s(x)}\sqrt{s(\xi)}\, g(x \mid \xi; \lambda_0)$ is a Hilbert-Schmidt kernel. From (4.113) we have

$$\int_a^b |g|^2 s(\xi)d\xi = |u(x, \lambda_0)|^2 \int_a^x s(\xi)|\psi(\xi, \lambda_0)|^2\, d\xi + |\psi(x, \lambda_0)|^2 \int_x^b s(\xi)|u(\xi, \lambda_0)|^2\, d\xi$$

$$\leq |u(x, \lambda_0)|^2\|\psi\|_s^2 + |\psi(x, \lambda_0)|^2\|u\|_s^2,$$

so that

$$\int_a^b\int_a^b s(x)s(\xi)|g|^2\, dx\, d\xi \leq 2\|u\|_s^2\|\psi\|_s^2.$$

Since we are in the limit-circle case, both $\|u\|_s$ and $\|\psi\|_s$ are finite and the assertion (4.118) has been proved.

Next we consider the homogeneous problem

$$Lw - \lambda sw = 0, \quad a < x < b, \quad B_a(w) = 0, \quad p(b)W(w, \bar{u}; b) = 0,$$
$$(4.119)$$

where $u(x, \lambda_0)$ is a solution of $Lu - \lambda_0 su = 0$ satisfying $p(b)W(u, \bar{u}; b) = 0$; that is, $u(x, \lambda_0)$ is the solution corresponding to a particular point on the limit circle for λ_0.

The differential equation in (4.119) can be rewritten

$$Lw - \lambda_0 sw = (\lambda - \lambda_0)sw,$$

so that

$$w(x, \lambda) = (\lambda - \lambda_0)\int_a^b g(x \mid \xi; \lambda_0)s(\xi)w(\xi, \lambda)d\xi, \qquad (4.120)$$

where g is given by (4.113). The same argument used to prove (4.116) when applied to (4.120) shows that $w(x,\lambda)$ satisfies the boundary condition $p(b)W(w, \bar{u}; b) = 0$. It is obvious from (4.120) that $B_a(w) = 0$, since $B_a(g) = 0$.

The integral equation (4.120) can be rewritten

$$\mu z(x) = \int_a^b k(x, \xi) z(\xi) d\xi, \tag{4.121}$$

where

$$\mu = \frac{1}{\lambda - \lambda_0}, \qquad z = \sqrt{s}w, \qquad k = \sqrt{s(x)}\sqrt{s(\xi)}g(x \mid \xi; \lambda_0).$$

Since k is a Hilbert-Schmidt kernel, (4.121) has at most denumerably many eigenvalues; hence there must exist a real number θ which is not an eigenvalue of (4.119). If we then repeat our derivation using $\lambda_0 = \theta$, k will be a real symmetric Hilbert-Schmidt kernel. The eigenfunctions of (4.119) must therefore form a complete orthonormal set with weight s.

EXAMPLE

Consider Bessel's equation of order 0 [see (4.87)],

$$-(xw')' - \lambda xw = 0, \quad 0 < x < 1, \quad p(x) = x, \quad s(x) = x. \tag{4.122}$$

At the regular point $x = 1$ we impose the boundary condition $w(1) = 0$. For $\lambda = 0$, the functions $\psi = \log x$ and $\varphi = -1 + A \log x$ are independent solutions, the first of which satisfies the boundary condition at $x = 1$. The condition $\lim_{x \to 0} p(x)W(\varphi, \bar{\varphi}; x) = 0$ is satisfied if and only if A is real. For any such particular choice of A, we can construct $g(x \mid \xi; 0)$; since $p(x)W(\varphi, \psi; x) = -1$,

$$g(x \mid \xi; 0) = (-1 + A \log x_<)(\log x_>) = \varphi(x_<)\psi(x_>). \tag{4.123}$$

Every solution of the integral equation

$$w(x) = \lambda \int_0^1 g(x \mid \xi; 0)\xi w(\xi) d\xi \tag{4.124}$$

clearly satisfies (4.122) and the boundary condition at the point $x = 1$. The boundary condition satisfied at $x = 0$ is easily calculated in the same way as was done for (4.116), and we find

$$\lim_{x \to 0} p(x)W(w, \varphi; x) = 0; \tag{4.125}$$

that is,

$$\lim_{x \to 0} [Aw - (A \log x - 1)xw'] = 0. \tag{4.125a}$$

Thus the integral equation (4.124) is equivalent to the differential system

$$-(xw')' - \lambda xw = 0, \quad 0 < x < 1, \quad w(1) = 0, \quad \lim_{x \to 0} [Aw - (A \log x - 1)xw'] = 0. \tag{4.126}$$

Now (4.124) can be rewritten

$$\mu z(x) = \int_0^1 k(x, \xi) z(\xi) d\xi, \tag{4.127}$$

where

$$\mu = \frac{1}{\lambda}, \qquad z(x) = \sqrt{x} w(x), \qquad k(x, \xi) = \sqrt{x\xi} g(x \mid \xi; 0).$$

The kernel $k(x, \xi)$ is a real symmetric Hilbert-Schmidt kernel. Hence the eigenfunctions of (4.127) form a complete set [note that $\mu = 0$ is not an eigenvalue of (4.127)], and so the eigenfunctions of (4.126) form a complete orthonormal set with weight $s(x) = x$.

Each possible real choice of A is (4.125a) yields a different eigenvalue problem; the one most frequently encountered is obtained by choosing $A = 0$. Then the boundary condition at $x = 0$ to be associated with (4.126) is merely

$$\lim_{x \to 0} xw' = 0. \tag{4.128}$$

Two independent solutions of the differential equation (4.126) are $J_0(\sqrt{\lambda}x)$ and $N_0(\sqrt{\lambda}x)$. Since $N_0'(x) \sim 2/\pi x$ near $x = 0$, only $J_0(\sqrt{\lambda}x)$ satisfies (4.128). Thus the boundary condition (4.128) is *in this case* equivalent to the requirement of finiteness at $x = 0$. The corresponding eigenfunctions are $J_0(\sqrt{\lambda_k}x)$, where λ_k is determined from $J_0(\sqrt{\lambda_k}) = 0$.

To find the normalization constant for these eigenfunctions, we can proceed in a number of different ways. Possibly the simplest is to imitate the derivation of (4.101). We then find that

$$\left\{ \frac{\sqrt{2} J_0(\sqrt{\lambda_k}x)}{J_0'(\sqrt{\lambda_k})} \right\}$$

is an orthonormal set with weight x over $(0, 1)$.

It is remarkable and somewhat unexpected that different choices of A in (4.125a) yield other orthonormal sets, for which there does not seem to be any use in practical applications. To find the eigenfunctions of (4.126) ($A \neq 0$), we let $w = CJ_0(\sqrt{\lambda}x) + DN_0(\sqrt{\lambda}x)$ and apply first the boundary condition at $x = 0$. Using the fact that near $x = 0$

$$J_0(\sqrt{\lambda}x) \sim 1, \qquad N_0(\sqrt{\lambda}x) \sim \frac{2}{\pi} \log x + \frac{2}{\pi} [\log(\sqrt{\lambda}/2) + \gamma];$$

$$J_0'(\sqrt{\lambda}x) \sim 0, \qquad N_0'(\sqrt{\lambda}x) \sim \frac{2}{\pi\sqrt{\lambda}x},$$

we find

$$D = -C \frac{A(\pi/2)}{1 + A[\gamma + \log(\sqrt{\lambda}/2)]}.$$

Applying the boundary condition at $x = 1$, we deduce that λ must satisfy

$$J_0(\sqrt{\lambda}) + A\left[\frac{\gamma + \log\sqrt{\lambda}}{2}\right]J_0(\sqrt{\lambda}) - A\frac{\pi}{2}N_0(\sqrt{\lambda}) = 0.$$

If the roots of this equation are labeled $\lambda_1, \ldots, \lambda_k, \ldots$, the eigenfunctions are proportional to

$$w_k(x) = J_0(\sqrt{\lambda_k}x) - \frac{A(\pi/2)}{1 + A[\gamma + \log(\sqrt{\lambda_k}/2)]}N_0(\sqrt{\lambda_k}x). \qquad (4.129)$$

EXERCISES

4.25 In the same vein as the example just preceding these exercises, discuss Bessel's equation of order v with $0 < v^2 < 1$. Show that (4.101) and (4.102) still hold.

4.26 *The Hankel transform of order* 0. Consider $-(xw')' - \lambda xw = 0$, $0 < x < \infty$. For $\lambda = 0$, two independent solutions are $w = 1$ and $w = \log x$. Since neither of these is of finite s norm over (l, ∞), ∞ is in the limit-point case. Of course $x = 0$ is of the limit-circle type. To construct $g(x\,|\,\xi; \lambda)$, we require that g be of finite s norm over $(0, \infty)$ and that $\lim_{x\to0} x(dg/dx) = 0$ (or equivalently that g be finite at $x = 0$). Show that for λ not in $[0, \infty)$,

$$g(x\,|\,\xi; \lambda) = \frac{\pi i}{2}J_0(\sqrt{\lambda}\rho_<)H_0^{(1)}(\sqrt{\lambda}\rho_>).$$

By appealing to the well-known formulas

$$J_0(-x) = J_0(x), \qquad H_0^{(1)}(x) - H_0^{(1)}(-x) = 2J_0(x),$$

and by using (4.44) or (4.95), obtain

$$\frac{\delta(x - \xi)}{x} = \int_0^\infty \mu J_0(\mu x)J_0(\mu \xi)d\mu. \qquad (4.130)$$

From (4.130) derive the pair of formulas

$$F_H(\mu) = \int_0^\infty xJ_0(\mu x)f(x)dx; \qquad (4.131)$$

$$f(x) = \int_0^\infty \mu J_0(\mu x)F_H(\mu)d\mu. \qquad (4.132)$$

Here $F_H(\mu)$ is *the Hankel transform of order* 0 of f and (4.132) is the inversion formula.

4.27 *The Hankel transform of order v.* Consider $-(xw')' + (v^2w/x) - \lambda xw = 0$, $0 < x < \infty$; $s(x) = x$, where v^2 is a given positive number and v is its positive square root.

By inspecting the solutions for $\lambda = 0$, show that $x = \infty$ is always in the *limit-point case* and that $x = 0$ is in the *limit-point case* when $v \geq 1$ and in the *limit-circle case* when $v < 1$. Construct the Green's function $g(x|\xi; \lambda)$ by requiring that it be of finite s norm over $(0, \infty)$ and, if $v < 1$, imposing a condition of finiteness at $x = 0$. Obtain

$$g(x|\xi; \lambda) = \frac{\pi i}{2} J_v(\sqrt{\lambda} x_<) H_v^{(1)}(\sqrt{\lambda} x_>).$$

Integrate along a large circle in the complex plane and use the relations

$$J_v(-x) = e^{v\pi i} J_v(x);$$

$$H_v^{(1)}(-x) = e^{-v\pi i}[H_v^{(1)}(x) - 2J_v(x)]$$

to show that

$$\frac{\delta(x - \xi)}{x} = \int_0^\infty \mu J_v(\mu x) J_v(\mu \xi) d\mu. \tag{4.133}$$

Obtain formulas similar to (4.131) and (4.132).

4.28 *The Mellin sine transform.* Consider again (4.89), but now over $0 < x < 1$. We impose the boundary condition $w(1) = 0$ at the regular point $x = 1$. Since $x = 0$ is in the limit-point case, the Green's function is unambiguously defined from

$$-(xg')' - \frac{\lambda g}{x} = \delta(x - \xi), \quad 0 < x, \xi < 1; \quad g|_{x=1} = 0, \quad \int_0^1 \frac{|g|^2}{x} dx < \infty.$$

Show that

$$g = \frac{i}{2\sqrt{\lambda}} x_<^{-i\sqrt{\lambda}}(x_>^{i\sqrt{\lambda}} - x_>^{-i\sqrt{\lambda}}).$$

Since g has a branch on the real λ axis and no other singularities, show that

$$x\delta(x - \xi) = \frac{2}{\pi} \int_0^\infty [\sin (v \log x)][\sin (v \log \xi)] dv. \tag{4.134}$$

Obtain the pair of formulas

$$\hat{F}_s(v) = \int_0^1 \frac{1}{x} [\sin (v \log x)] f(x) dx; \tag{4.135}$$

$$f(x) = \frac{2}{\pi} \int_0^\infty [\sin (v \log x)] \hat{F}_s(v) dv. \tag{4.136}$$

For want of a better term, we call $\hat{F}_s(v)$ the Mellin sine transform of $f(x)$; then (4.136) is the inversion formula. By making the substitution $y = \log x$, show the connection with the Fourier sine transform [(4.60) and (4.61)].

4.29 *The Mellin cosine transform.* Same exercise as 4.28, except that the boundary condition at $x = 1$ is $dg/dx|_{x=1} = 0$.

4.30 *The Kantorovich-Lebedev transform.* Consider Bessel's equation, where the role of the parameters has been interchanged,

$$-(xw')' + \mu x w - \frac{\lambda w}{x} = 0, \qquad 0 < x < \infty; \qquad p(x) = x, \quad s(x) = \frac{1}{x}.$$

Here μ is a *given real number* (which we take to be positive) and λ plays the role of the eigenvalue parameter. (This equation is discussed in Appendix B, Section B.3.) Setting $\lambda = 0$, we find the independent solutions $I_0(\sqrt{\mu}x)$ and $K_0(\sqrt{\mu}x)$, neither of which is of finite s norm in $(0, l)$. In (l, ∞), only K_0 is of finite s norm, so that $x = 0$ and $x = \infty$ are both in the *limit-point case*. The Green's function satisfies

$$-(xg')' + \mu x g - \frac{\lambda g}{x} = \delta(x - \xi), \quad 0 < x, \xi < \infty; \qquad \int_0^\infty \frac{|g|^2}{x}\, dx < \infty.$$

Show that

$$g(x|\xi; \lambda) = I_{-i\sqrt{\lambda}}(\sqrt{\mu}x_<)K_{-i\sqrt{\lambda}}(\sqrt{\mu}x_>).$$

Integrate along a large circle in the complex plane and then use (4.44) and the relations

$$K_{-\alpha}(x) = K_\alpha(x), \qquad I_{-\alpha}(x) - I_\alpha(x) = \frac{2}{\pi} \sin \pi\alpha\, K_\alpha(x)$$

to show that

$$x\delta(x - \xi) = \frac{2}{\pi^2} \int_0^\infty v \sinh \pi v\, K_{iv}(\sqrt{\mu}x)K_{iv}(\sqrt{\mu}\xi)dv. \qquad (4.137)$$

Obtain the pair of formulas

$$F_K(v) = \int_0^\infty \frac{f(x)}{x} K_{iv}(\sqrt{\mu}x)dx; \qquad\qquad (4.138)$$

$$f(x) = \frac{2}{\pi^2} \int_0^\infty v \sinh \pi v\, K_{iv}(\sqrt{\mu}x)F_K(v)dv. \qquad (4.139)$$

4.31 *The Modified Green's function.* Consider the regular eigenvalue problem

$$L\varphi - \lambda s\varphi = 0, \quad a < x < b; \quad B_a(\varphi) = 0, \quad B_b(\varphi) = 0. \quad (4.140)$$

There is no difficulty in translating this system into an eigenvalue integral equation by using the Green's function corresponding to a value of λ which is *not* an eigenvalue of (4.140). Sometimes the solutions of the homogeneous equation $L\varphi - \lambda s\varphi = 0$ are easily calculated only if λ is some particular number which may happen to be an eigenvalue of (4.140). We now explore the possibility of translating (4.140) into an integral equation by using the modified Green's function [see (1.89)] corresponding to the parametric value λ_1, which is a simple eigenvalue of (4.140).

Let $g(x|\xi; \lambda)$ be the ordinary Green's function satisfying

$$Lg - \lambda sg = \delta(x - \xi), \quad a < x, \xi < b; \quad (B_a g) = 0, \quad B_b(g) = 0.$$

Then by (4.42),

$$g(x|\xi; \lambda) = \sum_{n=1}^{\infty} \frac{\varphi_n(x)\bar{\varphi}_n(\xi)}{\lambda_n - \lambda}$$

and g is defined for each $\lambda \neq \lambda_1, \ldots$; moreover, g is symmetric $[g(x|\xi; \lambda) = \bar{g}(\xi|x; \lambda)]$ when λ is real $\neq \lambda_1, \ldots$. We observe that g cannot be constructed for $\lambda = \lambda_1$, but the function

$$g_M(x|\xi; \lambda) = g - \frac{\varphi_1(x)\bar{\varphi}_1(\xi)}{\lambda_1 - \lambda} = \sum_{n=2}^{\infty} \frac{\varphi_n(x)\bar{\varphi}_n(\xi)}{\lambda_n - \lambda}$$

does not have a singularity at $\lambda = \lambda_1$, so that we can define

$$g_M(x|\xi; \lambda_1) = \lim_{\lambda \to \lambda_1} g_M(x|\xi; \lambda) = \sum_{n=2}^{\infty} \frac{\varphi_n(x)\bar{\varphi}_n(\xi)}{\lambda_n - \lambda_1}. \tag{4.141}$$

It is easily seen that $g_M(x|\xi; \lambda_1)$ satisfies the system

$$Lg_M - \lambda_1 sg_M = \delta(x - \xi) - s(x)\varphi_1(x)\bar{\varphi}_1(\xi); \quad B_a(g_M) = 0, \quad B_b(g_M) = 0. \tag{4.142}$$

The solution of (4.142) is determined only up to a solution of the homogeneous system, $C\varphi_1(x)$. The particular solution (4.141) is symmetric and satisfies the condition

$$\int_a^b g_M(x|\xi; \lambda_1)s(x)\bar{\varphi}_1(x)dx = 0. \tag{4.143}$$

Now consider the integral equation

$$\mu w(x) = \int_a^b g_M(x|\xi; \lambda_1)s(\xi)w(\xi)d\xi. \tag{4.144}$$

Show that $\mu_k = 1/(\lambda_k - \lambda_1)$, $k = 2, \ldots$, are eigenvalues of (4.144) with corresponding eigenfunctions $w_k = \varphi_k$. Moreover, show that $\mu = 0$ is an eigenvalue with eigenfunction φ_1.

The integral equation (4.144) is equivalent to

$$\mu[\sqrt{s(x)}w(x)] = \int_a^b \sqrt{s(x)}\sqrt{s(\xi)}g_M(x|\xi;\lambda_1)[\sqrt{s(\xi)}w(\xi)]d\xi. \quad (4.145)$$

Since the kernel $\sqrt{s(x)}\sqrt{s(\xi)}\,g_M$ is symmetric, the set of all eigenfunctions of (4.145) will be a complete orthonormal set if

$$\int_a^b\int_a^b s(x)s(\xi)|g_M|^2\,dx\,d\xi < \infty.$$

Thus the eigenfunctions of (4.140) are complete with weight s.

In the regular case, this result has been established previously without using the modified Green's function. On the other hand, in singular problems, we shall often prove completeness on an ad hoc basis, and occasionally it is convenient to use a modified Green's function for this purpose (see Exercise 4.32, for instance).

4.32 *The Legendre equation.* Consider the equation

$$-[(1-x^2)u']' - \lambda u = 0, \qquad -1 < x < 1. \quad (4.146)$$

As was seen in (4.90), the points $x = \pm 1$ are of the limit-circle type. Explicit solutions of (4.146) can be found by setting $u = \sum_{n=0}^{\infty} a_n x^n$. Substitution in (4.146) yields the recursion formula

$$a_{n+2} = \frac{n(n+1)-\lambda}{(n+1)(n+2)}(a_n). \quad (4.147)$$

If we choose $a_1 = 0$, then $a_3, a_5, \ldots$ all vanish and we obtain an even solution of (4.146). Similarly, if $a_0 = 0$, then $a_2, a_4, \ldots$ all vanish, and we have an odd solution of (4.146). These two solutions are clearly independent solutions of (4.146).

Now, for either of these solutions, we have for n sufficiently large and real λ,

$$\frac{a_{n+2}}{a_n} > 1 - \frac{\varepsilon}{n}, \quad (4.148)$$

unless λ is of the form $k(k+1)$, where k is a nonnegative integer (in which case $0 = a_{k+2} = a_{k+4} = \cdots$ and the series reduces to a polynomial). From (4.148), by comparison with the series $\sum_{k=1}^{\infty}(x^k/k) = -\log(1-x)$, one can show that $\sum_{n=1}^{\infty} a_n x^n$ becomes infinite either at $x = +1$ or $x = -1$. Therefore, (4.146) has solutions which are bounded in $-1 < x < 1$, if and only if $\lambda = k(k+1)$. In this case there is one bounded solution which is a polynomial $P_k(x)$ of degree k; the polynomial $P_k(x)$, normalized so that $P_k(1) = 1$, is known as the kth *Legendre polynomial*.

To prove the completeness of the set $P_k(x)$, we use the modified Green's function discussed in Exercise 4.31. We consider the eigenvalue problem (4.146) with the requirement that u be finite at $x = \pm 1$. It follows that $\lambda = 0$ is an eigenvalue with normalized eigenfunction $u(x) = 1/\sqrt{2}$, so that $P_0(x) = 1$. The modified Green's function $g_M(x \mid \xi; 0)$ is the symmetric solution of

$$-[(1 - x^2)g_M']' = \delta(x - \xi) - \frac{1}{2}, \quad g_M \text{ finite at } x = \pm 1. \quad (4.149)$$

A straightforward calculation yields

$$g_M = \log 2 - \tfrac{1}{2} - \tfrac{1}{2} \log(1 + x_>)(1 - x_<). \quad (4.150)$$

It can be shown that

$$\int_{-1}^{1} \int_{-1}^{1} |g_M|^2 \, dx \, d\xi < \infty. \quad (4.151)$$

The integral equation

$$\mu w(x) = \int_{-1}^{1} g_M(x \mid \xi; 0) w(\xi) d\xi$$

has the eigenvalues $\mu_k = 1/\lambda_k$, $k = 1, 2, \ldots$, with the eigenfunctions $P_k(x)$, and also the eigenvalue $\mu = 0$ with the eigenfunction $P_0(x)$. By (4.151) it follows that the set $P_0(x), P_1(x), \ldots$ is a complete orthogonal set. Moreover, one can show that

$$\int_{-1}^{1} P_n^2(x) dx = \frac{2}{2n + 1}. \quad (4.152)$$

The boundary condition of finiteness at $x \pm 1$ can be replaced by $\lim_{x \to \pm 1} (1 - x^2)u' = 0$ obtained from $\lim_{x \to \pm 1} p(x)W(u, 1; x) = 0$.

4.33 *The Hermite equation.* Consider as in (4.88) the equation

$$-u'' + x^2 u - \lambda u = 0, \quad -\infty < x < \infty, \quad (4.153)$$

for which $x = \pm \infty$ are in the limit-point case. We look for solutions for which $\int_{-\infty}^{\infty} |u|^2 \, dx < \infty$. For the case $\lambda = -1$, we have shown that $\exp(x^2/2)$ and $\exp(x^2/2)\int_{0}^{x} [\exp(-t^2)]dt$ are independent solutions of the equation. The functions $u_1(x) = \exp(x^2/2)\int_{-\infty}^{x} [\exp(-t^2)]dt$ and $u_2(x) = \exp(x^2/2)\int_{x}^{\infty} [\exp(-t^2)]dt$ are therefore also independent solutions, the first of which is in $\mathcal{L}_2^{(c)}(-\infty, 0)$ and the second in $\mathcal{L}_2^{(c)}(0, \infty)$. We can therefore construct $g(x \mid \xi; -1)$. Show that

$$g(x \mid \xi; -1) = \frac{1}{\sqrt{\pi}} u_1(x_<) u_2(x_>).$$

Moreover, show that

$$\int_{-\infty}^{\infty} \int_{-\infty}^{\infty} |g|^2 \, dx \, d\xi < \infty, \qquad (4.154)$$

so that the eigenfunctions of (4.153) form a complete set. Make the substitution $u = z \exp(-x^2/2)$ to obtain

$$-z'' + 2xz' + z - \lambda z = 0.$$

By setting $z(x) = \sum_{n=0}^{\infty} a_n x^n$, find the recursion formula

$$a_{n+2} = \frac{(2n+1) - \lambda}{(n+1)(n+2)}.$$

Show that unless $\lambda = \lambda_k = 2k + 1$, where $k = 0, 1, 2, \ldots$, $u(x)$ will not be in $\mathscr{L}_2^{(c)}(-\infty, \infty)$.

To find explicitly the eigenfunctions of (4.153), we first note that $\exp(-x^2/2)$ is an eigenfunction corresponding to $\lambda_0 = 1$. By induction show that the eigenfunction corresponding to $\lambda_k = 2k + 1$ is $u_k = \exp(-x^2/2)H_k(x)$, where

$$H_k(x) = (-1)^k \exp(x^2) \frac{d^k \exp(-x^2)}{dx^k}, \qquad k = 0, 1, 2, \ldots,$$

are the *Hermite polynomials.* Prove that

$$\int_{-\infty}^{\infty} \exp(-x^2) H_k^2(x) dx = 2^k k! \sqrt{\pi}, \qquad k = 0, 1, 2, \ldots.$$

Show that $u_k(x)$ satisfies the integral equation

$$\theta y(x) = \int_{-\infty}^{\infty} \left[\exp \frac{(x^2 + t^2)}{2} \right] \left[\exp \left(-\frac{x^2 + t^2 - 2xt\alpha}{1 - \alpha^2} \right) \right] \frac{y(t)}{[1 - \alpha^2]^{1/2}} \, dt,$$

with α fixed, $0 < \alpha < 1$. What are the eigenvalues?

Hence show that, by an extension of the bilinear formula,

$$\left[\exp \left(\frac{x^2 + t^2}{2} \right) \right] \left[\exp \left(-\frac{x^2 + t^2 - 2xt\alpha}{1 - \alpha^2} \right) \right]$$

$$= (1 - \alpha^2)^{1/2} \sum_{n=0}^{\infty} u_n(x) u_n(t) \frac{\alpha^n}{n! 2^n}.$$

4.34 Consider Bessel's equation of order 0 with parameter λ over the interval (a, ∞), where $a > 0$. Let the boundary condition at $x = a$ be $u(a) = 0$. Find the spectral decomposition for this operator and the appropriate transform pairs.

4.35 Consider the Schrödinger equation

$$-u'' + q(x)u = \lambda u, \qquad -\infty < x < \infty, \qquad (4.155)$$

where

$$q(x) = \begin{cases} 0, & |x| < a; \\ v, & |x| > a, \end{cases}$$

where v is a given positive constant.

The problem arises in quantum mechanics in the study of the motion of a particle in a rectangular potential well. Show that there is a point spectrum (for $0 < \lambda \leq v$) containing only a finite number of eigenvalues. Show that every value of $\lambda > v$ is in the continuous spectrum. Find the spectral representation of the operator in (4.155).

SUGGESTED READINGS FOR CHAPTER 4

The letters E, I, and A indicate elementary, intermediate, and advanced books, respectively.

Spectral Theory
(I) Friedman, B., *Principles and Techniques of Applied Mathematics*, Wiley, New York, 1956.
(A) Hellwig, G., *Differentialoperatoren der mathematischen Physik*, Springer, Berlin, 1964.
(A) Neumark, M. A., *Linear Differentialoperatoren*, Akademie-Verlag, Berlin, 1960.
(A) Titchmarsh, E. C., *Eigenfunction Expansions Associated with Second-Order Differential Equations*, Oxford University Press, Oxford, 1946.
(I) Yosida, K., *Lectures on Differential and Integral Equations*, Interscience, New York, 1960.

APPENDIX A

A.1 STATIC AND DYNAMIC PROBLEMS FOR STRINGS AND MEMBRANES

(a) A taut string, lying on the smooth horizontal xy plane, is initially stretched, under a tension T, between two points on the x axis. A transverse load $f(x)$ measured in units of force/length, is applied to the string as in Figure A.1 and gives rise to a deflection $u(x)$ shown in Figure A.2. Any load

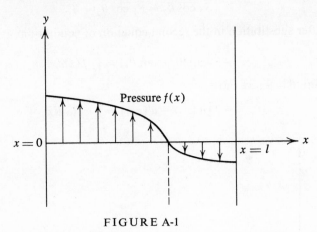

FIGURE A-1

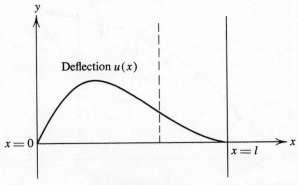

FIGURE A-2

or deflection is considered positive if it is in the positive y direction. In what follows we shall suppose that the load $f(x)$ is known as a function of x for the string in its deflected state.

Consider the portion of the deflected string between the x coordinates x_1 and x_2. As shown in Figure A.3, the loads acting on this portion of the string are the tensile forces S_1 and S_2 and the applied distributed load $f(x)$ which contributes solely a force in the y direction equal to $\int_{x_1}^{x_2} f(x)dx$. Since the table is smooth, there is no frictional force; moreover, gravity does not enter into the x and y equations of equilibrium, which are

$$S_2 \cos \theta_2 = S_1 \cos \theta_1;$$

$$S_2 \sin \theta_2 + \int_{x_1}^{x_2} f(x)dx = S_1 \sin \theta_1.$$

The first equation shows that the x component of tension is constant throughout the string and we shall identify this component with the initial tension T in the string. Thus

$$S_2 \cos \theta_2 = S_1 \cos \theta_1 = T,$$

and, after substitution in the second equation of equilibrium,

$$-T(\tan \theta_2 - \tan \theta_1) = \int_{x_1}^{x_2} f(x)dx.$$

Since $\tan \theta = u'$, we have

$$-T[u'(x_2) - u'(x_1)] = \int_{x_1}^{x_2} f(x)dx. \qquad (A.1)$$

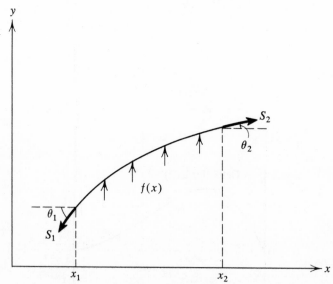

FIGURE A-3

If $f(x)$ is continuous, the theorem of the mean for integrals guarantees the existence of a number ξ, with $x_1 < \xi < x_2$, such that $\int_{x_1}^{x_2} f(x)dx = (x_2 - x_1)f(\xi)$. Therefore,

$$-T\frac{[u'(x_2) - u'(x_1)]}{x_2 - x_1} = f(\xi),$$

and, as $x_2 \to x_1$, the left side approaches $-Tu''(x_1)$ and the right side $f(x_1)$. We conclude that

$$- Tu'' = f(x), \tag{A.2}$$

at every point x where f is continuous. At points where f is not continuous we can still obtain useful information from (A.1); if f is piecewise continuous or merely integrable, then $\lim\limits_{x_2 \to x_1} \int_{x_1}^{x_2} f(x)dx = 0$, so that we at least know that u' remains continuous. On the other hand, if $f(x)$ is the generalized function $P\delta(x - \xi)$ corresponding to a concentrated force P at $x = \xi$, then we conclude from (A.1) that u' is discontinuous at $x = \xi$. Explicitly, we have

$$- T[u'(\xi+) - u'(\xi-)] = P. \tag{A.3a}$$

(b) If the string is embedded in an elastic medium which generates a restoring force proportional to the displacement, then (A.2) becomes

$$- Tu'' + ku = f, \tag{A.3b}$$

where k is the "spring constant" of the restoring medium.

(c) Consider the transverse vibration of a string [as in (a)] subject to a continuous transverse pressure $f(x, t)$. For the portion of the string between x_1 and $x_2 = x_1 + dx$, we have the equations of motion

$$S_2 \cos \theta_2 = S_1 \cos \theta_1,$$

$$S_2 \sin \theta_2 - S_1 \sin \theta_1 + f(x_1, t)dx = \rho \, dx \frac{\partial^2 u}{\partial t^2} (x_1, t),$$

where ρ is the mass density per unit length for the string in its rest position. Again we identify the constant x component of tension with the initial tension T. We obtain the partial differential equation

$$\rho \frac{\partial^2 u}{\partial t^2} - T\frac{\partial^2 u}{\partial x^2} = f(x, t), \tag{A.4}$$

by using arguments similar to those of (a). This equation is known as the *wave equation*.

If the string is immersed in a viscous medium, it will be subject to a resistive force proportional to the velocity. This would also be the case if the string were lying on a rough table instead of a smooth one. The differential equation then takes the form

$$\rho \frac{\partial^2 u}{\partial t^2} + \gamma \frac{\partial u}{\partial t} - T \frac{\partial^2 u}{\partial x^2} = f(x, t). \tag{A.5}$$

The above equation will be called the *dissipative wave equation*.

4. Consider the transverse vibrations of a taut membrane initially lying in the xy plane. The membrane is subject to a transverse pressure $f(x, y, t)$, that is, a pressure acting in a direction perpendicular to the initial plane of the membrane. If $u(x, y, t)$ is the deflection in the direction perpendicular to the xy plane, we find that u must satisfy the partial differential equation

$$\rho \frac{\partial^2 u}{\partial t^2} - T\left(\frac{\partial^2 u}{\partial x^2} + \frac{\partial^2 u}{\partial y^2}\right) = f(x, y, t), \tag{A.6}$$

where T is the tension in the membrane and ρ is the density per unit area, and $f(x, y, t)$ is measured in units of force/area.

A.2 STATIC AND DYNAMIC PROBLEMS FOR BEAMS AND PLATES

(*a*) Consider the static deflection of a beam of uniform cross section subject to a transverse load $f(x)$. Let V and M stand for the shear force and the bending moment on a cross section, respectively. The equations of equilibrium for an infinitesimal portion of the beam between x and $x + dx$ become

$$\frac{dM}{dx} = V, \qquad \frac{dV}{dx} = -f(x).$$

We can relate M to the deflection u by using Euler's assumption that plane sections remain plane after bending. If there is no net tensile force on a cross section, we find

$$-EIu'' = M,$$

where E is the modulus of elasticity and I is the moment of inertia of a cross section about the neutral axis. Using the previous relations between M, V, and f, we obtain

$$EI \frac{d^4 u}{dx^4} = f(x). \tag{A.7}$$

At a clamped end of a beam we must have $u = u' = 0$; at a simply supported end $u = u'' = 0$, since the moment must vanish; at a free end the moment and shear force both vanish, so that $u'' = u''' = 0$.

(b) If the beam is also under a net tensile force T, (A.7) becomes

$$EI \frac{d^4 u}{dx^4} - T \frac{d^2 u}{dx^2} = f(x).$$

If the beam rests on an elastic foundation, the appropriate equation is

$$EI \frac{d^4u}{dx^4} + ku = f(x).$$

(c) The transverse vibrations of a beam satisfy the equation

$$\rho \frac{\partial^2 u}{\partial t^2} + EI \frac{\partial^4 u}{\partial x^4} = f(x, t). \tag{A.8}$$

(d) The transverse vibrations of a plate are governed by the equation

$$\rho \frac{\partial^2 u}{\partial t^2} + D\nabla^4 u = f(x, t), \tag{A.9}$$

where D is the flexural rigidity of the plate and

$$\nabla^4 u = \nabla^2(\nabla^2 u) = \left(\frac{\partial^2}{\partial x^2} + \frac{\partial^2}{\partial y^2}\right)\left(\frac{\partial^2 u}{\partial x^2} + \frac{\partial^2 u}{\partial y^2}\right) = \frac{\partial^4 u}{\partial x^4} + 2\frac{\partial^4 u}{\partial x^2 \partial y^2} + \frac{\partial^4 u}{\partial y^4}.$$

A.3 THE EQUATION OF HEAT CONDUCTION

Consider the conduction of heat in a three-dimensional region R with boundary B. The thermal conductivity is a function of position $k(x) = k(x, y, z)$, and the specific heat per unit volume is also a function of position $c(x)$. We shall assume that there are given sources which generate heat at the rate $f(x, t)$ per unit volume per unit time within R (such sources might arise for instance from radioactivity). To derive a partial differential equation for the temperature $u(x, t)$, we consider an energy balance for an arbitrary subregion V of R between neighboring times t and $t + \Delta t$.

The total heat generated by the sources $f(x, t)$ within V is

$$\Delta t \int_V f(x, t)dV.$$

The heat flowing out of the boundary S of V is

$$\Delta t \int_S \left(-k\frac{\partial u}{\partial n}\right)dS,$$

where n is the outward normal to S. The increase of internal energy of V is

$$\int_V c\Delta u \, dV,$$

where $\Delta u(x, t) = \Delta t(\partial u/\partial t)(x, t)$ is the change in temperature at x between times t and $t + \Delta t$.

Assuming that no energy is converted to any form besides heat, we find, from conservation of energy,

$$\int_V f(\mathbf{x}, t)dV = \int_V c\frac{\partial u}{\partial t}\, dV - \int_S k\frac{\partial u}{\partial n}\, dS.$$

Since $k(\partial u/\partial n) = n \cdot k$ grad u, we conclude from the divergence theorem that

$$\int_S k\frac{\partial u}{\partial n}\, dS = \int_V \text{div}\,(k\,\text{grad}\,u)dV.$$

Hence

$$\int_V \left[c\frac{\partial u}{\partial t} - \text{div}\,(k\,\text{grad}\,u) - f(\mathbf{x}, t) \right] dV = 0,$$

for *every volume* V within R. Let us choose for V an infinitesimal volume surrounding a point $\mathbf{x}$; assuming that the integrand is continuous, we conclude that

$$c\frac{\partial u}{\partial t} - \text{div}\,(k\,\text{grad}\,u) = f(\mathbf{x}, t)$$

or

$$\frac{\partial u}{\partial t} - \frac{1}{c}\,\text{div}\,(k\,\text{grad}\,u) = \frac{1}{c}f(\mathbf{x}, t). \tag{A.10}$$

If k is constant, we obtain the simpler equation

$$\frac{\partial u}{\partial t} - \frac{k}{c}\nabla^2 u = \frac{f(\mathbf{x}, t)}{c}.$$

If c is a constant, it is usual to introduce the *thermal diffusivity* $a = k/c$, to obtain

$$\frac{\partial u}{\partial t} - a\,\nabla^2 u = \frac{f(\mathbf{x}, t)}{c}, \tag{A.11}$$

which is known as the *equation of heat conduction.*

APPENDIX B

B.1 BESSEL FUNCTIONS

Let α^2 be an arbitrary given complex number and let z be a complex variable. The ordinary linear differential equation of the second order,

$$\frac{d}{dz}\left(z\frac{du}{dz}\right) + \left(z - \frac{\alpha^2}{z}\right)u = 0, \tag{B.1}$$

is known as *Bessel's equation of order* α. According to this definition, the equations of order α and $-\alpha$ are one and the same equation. Any solution of Bessel's equation is called a *cylinder function*.

The *Bessel function* of order α, $J_\alpha(z)$, is defined by the series

$$J_\alpha(z) = \left(\frac{z}{2}\right)^\alpha \sum_{k=0}^{\infty} \frac{(-1)^k (z/2)^{2k}}{k!(\alpha + k)!}, \tag{B.2}$$

which we shall sometimes write

$$J_\alpha(z) = \left(\frac{z}{2}\right)^\alpha E_\alpha(z).$$

We note that the series for $E_\alpha(z)$ converges for all complex values of z, so that $E_\alpha(z)$ is an entire function of z. Thus when α is an integer, $J_\alpha(z)$ is an entire function of z, but when α is not an integer, $J_\alpha(z)$ has a branch cut (due to z^α) which we usually take along the real negative axis. Whether or not α is an integer, it is easily verified that $J_\alpha(z)$ is a solution of (B.1). The function $J_{-\alpha}(z)$, obtained from (B.2) by replacing α by $-\alpha$, is also a solution of (B.1). Moreover, the *Neumann function*

$$N_\alpha(z) = \frac{1}{\sin \alpha\pi} [\cos \alpha\pi J_\alpha(z) - J_{-\alpha}(z)], \tag{B.3}$$

and the *Hankel functions*

$$H_\alpha^{(1)}(z) = J_\alpha(z) + iN_\alpha(z);$$

$$H_\alpha^{(2)}(z) = J_\alpha(z) - iN_\alpha(z), \tag{B.4}$$

are all solutions of (B.1).

The general solution of (B.1) is a linear combination of two *independent* solutions. We must distinguish between two cases:

(a) If α *is not an integer*, then any two of the functions $J_\alpha, J_{-\alpha}, N_\alpha, H_\alpha^{(1)}, H_\alpha^{(2)}$ are independent. The general solution of (B.1) can therefore be written as a linear combination of any two of these five functions.

(b) If α *is an integer*, the functions J_α and $J_{-\alpha}$ are dependent. In fact, let α be a positive integer n; then the first n terms in the series for J_{-n} contain a factor of the form $1/(k-n)!$ with $k < n$; since this factor vanishes, we have

$$J_{-n}(z) = \left(\frac{z}{2}\right)^{-n} \sum_{k=n}^{\infty} \frac{(-1)^k(z/2)^{2k}}{k!(k-n)!}.$$

Introducing a new summation index $p = k - n$, we obtain

$$J_{-n}(z) = \left(\frac{z}{2}\right)^{-n} \sum_{p=0}^{\infty} \frac{(-1)^{p+n}(z/2)^{2p+2n}}{p!(p+n)!} = (-1)^n J_n(z). \tag{B.5}$$

The dependence of J_n and J_{-n} will be confirmed when we show later that their Wronskian vanishes.

The function $N_n(z)$ defined from (B.3) by taking the limit as $\alpha \to n$ is still a solution of (B.1), and is independent of $J_n(z)$. Any two of the functions J_n, N_n, $H_n^{(1)}$, $H_n^{(2)}$ are independent, and the general solution of (B.1) can be written as a linear combination of any two of these four functions.

B.2 WRONSKIAN RELATIONSHIPS

Let u_1 and u_2 be any two solutions of (B.1) (for the same value of α), and let $W[u_1, u_2; z]$ be their Wronskian; that is $W[u_1, u_2; z] = u_1 u_2' - u_2 u_1'$. Then, for any $z \neq 0$, it follows from the differential equation that

$$z W[u_1, u_2; z] = C,$$

where C is independent of z (but may, of course, depend on α). It will usually be easiest to determine C by considering the limiting value of the left side as $z \to 0$. For instance, if $u_1 = J_\alpha$ and $u_2 = J_{-\alpha}$, we have

$$J_\alpha = \left(\frac{z}{2}\right)^\alpha E_\alpha(z), \qquad J_\alpha' = \alpha\left(\frac{z}{2}\right)^\alpha \frac{E_\alpha(z)}{z} + \left(\frac{z}{2}\right)^\alpha E_\alpha'(z);$$

$$J_{-\alpha} = \left(\frac{z}{2}\right)^{-\alpha} E_{-\alpha}(z), \qquad J_{-\alpha}' = -\alpha\left(\frac{z}{2}\right)^{-\alpha} \frac{E_{-\alpha}(z)}{z} + \left(\frac{z}{2}\right)^{-\alpha} E_{-\alpha}'(z),$$

so that

$$\lim_{z \to 0} W[J_\alpha, J_{-\alpha}; z] = -2\alpha E_\alpha(0)E_{-\alpha}(0) = \frac{-2\alpha}{\alpha!(-\alpha)!}.$$

By a well-known property of factorial functions,

$$\frac{\alpha}{\alpha!(-\alpha)!} = \frac{\sin \alpha\pi}{\pi}.$$

Therefore,

$$W[J_\alpha, J_{-\alpha}; z] = -\frac{2 \sin \alpha\pi}{\pi z}. \tag{B.6}$$

We observe that this Wronskian vanishes if and only if α is an integer; thus J_α and $J_{-\alpha}$ are independent, unless α is an integer.

We can now easily establish the following formulas:

$$W[J_\alpha, N_\alpha; z] = \frac{2}{\pi z}; \tag{B.7}$$

$$W[J_\alpha, H_\alpha^{(1)}; z] = \frac{2i}{\pi z}. \tag{B.8}$$

B.3 THE MODIFIED BESSEL FUNCTION

The equation

$$\frac{d}{dz}\left(z\frac{du}{dz}\right) - \left(z + \frac{\alpha^2}{z}\right)u = 0, \tag{B.9}$$

differs from Bessel's equation only by the sign of the term zu. Since the formal substitution $t = iz$ reduces (B.9) to (B.1), we expect that the solutions of (B.9) will be cylinder functions of argument iz.

By tradition, the *modified Bessel function*,

$$I_\alpha(z) = \left(\frac{z}{2}\right)^\alpha \sum_{k=0}^\infty \frac{(z/2)^{2k}}{k!(\alpha+k)!}, \tag{B.10}$$

and the *Macdonald function*,

$$K_\alpha(z) = \frac{\pi}{2}\left[\frac{I_{-\alpha}(z) - I_\alpha(z)}{\sin \alpha\pi}\right], \tag{B.11}$$

have been used as the basic independent solutions of (B.9). These solutions are real when α and z are real and positive. The functions $I_\alpha(z)$ and $K_\alpha(z)$ are constant multiples of $J_\alpha(iz)$ and $H_\alpha^{(1)}(iz)$, respectively.

From (B.8) and the definitions (B.10) and (B.11), we obtain the Wronskian relationship

$$W[I_\alpha, K_\alpha; z] = -\frac{1}{z}. \tag{B.12}$$

B.4 THE BEHAVIOR OF CYLINDER FUNCTIONS AT ZERO AND AT INFINITY

If α has positive real part or if $\alpha = 0$, $J_\alpha(z)$ is the only solution of (B.1) that is bounded in a neighborhood of $z = 0$. Similarly, $I_\alpha(z)$ is the only solution of (B.9) that is bounded at the origin.

At $z = \infty$, we have the asymptotic formulas

$$H_\alpha^{(1)}(z) \sim \left(\frac{2}{\pi z}\right)^{1/2} \exp\left[i\left(z - \frac{\alpha\pi}{2} - \frac{\pi}{4}\right)\right] \tag{B.13}$$

$$H_\alpha^{(2)}(z) \sim \left(\frac{2}{\pi z}\right)^{1/2} \exp\left[-i\left(z - \frac{\alpha\pi}{2} - \frac{\pi}{4}\right)\right] \tag{B.14}$$

which are valid when $|\arg z| \leq \pi - \delta$, where δ is any positive number. From these formulas and (B.4) one can easily find asymptotic formulas for J_α and N_α. One can also show that $I_\alpha(z)$ is infinite at $z = \infty$, whereas

$$K_\alpha(z) \sim \left(\frac{\pi}{2z}\right)^{1/2} e^{-z}, \qquad |\arg z| \leq \pi - \delta. \tag{B.15}$$

Index

A

Abel's formula for the Wronskian, 60
Absolutely continuous functions, 145
Action of distribution, 28, 29, 31
Adjoint; *see also* Self-adjoint operators, Symmetry
  for differential system, 84
  formal, 40, 68
  for integral equation, 81, 212
  of integral operator, 212
  for linear equations, 80
  of matrix, 80, 152–54
  null space of, 171
  of transformation on Euclidean space, 152–54
  of transformation on Hilbert space, 170–80
Adjoint boundary conditions, 70
Adjoint Green's function, 71
Admissible pair, 170
Alternative theorems, 79–86
  for completely continuous operators, 187
  for differential equations, 82–86
  for equations in Euclidean space, 153–54
  for integral equations, 81, 221
  for linear equations, 79–81, 153
  for operators with closed range, 172

B

Banach spaces, 106
Basis
  dual, 138
  of eigenvectors, 160
  for Hilbert space, 119
  orthonormal, 123–24, 129
    characterization of, 127–28
  for vector space, 97
Bessel equation, 329–32
  eigenvalues of, 282
  Green's function for, 75, 77
  as singular problem, 301, 305–308, 313–15, 317, 321
Bessel functions, 329
  modified, 331
Bessel's inequality, 125
Bilinear concomitant, 69

Bilinear expansion
for Green's function, 261, 273, 290
for kernel, 238–40
Bilinear series: *see* Bilinear expansion
Bi-orthogonal set, 256
Boundary conditions, 64–69; *see also* Initial conditions
adjoint, 70
unmixed, 64, 66
Boundary value problem
regular, 269, 270
for second order equation, 64–91
singular, 269, 283–322

C

Cauchy principal value, 49
Cauchy sequences, 100
Closable operator, 142
Closed operator, 142, 168
Closed set. 114
Compact
operator: *see* Completely continuous transformation
set, 114, 164
Compatibility conditions,
see Consistency conditions
Complete orthonormal set, 127; *see also* Orthonormal basis
Completely continuous transformation, 185
alternative theorem for, 187
integral operator as, 192
Completeness
of metric space, 101–105
of orthonormal set, 127
Concentrated source: *see* Dirac delta function
Conjunct, 69
Consistency conditions, 80, 83, 85, 154, 201, 221, 265
Convergence
Cauchy, 100
of distributions, 42
in the mean, 117–18, 131
of test functions, 30

uniform, 131
weak, 133
Courant minimax principle, 225

D

Deficiency, 181
Degenerate eigenvalue, 213
Delta function: *see* Dirac delta function
Delta sequence, 24–27
Dense set, 114
Dependence
criterion for, 60
of set of functions, 59–60, 118
of set of vectors, 97, 118
Dimension of vector space, 97
Dipole, 25–26, 35
Dirac delta function, 6–7, 18–27, 33
expansion of, 273
sifting property of, 22–24
Distance function: *see* Metric
Distributional solutions of differential equations, 51–58
Distributions, 28–58
action on test functions, 28–29, 31
convergence of, 42
delta, 33
differentiation of, 37, 41
dipole, 35
divergent integrals and, 47–50
Fourier series of, 45–47
fundamental solution and, 54, 56
as linear functionals, 28, 31
operations on, 35–36
order of, 40
pseudofunctions and, 48–51
regular, 33
singular, 33
as solutions of differential equations, 53
values of, 37
Domain
of differential operator, 76
of function, 93, 95
of transformation, 95

E

Eigenfunctions
  completeness of, 219, 220
  of integral operator, 213
  normalization of, 274, 278
  orthogonality of, 213, 270
  of self-adjoint system, 220, 270
Eigenmanifold, 156
Eigenvalues
  approximations for, 228–36
  degenerate, 213
  existence of, 214
  extended problem of, 248–49
  extremal principles for, 162, 187–90,
    214–17
  of integral operator, 212–13
  multiplicity of, 156–57, 214
  simple, 213
  of transformation on Euclidean
    space, 154, 156
  of transformation on Hilbert space,
    181
Equal almost everywhere, 33, 105
Essentially regular transformation, 166
Existence and uniqueness
  of Green's function, 66
  for inhomogeneous integral
    equation, 221
  for initial value problems, 58, 59,
    61
Expansion theorem, 218
Extremal principles
  for eigenvalues, 162, 187–90, 214–
    17, 223–36
  for inhomogeneous equation,
    245–50

F

Finite part of divergent integrals, 48
Fourier-Bessel expansion, 308
Fourier coefficients, 125
Fourier cosine transform, 293
Fourier series
  of distributions, 44–46, 50, 51
Fourier sine transform, 287

Fourier sum, 125
Fourier transform, 47, 294
Fredholm integral equations
  of first kind, 195, 201
  of second kind, 195
Functionals, 134, 245; *see also* Linear
    functionals
Fundamental solution, 54, 62; *see also*
    Green's function
  causal, 56
  pole of, 62

G

Galerkin equations, 244, 245, 248
Galerkin's method, 244, 245
Generalized function, 34; *see also*
    Distributions
Generalized solutions of differential
    equations, 53
Gram-Schmidt procedure, 122
Green's formula, 70
Green's function, 1–18, 54–56, 65–69,
    71–78, 86–91, 219–20, 261–68,
    271–82, 284–95, 303–21
  adjoint, 70
  for Bessel's equation, 75, 77
  existence and uniqueness of, 66
  for initial value problems, 56, 66
  as integral operator, 12, 199, 219
  modified, 86–91, 316–19
  for regular boundary value
    problems, 66, 271
  for singular problems, 303–304
  singularities of, 274, 304

H

Hankel functions, 329
Hankel transforms, 315–16
Heat conduction equation, 327–28
Heaviside function, 20, 27, 34, 38
Heaviside sequence, 27
Hermite equation, 302, 320–21
Hermite polynominals, 321
Hermitian: *see* Symmetric

Hilbert-Schmidt operators: *see* Integral
    operators
Hilbert spaces
    definition of, 110
    functionals on, 135–39
    properties of, 116–35
    separable, 116
    transformations on, 140-46, 165–90

I

Impulse response, 78; *see also* Green's
    function
Impulsive source: *see* Dirac delta
    function
Indefinite operator 165, 224
Independence
    criterion for, 60
    of set of functions, 59–60, 118
    of set of vectors, 97, 118
Influence function: *see* Green's
    function
Initial conditions, 64, 67
Initial value problem, 59
    Green's function for, 56, 66
Inner product
    on complex linear space, 109
    on real linear space, 107
Inner product spaces, 107–114; *see
    also* Hilbert spaces
    complex, 109
    real, 107
Integral equations, 191–258
    approximate methods for, 241–50
    differential equations and, 199–206
    eigenvalue problem for, 195,
        212–20
    Fredholm, 195
    Volterra, 196
Integral operators
    adjoint of, 212
    complete continuity of, 193
    eigenvalues and eigenfunctions of,
        195–96
    Green's functions and, 199–206
    of Hilbert-Schmidt type, 193
    indefinite, 224

    kernel of, 192
    negative and nonnegative, 224
    nonsymmetric, 250–58
    positive and nonpositive, 224
    real, 225
    spectrum of, 212–20
Inverse operator, 12, 140, 151, 165–80

K

Kantorovich-Lebedev transform, 317
Kernel
    bilinear series for, 238–40
    Hilbert-Schmidt, 193
    of integral operator, 144
    iterated, 206, 239
    left iterate of, 251
    nonsymmetric, 250–58
    right iterate of, 251
    separable, 192, 198
    symmetric, 212
Kohn-Kato method, 235, 236

L

Lagrange's identity, 70
Least squares approximation, 124, 224
Lebesgue convergence theorem, 105
Lebesgue integral, 104–105
Legendre equation, 302, 319, 320
Legendre polynomials, 123, 130, 319
Limit circle case for singular problem,
    297, 301, 310–13
Limit point case for singular problem,
    297, 301, 310
Linear functionals
    boundedness of, 135, 137
    continuity of, 135
    on Euclidean space, 135–39
    extension of, 137
    on Hilbert space, 135–39
    norm of, 135
    Riesz representation theorem for,
        136
    on space of test functions, 31
Linear manifolds, 120, 121

Linear spaces, 96–99, 105–190; *see also* Vector spaces
Linear transformations: *see* Transformations
Locally integrable, 31

M

Macdonald functions, 331
Mapping: *see* Operator, Transformations
Matrix, 79, 146
Mellin cosine transform, 316
Mellin sine transform, 316, 317
Mellin transform, 308, 309
Mercer's theorem, 240
Metric, 100, 117
  generated by norm, 106
Metric spaces, 99–105, 114–**16**
  Cauchy sequences in, 100
  closed sets in, 114
  compact sets in, 114
  completeness of, 101
  convergence in, 100
  dense sets in, 114
  triangle inequality for, 100
Minimax principle, 225
Modified Green's function, 86–91, 317–19
  symmetric, 88
Multiplicity
  algebraic, 157
  geometric, 156

N

Negative operator, 165, 224
Neumann functions, 329
Neumann series, 206–211
  for Volterra equation, 209
Nonnegative operator, 165, 224
Nonpositive operator, 165, 224
Norm, 105, 117
  of functional, 135
  generated by inner product, 108
  metric generated by, 106

of s type, 296
of transformation, 140
Normal form of differential equation, 279
Normalization of eigenfunctions, 274, 278
Normed linear spaces, 105–107
Nullity of transformation, 153

O

One-to-one transformation, 93
Operator; *see also* Transformations
  bounded below, 277
  closable, 142
  closed, 142, 168
  continuous spectrum of, 181
  differentiation, 174
  extremal principles for, 162, 214, 226, 245
  point spectrum of, 181
  projection, 149
  regular value of, 181
  residual spectrum of, 181
  resolvent set of, 181
  shifts, 169
  spectrum of, 180
Order of distribution, 40
Orthogonal complement, 121
Orthogonal sets, 108, 120
Orthogonalization
  by Gram-Schmidt procedure, 122
Orthonormal basis, 123–24, 127–28, 129

P

Parallelogram law, 113
Parseval's identity, 127
Perpendicular: *see* Orthogonal
Poisson summation formula, 46, 47, 50
Polar identity, 164
Pole of fundamental solution, 62
Polynomials
  approximation by: *see* Weierstrass approximation theorem

Positive definite
    quadratic form, 112
    operator: *see* Positive operator
Positive operator, 165, 224
Projection, 121, 149
    operator, 149
    theorem, 129
Pseudofunction, 48–50

Q

Quadratic form, 112

R

Range
    of function, 93, 95
    of transformation, 95
Rank
    of matrix, 79
    of transformation on Euclidean
        space, 153
Rayleigh quotient, 227
Rayleigh-Ritz procedure
    for eigenvalues, 228
    for inhomogeneous equation, 245,
        248
Real operator, 225
Regular boundary value problem, 269
Regular distribution, 33
Regular point of differential equation,
    269, 297
Regular transformation
    on Euclidean space, 151
    on Hilbert space, 166
Resolution of the identity, 161
Resonance, 82–83
Riemann-Lebesgue lemma, 126, 185
Riesz representation theorem, 136
Riesz-Fischer theorem, 122
Ritz-Rayleigh: *see* Rayleigh-Ritz

S

Schrodinger equation, 322
Schwarz constants, 232

Schwarz inequality, 107, 109, 111,
    117
Schwarz iteration, 231
Schwarz quotients, 232
Secular equation, 156
Self-adjoint boundary value problem,
    71
Self-adjoint operators; *see also*
    Symmetry
    alternative theorem for, 172
    of differential type, 74, 219–20
    on Euclidean space, 152
    formally, 70
    on Hilbert space, 172
    of integral type, 212
Self-adjoint system, 71
Separable kernel, 192, 198, 242
Sets
    bounded, 184
    closed, 114
    closure of, 114
    compact, 114, 164, 184
    dense, 114
    exterior of, 116
    of measure zero, 105
    spanning, 119
Shift operator, 169
    modified, 169
Simple eigenvalue, 213
Singular boundary value problem, 269,
    283–322
    in limit-circle case, 297, 301
    in limit-point case, 297, 301
Singular distribution, 33
Singular point of differential equation,
    59, 297
Singular transformation
    on Euclidean space, 151
    on Hilbert space, 167
Spaces
    Banach, 106
    complex Euclidean, 110
    real Euclidean, 110
    Hilbert, 110, 116–90
    inner product, 107
    linear, 96–190
    metric, 99–105
    of n-tuples, 98, 103

separable, 116
    of square integrable functions, 111
    of test functions, 29
    vector, 96–190
Spanning set, 119, 128
Spectral resolution, 161
Spectral theorem, 160
Spectral theory of second order
    differential operators, 259–322
Spectrum
    continuous, 181
    of Hilbert-Schmidt operators,
        212–20
    point, 181
    residual, 181
    of self-adjoint operator, 184
    of transformation on Hilbert space,
        180–84
Step response, 78
Stirling's formula, 27
Successive approximations: *see*
    Neumann series
Superposition principle, 4, 78
Symbolic function, 34; *see also*
    Distributions
Symmetry
    of differential operator, 75–76
    of Green's function, 71
    of kernel, 212
    of transformation on Euclidean
        space, 152, 159
    of transformation on Hilbert space,
        172
System; *see also* Boundary value
    problem
    adjoint, 69–71
    self-adjoint, 71

T

Test functions, 28–30
    complex-valued, 34
    convergence for, 30
    space of, 29
Transformations, 94, 139–90, 191–258
    adjoint, 152, 170
    bounded, 140
    closable, 142

closed, 142, 168
commuting, 139
completely continuous, 185
continuous, 140
domain of, 139
eigenvalues of, 154
eigenvectors of, 154
on Euclidean space, 146–65
extensions of, 141
on Hilbert space, 139–46, 165–90
indefinite, 165
integral, 144, 191–258
inverse of, 95, 140, 151, 166
kernel of, 144, 192
linear, 140
negative and nonnegative, 165
null space of, 139, 143, 171
nullity of, 153
one-to-one, 139, 166
positive and nonpositive, 165
projection, 149
range of, 139, 171
rank of, 153
regular, 151, 166
self-adjoint, 152
singular, 151, 167
symmetric, 152, 159, 172
unbounded, 145
Translation of distribution, 35
Transposed matrix, 80
Triangle inequality, 100

U

Uniqueness: *see* Existence and
    uniqueness

V

Variation iteration, 231
Variational principles: *see* Extremal
    principles
Vector spaces, 96–99, 105–190
    basis for, 97–98
    complex, 96–97
    dimension of, 97
    inner product on, 107, 109
    normed, 104

Vector spaces (*cont.*)
  real, 96
Volterra integral equations, 196,
  209–211

W

Wave equation, 325–26

Weak solutions of differential
  equations, 53
Weierstrass approximation theorem,
  27, 115
Weyl's theorem, 297
Wronskians, 59–61
  Abel's formula for, 60
  for Bessel functions, 330–31
  Green's functions and, 272